D1591606

Teaching Language to Children with Autism or Other Developmental Disabilities

by

Mark L. Sundberg, Ph.D., and James W. Partington, Ph.D.

1998

Version 7.4

AVB Press
Advancements in Verbal Behavior

4425-C Treat Blvd. #210
Concord, CA 94521
www.avbpress.com

TEACHING LANGUAGE TO CHILDREN WITH AUTISM OR OTHER DEVELOPMENTAL DIS-
ABILITIES

1998
Version 7.4

Sundberg, Mark L., and Partington, James W.

ISBN #978-0-9818356-5-5

10 9 8 7 6 5 4

Publisher: AVB Press
               4425-C Treat Blvd. #210
               Concord, CA 94521
               www.avbpress.com

Dedicated to our teacher
Jack Michael

Acknowledgements

The main focus of this book is on how to use B. F. Skinner's (1957) analysis of verbal behavior as a guide for language assessment and intervention. The current version of the book represents over 25 years of research and revisions of the program. The book would have not occurred had it not been for Dr. Jack Michael, who not only taught us behavior analysis and Skinner's analysis of verbal behavior, but guided us through many years of attempting to develop the application of Skinner's analysis. The first version of this book was written by Mark Sundberg and made available in 1978. A revised version was then made available in 1979. These two early versions of the verbal behavior assessment and intervention program greatly benefited from the help of David Ray, Steve Braam, Mark Stafford, Thomas Rueber, and Cassandra Braam. These individuals played significant roles in the development of the program presented in the current book. In addition, much of this early work was conducted at the Kalamazoo Valley Multihandicap Center and would not have happened without the conceptual and administrative support of Dr. Jerry Shook. The third version was written and made available by Mark Sundberg in 1987 and was partially funded by The College of New Caledonia, British Columbia. The book was used as a course manual thanks to the efforts of Dr. John Douglas and Dr. David Polson. The fourth version was written and made available by Mark Sundberg in 1990, and the author thanks Dr. Ernest Vargas for his help with this version. The fifth and sixth versions were written by Mark Sundberg and James Partington in 1996 and 1997, and used as the text for a course at the College of Alameda taught by Mark Sundberg. These last two versions, like the current version, attempted to make the material more "user friendly," and represent several new developments as a result of the daily testing and adjustments of the procedures that occurred at STARS School, operated by Behavior Analysts, Inc. The efforts of the STARS staff who contributed to this program over that past seven years are greatly appreciated. Most importantly, our work would be meaningless if it were not for the children we serve, and their parents. We thank them for all they have taught us. Also, a special thanks to Cindy Sundberg for her contributions to the program, and for editing the past five versions of this book.

Finally, we would like to thank our families for enduring our seemingly endless work on this project. We owe a great deal to our wives (Cindy Sundberg and Terry Partington) and our children (John and Danny Sundberg and Scott and Sonja Partington) for their patience, support, and wonderful examples of verbal behavior.

Contents

Contents

Contents

Chapter 1

Introduction

There are several million children in the United States who have been diagnosed with some type of childhood disorder. The exact number is unknown, but some have suggested that 3-5 percent of America's children have some type of disorder (e.g., Birnbrauer, 1976; Snell, 1987), while others suggest that the number may be as high as 6-9 percent (e.g., Klob, 1973). Some of these disorders (e.g., learning disabilities, eating disorders) can be more successfully treated than others. Perhaps the most difficult disorders to treat, of the many childhood disorders identified in the American Psychiatric Association's Diagnostic and Statistical Manual (DSM IV, 1995), are mental retardation and pervasive developmental disorders (e.g., autism). These disorders are typically lifelong and require intensive treatment because of the significant intellectual, linguistic, social, and physical impairments associated with them.

Most, if not all, of the children who are diagnosed with mental retardation or autism have some type of language deficit. The most common language problem is the failure to learn to communicate in a manner that is characteristic of typical children. Some children may fail to acquire even a single word, while others may become mute, echolalic, or invent their own nonsensical language. These language problems are quite complex and usually require specialized intervention programs with highly trained teachers (e.g., Lovaas, 1977). The purpose of the current book is to help parents and educators understand these language deficits, and to provide them with a guide for individualized language assessment and training. The book will primarily focus on children with autism, but the assessment and treatment programs presented can be effective for a wide variety of other developmental disabilities that involve language deficits (e.g., mental retardation, Down Syndrome, Fragile X Syndrome, Asperger's Syndrome). Also, the programs presented in this book can be effective for adults with developmental disabilities who have language delays.

The Importance of Early Identification and Intervention

It has been frequently stressed that early intervention is critical for working with children who have severe language delays (e.g., Lovaas, 1977; Maurice, Green, & Luce, 1996). Treatment programs are often most effective when they are started at an early age. However, it is often hard for a parent to determine if their young child does indeed have a language delay, or is simply "slow to talk." Most parents are unsure as to whether their observations indicate a substantial language delay, or just represent late language development that is typical for many children. Even when parents begin to have concerns about their child's language development, they are often unsure as to when to seek professional assistance. Parents frequently hear stories from friends and relatives about other children who did not talk until three or four years of age, but who later went on to become very successful speakers. This situation is further complicated by the fact that some children with language delays may, in all other respects, appear to be developing in a normal manner (e.g., young children with autism). As a result, unless there are other strong indicators of developmental disorders or problems (e.g., Down Syndrome, rejection of parents attempts at social interaction, impaired motor skills, extreme fascination with only a few specific objects), parents frequently "hope for the best" and wait to see if the language skills finally begin to develop.

When a parent's concerns about the apparent delays in language acquisition become greater, they often express their observations to the child's pediatrician. Although there is a growing professional awareness of the developmental disorders that are associated with delays in language acquisition, it is still not uncommon for professionals to do little but monitor development until the child is clearly not developing in a typical manner. Professionals tend to err on the conservative side with young children. Pediatricians may avoid suggesting that the problem could be of a more serious nature, and in many cases the parent's concerns do dissipate as the child's language skills begin to develop in a relatively typical, but late, progression. This situation is frequently confirmed by parents of autistic children such as Catherine Maurice (1996), who

found that "the pediatrician typically denies or underplays the problem until the child's condition deteriorates to the point where a pediatric neurologist, a psychologist, or a psychiatrist will finally confirm the validity of our fears." It is often at this point in the process that either the problem is determined to be solely a delay in the development of the communication skills, or determined to possibly be a more serious developmental disorder (e.g., autism, mental retardation, expressive language disorder).

Thus parents of children with language delays have often consulted with numerous professionals prior to obtaining a somewhat clear indication of the seriousness of their child's language delays. However, during this information gathering period valuable time is often lost since no intervention plan has been developed. In addition, these parents may question their competence to teach their child the necessary skills and may fail to intervene for fear of worsening the problem.

Once the nature of the delays begin to unfold, it becomes clear that someone must determine what can be done to help the child acquire language. In many situations, children benefit greatly from early intensive intervention by a speech and language pathologist. However, some children are difficult to motivate to participate in the language training sessions, others lack the skills to follow directions, while others engage in disruptive behavior when attempts are made to have them participate in teaching situations. Parents are often unsure whether or not the child understands what is being requested of them, and hence are unsure of what they should do to get their child to learn a skill. It is difficult to require the child to do something that the parent isn't convinced that the child "knows how to do." Although there is a great desire to help the child, frequently there is a hesitancy to avoid "pushing" the child too fast, and parents and others can become quite frustrated.

In attempting to secure effective intervention services for the child, parents ultimately get directed to the services provided by the special education division of their public school system. Because the local school systems are now required to provide "free and appropriate" educational services to handicapped students (Public Law 94-142), there are often a wide variety of educational options for children with language and other developmental delays. Most children are able to benefit from the range of services available from the local school systems. However, some children are unable to make significant progress from the educational options that are made available through the public school system. This is a problem frequently encountered by young children with autism. Although there is a wide variation in the development of the children with this diagnosis, the research literature suggests that early and intensive intervention is critical for language acquisition (e.g., Lovaas, 1977). Unfortunately, many of these young children are not provided with an intensive program because they are deemed to be too young for lengthy instructional intervention.

Parents are often glad that services are being provided by caring professionals, but often feel the very real concern that the level of intensity or the quality of instruction is not adequate to ensure that the child is able to learn at their potential. Unfortunately, many educators have not had sufficient training on how to work with children who are difficult to teach. Those who do have appropriate training are frequently in classrooms where they are unable to provide the necessary intensity of individualized services due to the high student-to-teacher ratio. Parents sometimes feel caught between wanting to "push" the school system to do all that is possible for their child, and wanting to trust the judgment of the professionals who are responsible for educating their child.

Each child is a unique individual. Thus it is necessary to individually determine a child's educational needs and to design an intervention plan to directly meet those needs. It is extremely important that both parents and educators know the most effective methods for developing the child's language skills, and that both know how to intervene in such a manner as to avoid and reduce disruptive behavior. As a result of the child's individual needs, it has become clear that specific assessment and teaching skills are needed by those who work with children with severe language delays. The following sections will briefly discuss these negative behaviors and their relation to delayed language, and the special teacher skills necessary to work with severely language delayed children.

Delayed Language Development and Negative Behaviors

At present it is not exactly clear why some children fail to acquire language. However, it is clear that if language does not develop in a timely manner, it is reasonable to expect that various forms of negative or inappropriate behavior will occur. Most nonverbal or language delayed children have some type of behavior problem (e.g., tantrums, self-stimulation, property destruction, aggression, social withdrawal), and it is often easy to see how these behaviors come to function as the child's main form of communication. For example, if a nonverbal boy with autism wants to go outside and begins screaming and crying by the door and is let out, he will probably scream and cry the next time he wants to go out. It is often very difficult to ignore this behavior, especially if the child is in a social setting. The crying or screaming may be extremely loud and the parent or teacher can escape from the aversive sounds by letting the child out (which usually results in the cessation of screaming—a clear sign of its communication function). The parents or teachers may attempt to divert attention or somehow avert the problem, but it is often too late, the scream has already been reinforced by the adult. Early intervention is important, in part, because it avoids entrenchment. Otherwise, in several years and thousands of reinforced trials, the negative behavior will become a strong part of the child's repertoire and difficult to eliminate.

There are other types of negative behaviors that might come to function as language for a nonverbal child. For example, high rates of activity (i.e., hyperactive behavior) may produce specific attention (e.g., chasing, grabbing) by parents or program staff. Thus, when attention is strong as a motivator, running around may be equivalent to the vocal response "Chase me." Hyperactivity, as a way of inducing adults and peers to behave, is then reinforced, and this behavior is more likely to occur again in the future, especially when other means of getting attention are not easily available.

Increased rates of self-stimulation and social withdrawal can also be by-products of defective language skills. Language, after all, allows a child to interact with others in the environment and usually brings a child a large amount of attention and specific reinforcement from parents. A child who continues to fail at attempts to communicate may soon give up due to the punishing effects of failure and withdraw into his "own world" of rocking, spinning, or other repetitive behaviors. These behaviors are successful for the child because he controls the delivery of the reinforcement (unlike his ability to control the delivery of reinforcement from others in his environment). Body movement can be a strong reinforcer (like the runner who feels great after a long run). When other reinforcers are unavailable, a child's own body movement may provide the best reinforcement available at that moment.

All of the behaviors identified above may have other causes as well. In fact, they are typically controlled by a number of different variables (e.g., escape from tasks, self-gratification), but their direct relation to defective language is often unanalyzed. It is common to treat these negative behaviors simply as inappropriate behavior that must be reduced. Programs are frequently designed to eliminate a certain behavior (e.g., aggression) without consideration of its possible link to defective language. For example, a child may learn to push another child to get access to a toy. If he gets the toy, it is possible that the push becomes equivalent to the verbal response "I want that toy." A punishment procedure may reduce the aggressive behavior, but it may not solve the child's problem of not having a way to express a desire for the toy. Hence the effects of punishment may be only temporary, or other inappropriate behaviors may come to function as language. Eliminating an undesired behavior that is linked to a defective verbal repertoire without considering the language link is an example of the mistake of treating the symptom and not the cause. This book recomends that language training be a major part of most behavior reduction programs.

The Skills Necessary for Conducting Language Intervention

Establishing and implementing a language intervention program for children with severe language delays is complicated by a number of factors. First, those providing the intervention must have a specific set of teaching skills. It has been frequently pointed out that the techniques derived from Applied Behavior Analysis (i.e., behavior modification) have been the most successful approach for working with children with severe developmental disabilities such as autism (e.g., Lovaas, 1977; Maurice, Green, & Luce, 1996). Therefore, individuals who implement the day-to-day intervention pro-

grams with the children need to be skillful in the basic techniques of Applied Behavior Analysis. That is, each staff member must know how to , for example, use the basic techniques of shaping, prompting, fading, chaining, and differential reinforcement. These skills are not so easy to acquire, and at a minimum require some formal training. Readers who are not familiar with basic behavior modification are encouraged to consult one of the many books on this approach (e.g., Martin & Paer, 1995; Malott, Whaley, & Malott, 1994).

A second requirement for conducting daily language intervention for many children who are nonverbal is that staff must have some knowledge of the various types of augmentative communication. It has been repeatedly demonstrated that alternative forms of communication, such as sign language (e.g., Fristoe & Lloyd, 1977; Sundberg, 1980), picture communication systems (e.g., Mirenda, 1985; Reichle, York, & Sigafoos, 1991), and picture exchange systems (e.g., Bondy & Frost, 1993; Frost & Bondy, 1994), can be very successful in establishing communication skills for nonverbal children. Staff must not only know how to sign or how to arrange pictures, but also how to teach the child to use these special systems. These skills, like basic behavior modification, are complicated and require special staff training in order for most children to benefit. The issue of augmentative communication will be presented in more detail in Chapter 4.

A third requirement for establishing a language intervention program for nonverbal children is the use of an effective assessment and curriculum, as well as a language acquisition tracking system. The assessment is critical in order to pinpoint exactly what a specific child needs, and to identify a starting point for the language intervention program. The curriculum provides the parents and teachers with a guide to what to teach, and the tracking system ensures that the targeted skills are being acquired. There are a wide variety of language assessments available, but fewer curricula or tracking systems tailored specifically for nonverbal children.

This book presents a language assessment and a language curriculum along with specific procedures for teaching language and tracking its development. (A more detailed task analysis, curriculum, and tracking system is available in *The Assessment of Basic Language and Learning Skills* (Partington & Sundberg, 1998).) The assessment and language training programs contained herein are based on the behavioral analysis of language presented by B. F. Skinner (1957). We have organized the material into four sections and an appendix. The first section, "Preparing to Teach Language," presents the language assess-

ment program and the assessment interpretation program. In these chapters the reader will learn how to use the behavioral analysis of language to identify a child's language deficits, and how to determine an appropriate intervention program for the child. Guidelines for the selection of an appropriate response form (i.e., speech, sign language, picture systems) will also be presented in this section. The second section, "Beginning Language Training," describes specific procedures for establishing beginning language skills for nonverbal children. This section also contains a detailed language training curriculum. The third section, "Advanced Language Training," is a continuation of the procedures identified in section two. These materials are designed for the more advanced (but still delayed) language learner. The fourth section, "Elements of an appropriate teaching environment" presents issues relevant to the implementation of a language program in a child's home and school environment. Finally, the appendix contains more detailed information on a behavioral analysis of language.

Chapter 2
Language Assessment

There are a number of standardized language assessments that can be used for children with autism or other developmental disabilities (e.g., Illinois Test of Psycholinguistic Abilities, Peabody Picture Vocabulary Test, Preschool Language Scale, Test for Auditory Comprehension of Language). These assessments are typically divided into receptive and expressive sections. A child's language skills are tested by presenting him with an increasingly complex set of receptive and expressive tasks. The tests assess several aspects of language, including vocabulary, grammar, syntax, sentence construction, and the mean length of utterances (MLU) across both the comprehension (receptive) and production (expressive) of words and sentences. The primary goal of these language assessments is to identify a child's age-equivalent linguistic level. That is, how old are typical children who speak at about the same level as the child being tested? This level is obtained by a comparison of a child's score on the test to the average language abilities of a large group of typically developing children. The scores on the two parts are converted to obtain the child's chronological functioning level, and the scores are either summated (e.g., language age of 2.1 years) or presented individually (e.g., receptive functioning level of 3.2 years and an expressive functioning level of 2.4 years).

The results from these standardized tests can help professionals determine if a language problem exists. They can also provide important information about a child's language abilities. However, there are several limitations with this method of language assessment. First, since the assessments are standardized (like IQ tests) they involve a specific list of items that are presented out of context by a novel tester (an adult who does not regularly work with the child) in a novel testing environment (often an office or testing room that the child has never been in before). Correct responses are also not reinforced (standardized testing requires the tester provide neutral responses to answers in order to compare the child's performance to a norm). Thus, under these conditions, it is almost impossible to gain a true picture of a child's language abilities (especially given the abundant amount of research that shows a decrease in responding during extinction conditions). Yet this standardized testing is required by many school districts and states in order for a child to qualify for special speech and language services.

Another problem with standardized language assessments is that they do not provide teachers or parents with a specific starting point for developing a language intervention program. It is assumed that if a child's language age can be identified, then the teacher can develop a language intervention program and provide material that would be appropriate for that language age. However, there are many linguistic differences between, for example, an 8-year-old child with autism who scores at a 2-year-old level, and a typically developing 2-year-old child. These differences might include substantial variations in learning, such as the rate of language acquisition, spontaneity, verbal interaction, novel responding, and the prompt and reinforcement level required to evoke responses. In addition, finding an age-equivalent score does not help to identify specific linguistic problems, or help to suggest strategies for where and how to begin language intervention.

A final problem with standardized assessments is that they do not separate the several different types of expressive language. For example a child might be given credit for knowing the word "scissors" simply because he can identify a picture of scissors, but typically there are no measures of his ability to ask for scissors when he wants them but none are visible. As a result, important distinctions and verbal deficits are frequently not identified by standardized assessments (e.g., a defective ability to request desired items when they are absent). These aspects of language, identified as the functional use of language by Skinner (1957), are critical for the daily use of language in the child's natural environment.

An Alternative Approach to Language Assessment

The primary purpose of a language assessment should be to identify specific verbal deficits and serve as a guide for the development of an appropriate language intervention program for the individual being assessed. A behavioral analysis of language (Skinner, 1957) can be more productive in meeting this goal because it identifies the functional, as well as the structural, parts of a language repertoire. To get a clear understanding of a child's language deficits, we must assess language in a variety of contexts, under different stimuli and motivational conditions, and include both formal and informal trials along with parent and teacher observations. Finally, language assessment should be an ongoing process, rather than a one-time (or triennial) standardized event. As a result of this approach, the variables responsible for defective verbal development can be more clearly identified and tracked, and a more effective individualized intervention program can be developed. This chapter contains a language assessment based on these elements. This assessment is specifically designed for children who have very limited verbal skills (less than 100 words). A more detailed and advanced language assessment and tracking system can be found in Partington and Sundberg (1998).

Skinner's (1957) analysis of verbal behavior serves as the conceptual basis for the language assessment presented in the next two chapters. His functional analysis of verbal behavior suggests that the traditional framework of receptive and expressive language is an incomplete account of language, because it fails to identify many of the different environmental variables responsible for language. (Readers who would like a more detailed treatment of Skinner's analysis of verbal behavior should consult the appendix or Skinner's book.) The first published program that used Skinner's analysis of verbal behavior for language assessment was the *Parsons Language Sample* (Spradlin, 1963). Spradlin was a pioneer in the use of Skinner's analysis of verbal behavior for individuals with developmental disabilities, and he has inspired a number of follow-up projects on behavioral language assessment (e.g., Partington & Sundberg, 1998; Sloane & MacAuley, 1968; Sundberg, 1983; Sundberg, Ray, Braam, Stafford, Rueber, & Braam, 1979). Many elements of the following assessment are derived from Spradlin's early work, as well as the other assessment programs identified above.

Conducting a Language Assessment

There are several important factors to consider when attempting to determine a child's language abilities. First, an assessment is only a sample of a child's verbal behavior, so it is necessary to take special steps to assure that the sample is an accurate measure of a child's abilities. The objective is not to determine a child's entire vocabulary, but rather to obtain information about the strength of each type of language and the manner in which a child emits and acquires language. The assessment seeks to answer questions such as: "How strong are a child's requesting (manding) skills?"; "At what rate are new requests acquired?"; "What prompt levels are necessary to get a child to request?"; and "Will a child request items and activities from different people?" Issues such as these are examined in detail below. But before moving on to the actual assessment, there are a number of prelimi-

nary activities and issues to consider that might assist the assessor in obtaining the most accurate measure of a child's language skills.

Establishing Rapport

Prior to the assessment of a child's verbal skills it is important to establish rapport with the child. This, unfortunately, is rarely done (testers are often very busy and have a limited amount of time). Frequently, a child's language is assessed by an unknown person (e.g., a speech therapist assigned to do the mandatory three-year evaluations), who takes the child out of his daily environment (to a testing room) and presents him with novel verbal and nonverbal stimuli under extinction conditions (i.e., correct answers are not reinforced in most standardized testing). The odds are certainly against the child, because the results of an assessment are critical for teachers and parents who must provide daily language intervention for the child. The purpose of a language assessment should be to determine what aspects of a child's verbal behavior are weak and where to begin language instruction, hence it is extremely important that the person conducting the assessment have at least a reasonable degree of rapport with the child.

Establishing rapport is often very easy, and knowledge about the child's verbal repertoire can be obtained with the first interaction. However, a formal test should not be administered because the tester most likely does not have enough (stimulus) control over the child's behavior, and any test will reflect this brief history. Such control develops as a function of the reinforcement of a child's behavior. Therefore, one must know what functions as reinforcement for a child first, and then provide some of that reinforcement for appropriate responses. Simply playing and having fun with a child can help to establish stimulus control and establish the tester, and her behavior, as reinforcers. By spending this time with a child, the tester will enable the assessment to be much easier and clearly more valid. Failure to develop this rapport will result in an assessment of a very atypical sample of a child's verbal behavior.

Inappropriate Verbal and Nonverbal Behaviors

Inappropriate behavior such as aggression, screaming, crying, and self-abuse may be functioning as verbal behavior for a child. It will be useful to carefully analyze the antecedents and consequences of these behaviors and other inappropriate behaviors. Most nonverbal children have some form of communication that has been shaped over the years, and understanding these can be useful in developing a language intervention program.

The Testing Environment

There are three general circumstances under which a language assessment should be conducted: (1) observations of the child in his natural environment, (2) interviews with the child's parents and teachers, (3) and formal trial-by-trial direct examination of the child. A child's natural environment (classroom, home, or community), where he com-

fortably interacts with familiar things and people, provides the best circumstances to assess a verbal repertoire. It is important to observe verbal behavior under these circumstances, especially since so much of language occurs under the control of ongoing daily activities. However, this sample may be too small to provide all the necessary information. Therefore, interviews with individuals who know the child well will be essential for providing a more complete assessment. Parents and teachers are in a position to provide an abundant amount of information about a child. Questions should be presented clearly and unambiguously since it is often difficult for others to know exactly what is being assessed in a language assessment. The formal testing is necessary for presenting increasingly complex stimuli and recording specific responses. These procedures will be described in more detail in the upcoming sections.

Materials

A variety of materials are required to assess the different types of language skills presented below. For example, in order to assess the child's ability to name items, the tester must assemble a collection of objects and pictures. In order to assess the child's ability to request items and activities, the tester must identify and assemble items that function as reinforcements for the child. And, to assess the child's ability to engage in social and conversational language, the tester needs to use a specially designed series of verbal questions (e.g., fill-in-the-blank items or WH questions) and arrange (or observe) various social situations. Reviewing each assessment section and the test forms below can help a tester determine the most appropriate materials for a specific child.

Reinforcers

Standardized language assessments and psychological tests are conducted under conditions where correct responses are not reinforced (technically called extinction). However, research has shown that this practice can greatly reduce a child's score on these tests (Breuning & Davis, 1981; Young, Bradley-Johnson, & Johnson, 1982). The assessment program presented in this book encourages the use of reinforcers for correct responses in order to more precisely identify the child's actual language skills. Therefore, the tester should find out what reinforcers are effective for an individual and assemble them prior to beginning the formal testing procedures.

Summary

The purpose of a language assessment should be to determine what aspects of a child's verbal repertoire are weak and where to begin a language intervention program. Language assessments that focus on age-equivalent scores, and the traditional receptive and expressive distinction, are less useful to parents and teachers who simply need direction for working with a particular child. The tester should establish rapport with the child, interview the parents and teachers, gather individualized materials, and assess all the different types of verbal skills in both formal and natural situations, with correct responses being consistently reinforced. The assessment program described in the next

section identifies the specific skills that should be assessed and provide the tester with a criterion for scoring the child's performance in each area. The next chapter of the book then describes how to interpret the results of the assessment in order to establish an individualized language intervention plan.

The Behavioral Language Assessment

The behavioral language assessment contains 12 different sections that cover a variety of early language skills and related areas. Each section is broken down into 5 levels. The task of the person conducting the assessment is to determine which level most accurately represents the child's current abilities. The assessment is best suited for individuals who have very limited verbal skills. It is not meant to be a complete assessment of these skills, but rather a brief overview (for a more complete and advanced assessment of a child's language abilities see Partington & Sundberg, 1998). The initial assessment data is used to determine where to start the language intervention program. And, as discussed previously, language assessment needs to be ongoing, and adjustments to the intervention program should be made frequently based on the child's performance.

It is important that the scores for each skill be based upon the child's typical use of the skill. Specifically, the tester should not overestimate the child's skills by indicating emerging skills or skills that the child had demonstrated in the past but does not currently exhibit throughout the day. The information requested should be what the child typically does, and not what he is beginning to do or what he sometimes does.

Cooperation with Adults

Many nonverbal children are unwilling to cooperate with the requests made by adults. This problem occurs with typical children as well, mainly because adults frequently make children do things that they do not want to do (e.g., go to bed, sit in a chair, stay in a car seat, wash their faces). However, the degree of uncooperative behaviors may be more severe with a child who cannot talk or understand language. This can make it difficult to assess a child's language abilities, as well as teach him more effective language. For example, it may be hard to determine if a child *cannot* emit a response or *will not* emit a response. Identifying the degree to which a child will cooperate with adults can provide some important information, such as the potential need to include behavioral management procedures in the language training program. On the other hand, a child who is very cooperative with adults may be much easier to teach. The assessment forms contain five levels of cooperation, and the following discussion of each level should help the tester determine which level is most appropriate for the child being assessed.

1. Always uncooperative, avoids work, engages in negative behavior

Many nonverbal children remain nonverbal because they are very difficult to work with. These children may run from adults, avoid making eye contact, and emit various forms of negative behaviors when required to work (e.g., crying, screaming, hitting, self-injurious behaviors, destructive behaviors).

2. Will do only one brief and easy response for a powerful reinforcer

This type of child may respond, but they may be only simple responses and may require a lot of prompting and powerful reinforcers. Often these children will grab the reinforcer and immediately attempt to get away from the adult. Negative behavior may also be prominent when the child is asked to comply with tasks or give up reinforcers.

3. Will give 5 responses without disruptive behavior

Some children will work for a few trials without disruptive behavior, but they may still need a powerful reinforcer on each trial and long breaks. These children may not engage in disruptive behaviors for short work periods, but if the time is extended too far, negative behavior may occur. However, these children are more workable since they are attending and responding, and less time is spent dealing with negative behavior.

4. Will work for 5 minutes without disruptive behavior

Once a child will work with an adult for an extended period of time without disruptive behavior, instruction becomes more fruitful. These children may still need breaks after short intervals, but they are usually easy to get back on task. Less reinforcement may also be required to keep the child interested in working.

5. Works well for 10 minutes at a table without disruptive behavior

A strong cooperative repertoire can be seen in a child who will sit at a table and work with an adult on language and related tasks for extended periods of time, without emitting disruptive behaviors.

Requests (Mands)

The purpose of this section is to determine how a child gets his/her needs and wants known (*manding* is the term Skinner uses for this type of language—see the appendix for a more detailed treatment of manding). Typical children acquire this verbal skill quite quickly and often do so without much instruction. However, some children do not learn how to use words to ask for what they want. Often these children develop negative behaviors as a way of communicating. Some children may satisfy their needs by not talking, but by simply getting reinforcers themselves. Other children may be able to emit a few words or signs but do not do so without prompts, while others have no problem manding for their reinforcers. The assessment forms contain 5 levels of manding and the following discussion of each level should help the tester determine which level is most appropriate for the child being assessed.

1. Cannot ask for reinforcers or engages in negative behavior

Some children are completely nonverbal and do not indicate that they are hungry, thirsty, or in need of assistance. It may be that the child simply gets the desired reinforcers himself, or it may be that reinforcers are regularly provided and he does not need to ask for them. The child may have a physical disability (severe cerebral palsy) and may not have the muscle control to indicate specific needs. Or it may be that very little functions as reinforcement for the child, thus his needs and wants are very limited.

Other children may use negative behaviors as a way to get adults to provide them with what they want. Negative behavior can be a very effective form of communication for a nonverbal child. As previously discussed, it is quite common for children to acquire these behaviors because of their immediate effects on adults. The behaviors can be as mild as whimpers or social withdrawal or as intrusive as physical aggression and self-injurious behavior. The defining features of this behavior as language is that when the child wants something they engage in a type of negative behavior rather than using words, and after they are provided with the desired reinforcer, the negative behavior ceases.

2. Pulls people, points, or stands by reinforcing items

There are many ways in which a child can indicate that they want something without talking. Some of the more common ways observed with nonverbal children are pulling adults to the reinforcer (e.g., the door, the refrigerator, the tub), pointing to a desired items, or standing by what they want. These all have a communicative function in that they let the adult know what the child wants. This behavior is typically seen as an improvement over negative behavior, but it is not uncommon to see both types of behavior in one child. For example, a child may pull the adult to the car, but, when told he can't go for a ride, may resort to a tantrum. The pull and tantrum may both be types of communication (specifically, mands).

3. Uses 1–5 words, signs, or pictures to ask for reinforcers

A child may have a few words or signs, or may be able to point to or exchange a few pictures in order to obtain reinforcement, and he may use them accurately (e.g., up, eat, doggie, mama). They may occur only a few times a day and may even require some prompting. A child with some words may also emit the behaviors identified in levels 1 and 2, but these behaviors are different in that at least some manding does occur with standard words or signs.

4. Uses 5-10 words, signs, or pictures to ask for reinforcers

Once a child begins to acquire the ability to request reinforcers, it is common for the rate of requesting to increase (e.g., continually asking for a cookie). Also, it may become easier to teach new words and the number of different requests begins to increase. Prompts are typically not required and the responses may occur under a variety of situations.

5. Frequently requests using 10 or more words, signs, or pictures

A strong requesting repertoire can be seen in a child who can easily—and readily and frequently— ask for a wide variety of rein-

forcers. The child uses carrier phrases such as "I want..." and "Can I..." However, this child may still have deficits in this area and may benefit from the sections in the book on teaching advanced manding (especially Chapter 12).

Motor Imitation

The purpose of this section is to determine if a child can physically imitate motor movements modeled by adults. Children acquire a number of important skills through imitation of adults and other children. Strong imitation skills can be very valuable to a nonverbal child in that they can often acquire sign language quickly as a form of communication. Motor imitation can also foster the development of vocal imitation and may provide a good starting point for nonvocal children. In addition, imitation is also important for the development of play skills and social interaction, and like the other skills identified here, imitation should be frequently monitored for a child with language delays.

1. Cannot imitate anybody's motor movement

Some children cannot imitate any motor movements modeled by others. These children may also not attend to others or show much interest in the actions emitted by others.

2. Imitates a few gross motor movements modeled by others

Gross motor movements such as jumping, clapping, running, and raising up arms are often easier to imitate than fine motor movements such as wiggling a finger.

Many nonverbal children can at least emit a few of these imitative responses when prompted. Some may imitate a few movements modeled by other children or by characters on TV or a video.

3. Imitates several gross motor movements on request

Once a few imitative responses are acquired, it is often not too difficult to teach other large motor imitative responses such as kicking, twirling around, falling down, climbing stairs, and so on. This child may still have a difficult time imitating small motor movements and may not spontaneously imitate others.

4. Imitates several fine and gross motor movements on request

A child who can initiate a variety of fine and gross motor movements has a reasonably strong imitative repertoire. However, the child may not do so unless prompted, and he may not imitate novel responses without specific training.

5. Easily imitates fine or gross movements, often spontaneously

A strong imitative repertoire can be seen in a child who easily imitates the motor behavior of others and emits the behavior spontaneously. New behaviors can be imitated correctly on the first trial (at least approximations) and often occur without prompts.

Vocal Play

Typical children engage in a substantial amount of vocal play or babbling. This vocal activity plays an important role in language development because such behavior not only strengthens the vocal cords but allows for the random mixture of sounds that often accidentally produces words that parents may react to and reinforce. Many potentially nonverbal children can be identified by their failure to engage in vocal play during the first year of life. The existence of substantial vocal play for a nonverbal child can be a good predictor for the easy development of vocal imitation (echoic behavior) and eventually other types of verbal behavior.

1. Does not emit any sounds (mute)

Some children do not babble or emit any recognizable English phonemes. These children may scream, cry, or otherwise emit sounds, but they are not typical speech sounds. Sometimes these children are hard to reinforce—little seems to excite them— and they may seem unhappy and sullen.

2. Makes a few speech sounds at a low rate

This child may make a few recognizable sounds, but the sounds do not occur very often, nor do they have much variation. The sounds may occur only when the child is very excited or in some way prompted to speak. The vocal sounds, however, are clearly not emitted in a form of play by the child. That is, it does not appear that the child is having fun (i.e., smiling and laughing) while they are emitting the sounds. Also, the sounds may always be the same and may be emitted with the same intonation.

3. Babbles many speech sounds with varied intonations

This child may emit a number of speech sounds and may show some variation in intonation, volume, and pitch. He may actually appear to occasionally babble in a manner similar to typical children, but understandable words are rare. The rate of babbling and variation of speech sounds is also lower than a typical child in the babbling stage of language development.

4. Babbles frequently with varied intonation and says a few words

This child may babble and engage in vocal play frequently and may even emit a few recognizable words. His vocal behavior shows substantial variation and may be emitted while he is engaged in play with toys. It may also appear that the child is talking to the toys or providing a script to his play. However, most of the sounds are not recognizable as words.

5. Babbles frequently and says many clearly understandable words

A strong vocal play repertoire would be demonstrated by a child who frequently vocalizes with a mixture of sounds and recognizable words while he is playing or engaging in daily activities. It may also appear that the child is attempting to communicate, and in many instances appears to be sure about what he is saying, even though it may not be understood by adults. These children are often easy to reinforce and get excited easily.

Vocal Imitation (Echoic)

A child's ability to repeat sounds and words is very important to language acquisition. If a nonverbal child cannot repeat any

sounds or words, it may be very difficult to teach him vocal communication. A child such as this may likely be a candidate for the use of sign language or pictures (depending on the other factors identified in Chapter 4). A child who has a strong vocal imitation repertoire, but is still unable to ask for reinforcers or label items in the environment, may be able to learn these skills quickly given the appropriate teaching procedures.

1. Cannot repeat any sounds or words

A number of nonverbal children are unable to repeat any sounds or words when asked to do so. These children may also not babble much and may exhibit negative behavior when attempts are made to get them to repeat sounds.

2. Will repeat a few specific sounds or words

Some nonverbal children can at least echo a few sounds or words (e.g., "mama," "bye"). However, these children may not do so very willingly. It may require some effort to get them to copy an adult's words. Extensive prompting and strong reinforcers may be necessary. These children may also display some negative behavior when asked to engage in this task.

3. Will repeat or closely approximate several sounds or words

Children who can echo a number of different sounds and words, and will easily do so on command, are demonstrating some good echoic skills. These children may not require much prompting or reinforcement, and they may not engage in any negative behavior to escape or avoid the task. The echoic responding may also occur often throughout the day.

4. Will repeat or closely approximate many different words

When a child is able to closely echo a wide variety of words without prompts, strong reinforcers, or negative behaviors, he is beginning to demonstrate a functional echoic repertoire. A child at this level may also show enjoyment in copying sounds and may copy other children or words heard on TV or on a video.

5. Will clearly repeat any word, or even simple phrases

A strong echoic repertoire can be seen in a child who will easily and clearly repeat almost any word. This child may also spontaneously echo words and phrases that he hears in his natural environment from a wide variety of sources.

Matching-to-Sample

The ability to match pictures, designs, and shapes to identical samples often reveals a number of important abilities. A child who is successful at these tasks is often one who can, among other things, attend to visual stimuli, discriminate between differing stimuli, and emit specific motor behaviors to complete a task. This type of task is often seen on IQ tests, and it is frequently discussed by psychologists as a measure of cognitive ability. There are many elements of this skill that are relevant to language training and language development, and important information about a nonverbal child can be obtained by determining the

degree to which he can match similar stimuli.

1. Cannot match any objects or pictures to a sample

Many nonverbal children cannot match identical objects or pictures to provided samples. This task may be particularly difficult for children who engage in a substantial amount of self-stimulation (e.g., flapping, twirling, or object stimulation), because their tendency is to focus on stimming with the object rather than matching it to a similar object.

2. Can match 1 or 2 objects or pictures to a sample

Some children may be able to match a few objects or pictures together, but it may require a substantial amount of prompting and reinforcement. Errors are common, and the task might be met with a wide variety of negative behaviors in an attempt to avoid or escape the task.

3. Can match 5 to 10 objects or pictures to a sample

A nonverbal child who readily matches several common objects and pictures to a presented sample, without much resistance, is demonstrating a beginning level of this skill. The stimuli may need to be specific stimuli and perhaps even reinforcing stimuli (e.g., favorite Disney characters). Attempts may fail to get the child to match more abstract stimuli or to complete block designs. These attempts may also be met with negative behaviors.

4. Can match 5 to 10 colors, shapes, or designs to a sample

A more advanced demonstration of this skill can be seen in a child who can match a variety of stimuli to each other. These stimuli may include colors, shapes, geographical drawings, and a wide variety of pictures and objects. The task may be performed without resistance and may even appear as a form of entertainment for the child. However, the child may be unsuccessful with matching blocks to a design card.

5. Can match most items and match 2 to 4 block designs

A strong matching-to-sample repertoire would be demonstrated by a child who could match a wide variety of stimuli, as well as complete block design cards that have specific patterns to copy. The child may be able to select the specific blocks from a large box of blocks and be successful with other shapes as well. This child may also be able to match objects to pictures, line drawings to pictures, and sort specific items (e.g., foods vs. animals).

Receptive Language

A child's ability to understand and act upon specific words and phrases is a key indicator of his ability to acquire other types of language. However, as is commonly known, strong receptive language is not a guarantee that a child will readily acquire expressive language. There are several important aspects of receptive language that can be used to teach expressive language, and the strength of receptive skills can often predict the rate at which other types of verbal behavior can be acquired.

1. Cannot understand any words

Some children do not specifically react to any words emitted by their caretakers. Simple instructions such as "Stand up," "Sit," "Jump," and "Come here" do not evoke a correct response. Even in a strong context of, say, everyone going to the dinner table, the child may not respond to spoken words. These children may exhibit a wide variety of negative behaviors, including tantrums, whining, social withdrawal, self-injurious behavior, and physical aggression.

2. Will follow a few instructions related to daily routines

Perhaps the easiest types of instructions to follow are those that are given in context of an ongoing activity. Many nonverbal children will go along with verbal instructions, but they are often extensively prompted. That is, there are many stimuli combining to evoke the response (e.g., when everyone is about to leave, the verbal stimulus "Go get your coat" may evoke the correct response, in part, because the child sees everybody preparing to leave).

3. Will follow a few instructions to do actions or touch items

A more advanced type of receptive language can be seen in a child who will follow instructions to engage in a specific behavior out of context (e.g., "Jump," "Sit," "Clap"). In addition, the child may be able to touch or pick up a few specific items or pictures when asked to do so (e.g., "Touch the cookie," or "Give me Pooh Bear"). This behavior may require extensive prompting and may also evoke negative behaviors when the child is pressed to emit more complicated behaviors, such as pointing to a specific item when it is presented within a large array of items.

4. Can follow many instructions and point to at least 25 items

Many nonverbal children can discriminate between a wide variety of objects, pictures, and people and will do so easily on command (e.g., "Touch the cat," "Where's daddy?"). These children may also be able to distinguish between items that are similar to each other (e.g., dog and cat, cookie and cracker), and they will comply with the instructions without much prompting or negative behavior. They may also be able to follow a wide variety of instructions given by different people in different settings (e.g., "Can you dance?" "Go get your puppy").

5. Can point to at least 100 items, actions, persons, or adjectives

A strong receptive repertoire can be seen in a child who can easily distinguish between a large number of items. These items can be objects, pictures, people, colors, and so on. Often, the acquisition of new receptive skills is fast, and it generalizes to different items and people with little effort. These new responses may also occur with very little prompting or negative behavior on the part of the student.

Labeling (Tacting)

The ability to verbally label common items and actions is a major cornerstone of language development (*tacting* is the term Skinner uses for this type of language, see the appendix for a more detailed treatment of tacting). This skill is very different from the receptive identification of items and actions previously discussed in that it involves a child doing the talking rather than the adult (this is one of the differences between being a listener and being a speaker). Labeling items is a more difficult skill, because the child must not only come up with the correct word, but must be able to have the vocal control to independently pronounce the word (weakness in vocal control is often where sign language and pictures as temporary alternatives to speech can be beneficial). Children who do not acquire this skill are at a great loss, especially since they often need to know the name of things before they can ask for them or talk about them.

1. Cannot identify any items or actions

A very obvious feature of most nonverbal children is that they cannot verbally name common items in their environment. However, some of these children may be able to ask for some of the things they want, repeat words, and even receptively distinguish between items, but they cannot say the name of an item when presented the item and asked to identify it. These children may also emit negative behaviors (e.g., whining, crying, hitting) in an attempt to escape or avoid instructional situations where they are pushed to provide the name of items.

2. Identifies only 1 to 5 items or actions

Typically, the first items that a child can name are highly reinforcing objects and activities, such as the parents, pets, foods, or certain types of play or toys. These objects come to control language because of their reinforcing value. Also, they are objects that are constant and important features of a child's life. Thus the first types of labels that a child learns often involve these words.

3. Identifies 6 to 15 items or actions

A more advanced naming ability can be seen in a child who can easily identify several of the common items in his environment (e.g., dog, car, ball, book, shoe, key, bed). The responses may occur immediately without many errors or prompts. However, the child may not be able to correctly respond if variations of the items (or pictures of the items) are used, or if unfamiliar adults attempt to get the child to name items.

4. Identifies 16 to 50 items or actions

Typically, the size of a child's vocabulary begins to grow more quickly as he experiences success in naming activities. He may now be able to identify many variations of the same object (e.g., different types of cars, pictures of cars) and may do so for several different adults without prompts or negative behaviors. In fact, the child may even begin to spontaneously identify some items and actions in his natural environment.

5. Identifies over 100 items or actions and emits short sentences

A strong ability to label items and actions can be seen in a child who easily and quickly acquires new words and retains those words without much retraining. The child may also begin to say combinations of words in describing things in his environment (e.g., "Doggie all gone," "Bye, bye mommy," "Kitty goes meow").

Receptive by Function, Feature, and Class

Often a child can react to an object when given the name of the object, but not when told something about the object or when given a verbal instruction that varies from the specifically trained instruction. For example, a child may be able to touch a car when asked to "Touch the car," but not when asked to "Touch the one you ride in," or "Touch the one that mommy drives." It is important that a child be able to correctly respond to the many variations of verbal instructions that are related to everyday objects and actions in his environment. It would be a very limited skill if a child could only react to a car when someone specifically said the word "car."

1. Cannot identify items based on information about them

Some children may be able to receptively identify a number of items, but they may only be able to do so when given the specific name of the item and not when told something about the item. These children may, or may not, have an extensive receptive repertoire, depending on the specific training that they have received. However, it is not uncommon to find children who can discriminate between dozens of items, but cannot respond correctly when the verbal instruction is changed to describe some feature (e.g., "It has a handle"), function (e.g., "You drink from it"), or class (e.g., dishes).

2. Will identify a few items given synonyms or common functions

There are several very common descriptors of some items that a child may be able to correctly respond to with little training. For example, when shown a cat along with other pictures, the child may be able to find the one that says "meow." Synonyms are another type of a varied verbal stimulus that might easily evoke a correct receptive response. For example, "Touch the kitty" might easily evoke a correct response to a picture of a cat.

3. Will identify 10 items given 1 of 3 functions or features

Some children are able to identify a number of items when given either the functions of the items and/or features of the items. Functions are the things that one can do with the item. Features may be parts of an item that are characteristic of the item such as its elements, color, shape, texture, etc. For example, the child may be able to touch the ball when asked to "Touch the one that bounces," or when asked to "Touch the round one."

4. Will identify 25 items given 4 functions, features or classes

A child may also be able to receptively identify an item when given the class to which that item belongs. For example, the child may be able to touch the toy car

when asked to touch the "toy." When the child can touch a number of different items given a variety of verbal descriptors, they are beginning to acquire a skill that is likely to be frequently encountered in the natural environment.

5. Will identify 100 items given 5 functions, features, or classes

A strong receptive-by-feature-function-and-class repertoire can be seen in a child who easily identifies a wide variety of items and actions when given various information about those items and actions.

Intraverbal

Many language-delayed children have difficulty answering questions and participating in meaningful conversations. Some may be able to answer a few simple questions (e.g., "What is your name?" "What do you like to eat?"), while many cannot. These conversational language skills are very important for social interaction, as well as for the acquisition of academic skills. Conversational skills are clearly a type of language skill that is different from requesting reinforcers (mand) and from labeling objects, actions, and adjectives, etc. (tact). In fact, they are so different that many children with autism or other developmental disabilities never acquire conversational skills, despite a speaking vocabulary of hundreds of words. (Actual conversations are more complicated than the simplification presented here, but for purposes of this assessment these skills form the foundations of conversations. A more detailed treatment of this topic can be found in Chapter 11)

Skinner (1957) calls this significant and separate type of language skill *intraverbal* behavior. (Readers who would like a more detailed treatment of intraverbal behavior, and the wide range of skills it encompass, are referred to the appendix.) The purpose of this part of the assessment is to determine if the child has some of the rudimentary skills necessary for engaging in conversations. An important aspect of this part of the assessment is to ensure that the child is responding to the tester's words and not to any objects that might be present (e.g., the ability to say "dog" when asked to name an animal is caused by the word "animal" and not by the visual presence of a dog).

1. Cannot fill in missing words or parts of songs

One of the simplest types of a rudimentary conversation acquired by typical children is their ability to fill in missing words from songs (e.g., "The itsy bitsy...") and frequently heard phrases (e.g., "The kitty says..."). Also, completing simple word associations such as "Mommy and..." are early forms of conversations. Children who are unable to correctly respond to these verbal-only stimuli may, however, be able to identify a number of objects and ask for some reinforcers.

2. Can fill in a few missing words or provide the sounds of animals

Many children are able to verbally respond to some of the words and phrases they hear. Often these words and phrases are related to their favorite activities or reinforcers, such as videos, TV shows, and songs. For example, a child who enjoys watching Winnie the Pooh videos may be able to complete the phrase "Winnie the..." Commonly associated (and reinforcing) objects and sounds may also occur early, such as animal sounds. A child who enjoys cats may be able to complete the phrase "A kitty says..."

3. Can fill in 10 non-reinforcing phrases or answer 10 questions

It is a little more difficult to fill in phrases involving topics that are not directly relevant or highly reinforcing to the child. For example, if a child can fill in phrases such as "You sleep in your..." or, "You bounce a..." then he is beginning to demonstrate stronger conversational skills. The ability to correctly answer specific questions is also more difficult than simply completing phrases relating to reinforcing words. Questions such as "What do you eat?" "What is your Name?" may emerge early because of their interest to the child (food) and the frequency of contact with the question (children are frequently asked their names).

4. Can fill in 20 phrases or can answer 20 questions with variation

A child who scores at this level is able to fill in a number of statements and answer questions concerning issues directly relevant to his life. The answers are typically quick and do not require any prompting. In addition, the responses are not always the same "rote" words. For example, if asked to name some foods, the child can provide a variety of foods and in a different order each time.

5. Can answer at least 30 questions with variation

A child who can easily answer a number of specific questions, and does so with obvious variation in his answers, is beginning to demonstrate emerging conversational skills.

Letters and Numbers

A surprising number of children with autism learn to identify letters and numbers before they learn to label many objects. Some children may even be able to read several words even though they may have limited labeling, requesting, and conversation skills (this condition is often identified as hyperlexia). While this situation is generally rare (children are not expected to be able to identify numbers and letters at this level), it may provide the tester with some valuable information about the child. In addition, this information may be helpful in designing an intervention program. The purpose of this part of the assessment is to determine if the child knows any letters, numbers, or written words.

1. Cannot identify any letters, numbers, or written words

A child who scores at this level is unable to identify any letters or numbers. It would not be uncommon for a child to have high scores on many of the other areas and a low score on letters and numbers. This low score should not be interpreted as an indicator for intervention, because there may be many other important language skills that the child should learn before letters and numbers.

2. Can identify at least 3 letters or numbers

If the child can label or receptively identify a few letters or numbers they should be given a score of 2. If the child appears to enjoy these activities and acquires new letters quickly, then work should continue on these skills. However, if a substantial number of training trials were required to obtain these successful responses, and the child has low scores in other areas, letters and numbers should probably be put on hold for a while.

3. Can identify at least 15 letters or numbers

A child at this level can label or receptively identify several letters or numbers. A child who scores at this level shows good discrimination skills and could probably acquire a number of additional responses.

4. Can read at least 5 words and identify 5 numbers

Some children can read several words, typically as whole word reading. For some of these children, this type of reading may be very useful for the child and may even help establish other types of language skills. For nonvocal children who score at this level, written words may be an effective form of augmentative communication. The child might also benefit from more intensive training on beginning math skills.

5. Can read at least 25 words and identify 10 numbers

If a child can read 25 words, then reading should be a regular part of his daily program. A number of tasks can be introduced that may help facilitate other aspects of language (e.g., object-word matching, RFFC with words). If the child has very weak vocal or sign skills, but is able to read at this level, he may greatly benefit from the use of written words as a form of augmentative communication. The ability to identify 10 numbers also indicates that various math related activities would be appropriate.

Social Interaction

Many children who have severe language delays also have obvious social deficits. One major reason for this is that much of social behavior involves language. However, some children are quite social and do attempt to interact, or at least try to be near others. However, efforts to teach social interaction to children with autism often fail, in part due to language deficits, but also due to a number of other complex issues related to social interaction that make this training difficult (see Chapter 11).

1. **Does not initiate interactions with others**

   A child at this level is usually uninterested in other people and typically prefers to be isolated. Many children with autism avoid contact with others and often engage in negative behavior when the interaction is forced.

2. **Physically approaches others to initiate an interaction**

   Some children will at least approach other people that they know well, but they may retreat if interaction is requested. These children might engage in some parallel play with other children and may interact with important figures in their life, such

as their parents or a favorite sibling. However, they almost never interact with unfamiliar adults or children.

3. **Readily asks adults for reinforcers**

   A child at this level may approach adults and ask for reinforcers. Many children at this level will still not interact with peers but will interact with several adults. These children may approach peers, but typically do not talk to or interact with the peers.

4. **Verbally interacts with peers with prompts from adults**

   Some children will only interact with peers when prompted to do so by adults. These children might also display attempts to interact with peers and even watch peers play. They also often act like they really would like to play with the other children.

5. **Regularly initiates and sustains verbal interactions with peers**

   A child at this level will seek out other children and play and talk with them (without prompts).

The Behavioral Language Assessment Form

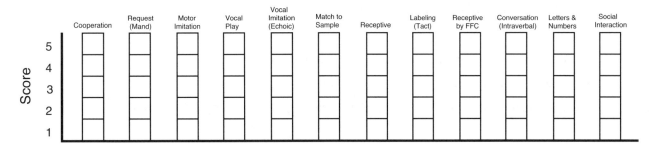

For the following questions, indicate the level of performance that best describes the learner's typical level of performance.

1. COOPERATION WITH ADULTS _____ (enter score)

How easy is it to work with the child?

    1. Always uncooperative, avoids work, engages in negative behavior

    2. Will do only one brief and easy response for a powerful reinforcer

    3. Will give 5 responses without disruptive behavior

    4. Will work for 5 minutes without disruptive behavior

    5. Works well for 10 minutes at a table without disruptive behavior

2. REQUESTS (Mands) _____

How does the learner let his needs and wants be known?

    1. Cannot ask for reinforcers, or engages in negative behavior

    2. Pulls people, points, or stands by reinforcing items

    3. Uses 1-5 words, signs, or pictures to ask for reinforcers

    4. Uses 5-10 words, signs or pictures to ask for reinforcers

    5. Frequently requests using 10 or more words, signs, or pictures

3. MOTOR IMITATION _____

Does the learner copy actions?

    1. Cannot imitate any motor movements

    2. Imitates a few gross motor movements modeled by others

    3. Imitates several gross motor movements on request

    4. Imitates several fine and gross motor movements on request

    5. Easily imitates any fine or gross movements, often spontaneously

4. VOCAL PLAY _____

Does the learner spontaneously say sounds and words?

    1. Does not make any sounds (mute)

    2. Makes a few speech sounds at a low rate

    3. Vocalizes many speech sounds with varied intonations

    4. Vocalizes frequently with varied intonation and says a few words

    5. Vocalizes frequently and says many clearly understandable words

5. VOCAL IMITATION (Echoic)_____

Will the learner repeat sounds or words?

    1. Cannot repeat any sounds or words

    2. Will repeat a few specific sounds or words

    3. Will repeat or closely approximate several sounds or words

    4. Will repeat or closely approximate many different words

    5. Will clearly repeat any word or even simple phrases

6. MATCHING-TO-SAMPLE _____

Will the learner match objects, pictures, and designs to presented samples?

    1. Cannot match any objects or pictures to a sample

    2. Can match 1 or 2 objects or pictures to a sample

    3. Can match 5 to 10 objects or pictures to a sample

    4. Can match 5 to 10 colors, shapes, or designs to a sample

    5. Can match most items and match 2 to 4 block designs

7. RECEPTIVE _____

Does the learner understand any words or follow directions?

    1. Cannot understand any words

    2. Will follow a few instructions related to daily routines

    3. Will follow a few instructions to do actions or touch items

    4. Can follow many instructions and point to at least 25 items

    5. Can point to at least 100 items, actions, persons, or adjectives

8. LABELING (Tacts) _____

Does the learner label or verbally identify any items or actions?

1. Cannot identify any items or actions

2. Identifies only 1 to 5 items or actions

3. Identifies 6 to 15 items or actions

4. Identifies 16 to 50 items or actions

5. Identifies over 100 items or actions and emits short sentences

9. RECEPTIVE BY FUNCTION, FEATURE, AND CLASS _____

Does the learner identify items when given information about those items?

1. Cannot identify items based on information about them

2. Will identify a few items given synonyms or common functions

3. Will identify 10 items given 1 of 3 functions or features

4. Will identify 25 items given 4 functions, features, or classes

5. Will identify 100 items given 5 functions, features, or classes

10. INTRAVERBALS _____

Can the learner fill in missing words or answer questions?

1. Cannot fill in missing words or parts of songs

2. Can fill in a few missing words or provide animal sounds

3. Can fill in 10 non-reinforcing phrases or answer at least 10 simple questions

4. Can fill in 20 phrases or can answer 20 questions with variation

5. Can answer at least 30 questions with variation

11. LETTERS AND NUMBERS _____

Does the learner know any letters, numbers, or written words?

1. Cannot identify any letters, numbers, or written words

2. Can identify at least 3 letters or numbers

3. Can identify at least 15 letters or numbers

4. Can read at least 5 words and identify 5 numbers

5. Can read at least 25 words and identify 10 numbers

12. SOCIAL INTERACTION _____

Does the learner initiate and sustain interactions with others?

1. Does not initiate interactions with others
2. Physically approaches others to initiate an interaction
3. Readily asks adults for reinforcers
4. Verbally interacts with peers with prompts
5. Regularly initiates and sustains verbal interactions with peers

Chapter 3

Interpreting the Behavioral Language Assessment

The purpose of the behavioral language assessment is to provide the tester with enough information to design an individualized language intervention program for a specific child. The results of the initial assessment will vary considerably across children who may have identical diagnostic labels. In fact, it is common for children with the same diagnosis (e.g., autistic disorder) to have significantly different scores in each area of the assessment. These differences in skills make it important to carefully develop an individualized intervention program, rather than attempt to implement a general program for a group of children with the same diagnostic label.

An Item-by-Item Analysis of the Initial Assessment

The assessment is designed to reflect the average performance of typical two- to three-year-old children. Most of these children would receive a score of five on each of the areas in the assessment (with the possible exception of the numbers and letters section). This level of linguistic performance allows typical children to learn from their everyday experiences, and it enables them to effectively engage in social interactions with both peers and adults. Children with severe language delays, who have failed to acquire even the simplest levels of communication, would receive scores in the 1-to-2 range. Most other children with language delays will fall somewhere in between these two ends of the continuum. Scores on each of the separate items can reveal important information about the child and may play a significant role in guiding the establishment of the child's intervention program. The following item-by-item analysis is provided to assist the tester in interpreting the results of the assessment.

Cooperation with Adults

A child who scores a 1 or 2 in this area is mostly uncooperative and may be difficult to teach. This type of child will probably require that some specific behavior management procedures be implemented along with the language program. These procedures are described in Chapter 5. A child who scores a 3 or 4 may still require special procedures but in general will be easier to teach. A child who scores a 5 should readily participate in a language intervention program.

Requests (Mands)

A child who scores a 1 or 2 on the mand assessment will benefit from an immediate and intensive focus on teaching him to use words, signs, or pictures to request his reinforcers. Successful intervention with this type of child may also require that behavior intervention procedures be incorporated into the language intervention program. Both the mand procedures and the behavior intervention procedures recommended for this type of a child are described in Chapter 5. A child who scores a 3 in this area will also require an intensive mand training program. However, a score of 4 or 5 will allow the trainers to focus on some other language areas in addition to the mand training.

Motor Imitation

A child who scores a 1 on the motor imitation assessment will benefit from an immediate focus on this skill. This child would probably not be a candidate for sign language (unless the score on vocal imitation is also a 1, then signs are probably indicated over speech as an immediate response form). If the child scores a 2 in this area, training on motor imitation should still be a major focus of the intervention plan (these procedures are described in Chapter 6). A child who receives a 2, but fails to score above 1 on vocal imitation, would probably be a candidate for sign language. A higher score on vocal imitation may indicate a focus on speech as a response form, but this decision will probably require a further analysis (see Chapter 4 for more information). A score of 3 or 4 on motor imitation will allow the trainers to focus on other areas, but still they should continue to work on improving the child's ability to imitate others. A score of 3 or 4 on imitation and a score of 1 or 2 on echoic would most likely indicate that the child could benefit from the initial use of sign language as a response form. A score of

5 on imitation would indicate that intervention is not necessary in this area, but it may be used to develop sign language, play skills, social interaction, or as interspersal trials (i.e., mixing previously acquired responses in between the more difficult responses) to increase the child's success rate in language training activities.

Vocal Play

A child who scores a 1 or 2 on vocal play will benefit from special procedures to increase this behavior (these procedures are described in Chapter 6). If a child with a score of 1 or 2 also scores lower on the vocal imitation than on the motor imitation, then the child may benefit from sign language. A nonverbal child who scores 3 or 4 on vocal play may be able to quickly acquire vocal language, provided the appropriate training is given. A score of 5 on vocal play (and the absence of other obvious signs of disorders) is a possible indicator that the child (if less than 3 years old) may simply be a late talker.

Vocal Imitation (Echoic) and Articulation

A score of 1 on vocal imitation indicates that it may be quite difficult to immediately teach the child vocal language. If the child also receives a score of 2 or more on motor imitation, then he may make faster progress with sign language. A score of 2 may make it possible to pursue speech, depending on the score on imitation and vocal play. Procedures to increase vocal imitation skills are described in Chapter 6. A score of 3 or 4 on vocal imitation clearly indicates that speech is the desired response form. A score of 5 on vocal imitation (and the absence of other obvious signs of disorder) is also a possible indicator that the child (if less than 3 years old) may be a late talker, unless vocal imitation is too strong (i.e., echolalia).

Matching-to-Sample

A score of 1 on matching-to-sample tasks indicates that the child is unable to attend to visual stimuli or discriminate among visual stimuli (providing that the child at least tries). A nonverbal child who is unable to match items would most likely not be appropriate for a picture communication system (see Chapter 4 for more information). Procedures to increase matching skills are described in Chapter 6. A child who scores a 2 or 3 on matching-to-sample tasks is showing the beginning signs of this skill, and procedures to strengthen this important ability should be included in the child's curriculum. A score of 4 or 5 presents a child with a well-developed matching ability. A nonverbal child who scores this high on matching, and very low on vocal and motor imitation, may be successful on a picture exchange or picture pointing system (but see Chapter 4).

Receptive Language

A child who has a score of 1 on the receptive assessment will benefit from an immediate focus on this skill. This child may also require that behavior intervention procedures be incorporated into the language intervention program. Both the receptive procedures and the behavior intervention procedures recommended for a child scoring

at this level are described in Chapter 6. A child who scores a 2 or 3 in this area will also require an intensive receptive training program. However, a score of 4 or 5 will allow the trainers to focus on other language areas, in addition to receptive training.

Labeling (Tacting)

A child who has a score of 1 on the tact assessment, and a low score on the mand assessment, should receive mand training rather than tact training at this time (see Chapter 5). If the child can already request several reinforcers (or is beginning to acquire this skill), then initial tact training should be initiated (see Chapter 6). A child who scores a 2 or 3 in this area should begin to receive more intensive tact training (see Chapter 7), along with training on the other types of language discussed thus far. If a child scores a 4 or 5 on the tact assessment, then he should be ready for more advanced types of language training (see Chapters 8, 9, 10, and 11).

Receptive by Function, Feature, and Class (RFFC)

A score of 1 or 2 on RFFC is not uncommon for a child who has a very small vocabulary. Typical children do not develop this skill until they have acquired a number of tacts and receptive responses. If the child does have at least 50 tacts and receptive responses, it is probably appropriate to begin working on developing RFFC skills. Procedures for teaching RFFC can be found in Chapter 8. A child who scores a 3 or 4 in the RFFC area probably has a fair amount of language and is ready for training on conversation skills. Procedures to develop conversation skills can be found in Chapter 9. A score of 5 on RFFC presents a child who has some relatively sophisticated language comprehension skills, but may have verbal deficits in other areas (e.g., conversational skills). A child who has this level of skills may benefit from the more detailed language assessment (Partington & Sundberg, 1998) and the procedures and techniques described in Section 3 of this book.

Intraverbal

A score of 1 or 2 on the intraverbal assessment can be expected for a child who has a labeling and receptive vocabulary of less then 50 words. Such a child may not be ready for intensive training on conversational skills, unless they score at least a 3 on the RFFC assessment. A score of 3 on intraverbal, and scores of 4 or 5 on labeling, receptive, and RFFC probably indicates that a substantial amount of language training time should be spent on developing conversational skills. Procedures for training this type of language can be found in Chapter 9. A score of 4 or 5 on the intraverbal indicates that a child's basic conversational skills are emerging, but the child may benefit from the advanced intraverbal training procedures presented in Chapter 11.

Letters and Numbers

A score of 1 or 2 on letters and numbers can also be expected for a child who has not acquired a sizable number of labeling and receptive responses. Therefore, training on numbers and letters would not be appropri-

ate for a child with a minimal speaking vocabulary (unless the child presents some savant-like abilities in this area, which is not uncommon for some children with autism). A child with a score of 3 or 4 on letters and numbers might benefit from some additional training in this area, especially if his labeling, receptive, and conversational scores are 4 or 5. However, it should be kept in mind that typical children do not readily acquire reading or math skills until they have thousands of words in their speaking vocabulary. Therefore, it is important to not overstress this skill, unless, as previously mentioned, the child shows some unique ability to acquire reading and math. A score of 5 on this part of the assessment may indicate that the child could benefit from further assessment (Partington & Sundberg, 1998) and instruction on these skills. Procedures to teach more advanced reading and math skills to children with language delays are not presented in this book, but they can be found in a number of academic programs designed for typical children (e.g., Distar Reading and Distar Math programs).

Social Interaction

A score of 1 or 2 is characteristic of many children with autism and other developmental disabilities, especially if their scores are low on the other sections of the assessment. A child who has very weak verbal skills is unlikely to be successful at social interaction; in fact, the child may experience a substantial amount of social punishment for attempts to socially interact. A child who scores at this level will probably benefit more from a focus on developing the prerequisite verbal skills (e.g., labeling, requesting, receptive, RFFC, and rudimentary conversation) before attempting to place an emphasis on social interaction. A child who scores a 3 or 4 is beginning to demonstrate the ability to verbally interact with others, and may benefit from the procedures described in Chapter 11. A score of 5 demonstrates a child's readiness for more advanced social training, and that the natural contingencies that shape more advanced social interaction are most likely operative in this child.

Setting up an Intervention Program

In order to establish an effective intervention program for a particular child, the tester must identify the most appropriate starting point for initial training. It is important that the tester not simply pick the areas with the lowest scores and recommend training begin in those areas. Instead, the tester should review each skill in relation to the entire set of skills identified in the assessment. For example, it would not be appropriate to attempt to teach conversational relationships between words to an individual who cannot label or receptively identify objects and actions. Also, it is usually best to focus on the development of a few key language areas at one time, even though the child may have weaknesses in several of the areas reviewed by the assessment. The selection of the initial objectives for language training is critical for both the child and the person conducting the language training program. It is important to ensure that the participation in the training is relatively fun for the learner and produces outcomes that are likely to be maintained by the

effects of using those skills in the learner's everyday activities. It is also very important to ensure that the instructor is able to observe the learner acquiring skills in a relatively short period of time, in order to maintain his motivation to continue conducting language training activities. Although only a few areas will be selected for the initial intervention, the focus of intervention will be continuously changed as the student acquires new skills. Making these necessary changes will require that someone carefully monitor the child's progress (or lack or progress) and frequently adjust the program accordingly.

In general, the overall strategy of the language intervention program is to develop the child's skills such that he could score at least a 5 on each of the areas of the assessment (with the possible exception of the letters and numbers section). Although a child may have received a score of 5 on some of the areas, he still may need to continue to develop skills in these areas. A score of 5 in a specific area may indicate that that particular skill area may not require as intensive intervention as those skills with a lower score. Section 3 of this book will provide the reader with assessment and teaching recommendations for children who have scored above 5 on the initial assessment.

In an effort to assist the tester in interpreting the assessment, the following five case histories and test profiles will be presented. Each case is presented as representing a general level of verbal skills. It has been our experience that a large number of children experiencing early language delays fall close to one of these levels. There are, of course, several possible combinations of scores and each child will be different, but these case histories may provide the tester with a model for interpreting the assessment and establishing an appropriate intervention program for a specific child.

Five Model Profiles

Level 1 Profile

The first level represents a child who has very few verbal skills and is difficult to teach. This child also may display a variety of behavior problems. A child who is at Level 1 will score mostly ones on the assessment but may have a few twos, probably in the receptive, mand, echoic, or imitation areas (Table 3-1).

Michael

General Observations

Michael is a 3-year-old boy who has been diagnosed as having an autistic disorder. Michael currently attends a special day class in a public school. In addition, Michael receives speech and language therapy twice a week after his school program. Michael lives at home with his parents and two older siblings. The parents have frequently expressed concern about Michael's lack of effective communication skills, his noncompliance with instructions, his temper tantrums, self-stimulation, and his lack of social interaction with peers. Michael does have a few specific reinforcers that he is interested in (e.g., gummy bears, Peter Pan video), but when he is required to work for them, he loses interest.

Table 3-1 — Current Communication Skills

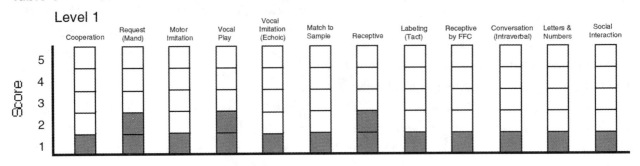

Cooperation with Adults

Michael does not readily comply with instructions or requests. He does follow a few instructions, but only when the situational context provides him with multiple cues (i.e., prompts) as to what is being requested from him. For instance, he will come to the table when called if he is hungry, and his parents are standing at the table with food on his plate, and a parent has recently spent time in the kitchen preparing the food in his sight. Michael is also likely to respond to highly reinforcing instructions where responses are clearly followed by a desired item or activity (e.g., "Let's go for a ride"). Michael does not comply with specific (out of context) instructions, even when he has previously demonstrated that he knows what is being requested of him. Attempts to have him comply with known requests usually result in him engaging in disruptive behavior (e.g., whining, crying, attempting to grab desired items from the parents). In other situations where he is requested to respond, he will simply walk away from the person and attempt to gain access to another reinforcing item.

Requesting (Manding)

Michael does not use words to ask for his needs and wants. However, he has occasionally said "Up" to be lifted up. His method of asking for his needs and wants typically consist of pulling his parents to the location of a desired object (e.g., pulling them to the refrigerator) or whining and crying until he gets what he wants. Attempts to get Michael to use words to ask for reinforcers typically results in whining or running away and not responding with words. While Michael clearly wants reinforcers (e.g., a gummy bear), his tendency to respond clearly drops when a specific demand is placed on him. For example, Michael will readily take a gummy bear if it is offered to him, but if he is asked to perform a clearly known task in order to get the gummy bear, he no longer wants the candy and looks for a free reinforcer (e.g., a stim-toy such as lint).

Motor Imitation

Michael has never been observed to imitate the actions of others. When asked to imitate an action, he will not (or cannot) comply.

Vocal Play

Michael will occasionally say a few sounds and approximations to words when by himself, but when asked to say specific sounds or words he will not respond.

Vocal Imitation (Echoic) and Articulation

Michael's echoic repertoire is extremely weak. He has never demonstrated any ability to repeat a sound or word when asked to do so.

Matching-to-Sample

Although Michael has been observed to independently place a few puzzle pieces in their correct position in an inset puzzle board, he will not do this or other matching tasks on request. He is unsuccessful at all specific attempts to get him to match objects or pictures with identical items. Thus, while he appears to be able to demonstrate some rudimentary matching skills, he cannot readily match items to samples of those items.

Receptive Language

Michael can follow some instructions associated with routines and everyday activities (e.g., "Time to eat," "Go to the table"), but he will only follow them if he wants to (e.g., he is hungry), and there are contextual cues. He is unable to receptively distinguish between items when asked to do so. For example, when presented with two items, and asked to touch a specific item, he is unable to successfully comply with the request.

Receptive by Function, Feature, and Class (RFFC)

Michael is unable to point to any stimuli when given verbal information about the item (e.g., "Touch the one you eat with").

Labeling (Tact)

Michael cannot name any of the familiar items in his environment.

Intraverbal

Michael is unable to complete any fill-in-the-blank songs or phrases or engage in any type of simple word association or conversation.

Letters and Numbers

Michael cannot identify any letters or numbers.

Social Interaction

Michael occasionally approaches his parents when he needs or wants something that he is unable to get by himself. However, he will not approach others if it is possible to get his needs met without engaging in social interactions.

Language Skills Analysis and Recommendations

Michael requires some specialized teaching because he is nonverbal, noncompliant, and has learned to obtain his reinforcers with negative behaviors. The two most important areas to focus on now for Michael are compliance training and mand training (see Chapter 5 for the specific procedures). Training in both of these areas will require some intensive instruction in order to be successful. Michael must learn to ask for what he wants using specific words or sign language without physical or imitative prompts (see Chapter 4 for guidelines on deciding whether speech or some form of augmentative communication would be appropriate for a child such as Michael). Also, Michael needs to learn to comply with adult instructions and should receive intensive intervention in this area as well. Michael must learn that he must to do something specific in order to get a reinforcer. A compliance-training program can be designed so that it is fun and seems like play to Michael, while establishing control over his behaviors. Once compliance is stronger and specific words or signs are learned as requests, it should be much easier to teach Michael some of the other language skills identified above.

Some Suggested IEP Objectives

1. Michael will learn 10 expressive words or signs (mands) for his reinforcers.

2. Michael will use his words or signs to ask for reinforcers at least 20 times per day.

3. Michael will immediately comply with at least 25 different instructions per day without emitting negative behavior or attempts to escape.

4. Michael will comply with 10 different motor instructions (e.g., jump, run).

5. Michael will imitate at least 10 different motor actions when asked to do so.

6. Michael will echo at least 5 different sounds or words when asked to do so.

7. Michael will receptively identify 20 different items when asked to do so.

Level 2 Profile

A child who scores around Level 2 is likely to have some simple forms of communication and be a little more cooperative with adults. However, this child may also display a variety of behavior problems. A Level 2 child will score mostly twos on the assessment, but may have a few threes, probably in the receptive, mand, echoic, or imitation areas (Table 3-2). A child at this level will probably still require an intensive (and possibly one-to-one) language intervention program.

David

General Observations

David is a 4-year-old boy who has recently been diagnosed as having an autistic disorder. David currently attends school in a special education classroom that has ten children with various developmental disabilities, and one teacher with two aides. David lives at home with his parents and older sister. The parents have concerns about David's failure to understand simple directions and his failure to learn the names of common objects. They have recently been successful in teaching him a few signs for his favorite items, but he is not using the signs consistently. David's teacher noted that he was unable to follow along with the group activities even when provided with numerous physical and gestural prompts. He also was unable to follow most verbal instructions and lacked the language skills to verbally interact with his peers. However, David is reinforced by a number of different items and activities (e.g., music, bubbles, toy cars, playing with balls, roughhousing, tickles, and a wide variety of food items).

Table 3-2 — Current Communication Skills

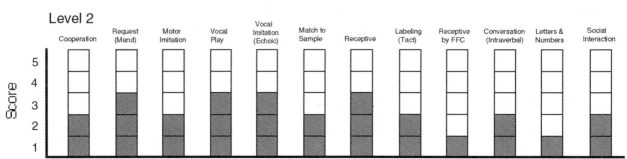

Cooperation with Adults

David does not readily comply with instructions or requests, especially when he is required to give up reinforcers (e.g., coming in from outside), or when he is asked to perform academic or language tasks. For example, he does not follow more than a few instructions that require him to use his signs or engage in activities that he is not interested in, such as fine motor tasks. He has difficulty with these tasks and hence tends to refuse to continue to participate whenever he makes a mistake. In situations that require him to give many responses without reinforcers being made available, he will typically walk away from the task.

Requests (Mands)

David is able to request three items and activities using sign language combined with the first sounds of those words. He can request "Eat," "Up," and "Ball." David will allow others to physically prompt him to make a few other signs including "book," and "swing," but he will not sign these words independently. Otherwise, he will typically cry or tantrum in order to get his wants known.

Motor Imitation

David can imitate few gross motor movements, but he requires a fair amount of verbal prompting and the immediate delivery of reinforcement. He is able to imitatively clap his hands, kick a ball, put his hands on his head, and tap a stick to a drum. He is unable to imitate any fine motor movements, such as picking up items with a pincer grasp or pointing to items with only his index finger.

Vocal Play

David makes a variety of speech sounds with different inflections, especially while playing. However, these vocalizations are only rarely identified by others as being specific words.

Vocal Imitation (Echoic) and Articulation

David will often attempt to imitate a word with an approximation when he is highly motivated for a clearly available reinforcer. For example, when he is requesting items using sign language, he can echo "uhh" for up, "bah" for ball, and "ee" for eat. However, he will quickly attempt to leave (escape) a situation in which he is not successful in vocally imitating a word (i.e., after two unsuccessful attempts to say the word or sound).

Matching-to-Sample

When given an object or a picture of an item that is one of David's favorite reinforcers (e.g., a ball), and a display of two objects or pictures, one of which is identical to his object or picture, David can place the object or picture with the identical item. He is unable to match many items and pictures, especially those items or pictures that are not of interest to him. David is also unable to match colors or shapes.

Receptive Language

David can follow a few instructions without contextual cues (e.g., "Come here," "Raise your arms," and "Clap hands" without any gestural prompts provided). He can also follow numerous instructions in the context of ongoing activities (e.g., "Throw it away," after drying his hands with a paper towel). David is able to follow directions to select and give approximately 5 commonly encountered objects upon request when they are presented in an array of 2 items on a table. However, he is unable to receptively identify pictures of items.

Receptive by Function, Feature, and Class (RFFC)

David cannot point to any objects or pictures when given specific verbal information about the item, but not its specific name. For example, he cannot touch a dog or a cat when asked to touch the one that says "woof, woof" or "meow."

Tact

David can label a few items including some reinforcing items (i.e., food, ball, and music) and cat and dog. He is unable to tact any actions, people, colors, or letters.

Intraverbal

David can fill in a few missing words from some favorite songs (e.g., "Winnie the..."), and approximate "meow" when someone says "A kitty says..." However, he cannot answer any specific questions or fill in any words from common phrases.

Letters and Numbers

David does not know any letters or numbers.

Social Interaction

David frequently approaches his parents and other familiar adults, and, if prompted, he will ask for his favorite items using sign language. He does enjoy being near others and is reinforced by people smiling at him.

Language Skills Analysis and Recommendations

The most important areas to focus on for David at this time are for him to learn to ask (mand) for a wider variety and a greater number of items and activities (Chapter 5), and to increase his motor and vocal imitation skills (Chapters 6 and 7). David could also benefit from some beginning training on labeling (tact) and receptive language (Chapters 6 and 7). However, it is very important to continue his success in being able to gain access to reinforcing items and events with specific signs and/or vocalizations. By increasing his range of requests, it will be easier to maintain his motivation to participate in a wide variety of learning tasks. Because of his poor echoic skills, his low motivation to participate in vocal imitation tasks, and his poor fine motor skills, it would be desirable to continue to teach him signs that do not require fine motor movements. At the same time, he should be working on imitating a wider variety of fine motor movements and simple vocalizations. He should also be encouraged to vocalize as he uses his signs (especially when he is attempting to gain access to powerful reinforcers). In addition, David should continue to develop his matching-to-sample skills and other nonverbal tasks, while slowly increasing the number of responses, or the amount of time working on tasks, prior to earning a reinforcer.

Some Suggested IEP Objectives

1. David will learn 10 new signs or words (mands) for his reinforcers.

2. David will use his signs or words to ask (mand) for reinforcers at least 30 times per day.

3. David will echo approximations to at least 15 different sounds or words upon request.

4. David will comply with a total of 10 different motor instructions (e.g., jump, run).

5. David will imitate at least 20 different motor actions when asked to do so.

6. David will receptively identify 10 different items when presented in an array of 2 items or pictures.

7. David will be able to tact (name) a total of 10 different items or pictures.

8. David will be able to match objects to corresponding pictures presented in an array of three pictures, and pictures to objects in a similar array.

Level 3 Profile

A child who scores around Level 3 is likely to have some more advanced communication skills, be more cooperative with adults, and acquire new words or signs at a quicker pace. However, this child may also display a variety of behavior problems. A Level 3 child will score mostly threes on the assessment, but may have a few fours, probably in the receptive, mand, echoic, or imitation areas (Table 3-3). A child at this level will still probably require an intensive language intervention program.

Sara

General Observations

Sara is a 5-year-old girl who has recently been diagnosed as having a pervasive developmental disorder. Sara currently attends a communicatively handicapped class operated by the county school system. She lives at home with her natural parents and two sisters, one younger and one older. The parents have concerns about Sara's slow language development and her inappropriate behaviors that consist of non-compliance and temper tantrums. Sara is reinforced by a wide variety of items and activities (e.g., food, toys, swings, videos, rides), and she will often work and play independently at tasks and fun activities for extended periods of time.

Table 3-3 — Current Communication Skills

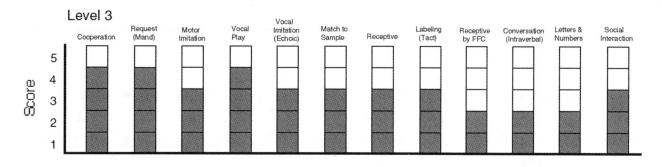

Cooperation with Adults

Sara is usually cooperative with adults and will follow instructions, but if she does not want to do what adults want her to do, she will scream, cry, hit, and often fall to the floor. The tantrums are brief in duration but quite disruptive. Sara will sit at a table and do academic and language tasks for brief periods of time, but when she is ready to get up she will tantrum if she is not allowed to do so.

Requests (Mand)

Sara can ask for a number of her reinforcers, but it is often hard to understand what she is saying. When she is not understood, or if the reinforcer is not immediately delivered, she will often tantrum or attempt to hit the adult.

Motor Imitation

Sara can imitate the motor behavior of others, but she only does so when she is prompted (i.e., she does not spontaneously imitate others). She has difficulty with fine motor imitation and often tantrums when attempts are made to teach her better skills.

Vocal Play

Sara engages in a substantial amount of spontaneous vocal play (especially while playing with toys and watching videos). She emits a wide variety of words and phrases, with varied intonations and pitch. These vocalizations could be best characterized as "happy sounds."

Vocal Imitation (Echoic) and Articulation

Sara can echo several words and phrases, but usually they are approximations to the presented model. She has particular difficulty with the sounds "rrr" and "lll," as well as several blends (e.g., "st," "sp," "fl"), and if she is pushed too much to say these sounds, she will tantrum.

Matching-to-Sample

When given an item or picture of an item and a display of two items or pictures, one of which is exactly identical to her item or picture, Sara can place the objects and pictures with the identical item. She cannot match items and pictures to other items or pictures that are not exactly identical to her item (e.g., different colored cups). Sara is also unable to match a sequence of colored blocks.

Receptive Language

Sara can follow instructions associated with familiar routines and everyday activities (e.g., "Get your coat," "Sit down"), and she can follow instruction to do simple actions out of context (e.g., "Jump," Clap your hands"). Also, Sara can make simple discriminations between approximately 10 objects when shown 2 objects at a time.

Receptive by Function, Feature, and Class

Sara is unable to point to any objects or pictures when given verbal information about them but not their specific name (e.g., "Touch the one you ride").

Labeling (Tacting)

Sara can name approximately 10 common objects and pictures. However, her articulation is poor, and the listener needs to know what word she is trying to say. Sara cannot correctly identify any actions or correctly use adjectives, prepositions, or pronouns. When pushed to respond, Sara will often tantrum.

Intraverbal

Sara's intraverbal skills are the weakest of the different types of expressive language. However, she can correctly respond to a few fill-in-the-blank type questions involving songs and animal sounds, but she cannot answer "Wh" questions, or verbally categorize objects, or verbally sequence activities. For example, she can say "cat" when asked to name an animal that goes "meow," but was unable to specifically name any animals. As with some of her other language tasks, Sara will often tantrum when pushed to respond.

Letters and Numbers

Sara can receptively identify the letters A, B, C, and S and the numbers 1 and 2, but cannot label them.

Social Interaction

Sara demands a lot of attention from adults. Most of her interactions revolve around her specific wants, rather than any conversation or playful interactions. She does not socially interact with other children, but will tolerate them being near her.

Language Skills Analysis and Recommendations

The most important area to focus on for Sara at this time is her mand repertoire (Chapter 5). Sara may also be a candidate for speech therapy and/or for sign language as a temporary support for her vocal behavior (see Chapter 4). Also, Sara needs to learn to identify (tact) a wider variety of objects and pictures (Chapter 7) and improve her imitation skills (Chapter 6). In addition to intensive language training, Sara could probably benefit from a consistent behavior intervention program.

Some Suggested IEP Objectives

1. Sara will immediately comply to at least 20 different verbal instructions per day without emitting negative behavior or attempts to escape.

2. Sara will be able to ask for 10 different reinforcing items.

3. Sara will correctly echo at least 50 different sounds or words upon request.

4. Sara will imitate at least 25 different fine and gross motor actions when asked to do so.

5. Sara will be able to receptively discriminate between 40 different objects when asked to do so.

6. Sara will be able to label 40 different objects or actions.

7. Sara will have less than one tantrum per day.

Level 4 Profile

A Level 4 child will score mostly fours on the assessment, but may have a few fives, probably in the cooperation, receptive, mand, echoic, or imitation areas (Table 3-4). This level of performance is generally indicative of a learner who has acquired the ability to request several reinforcing items and activities, can receptively understand several words and directions, has good imitation skills, has the ability to label numerous common items, and will participate in language acquisition activities. However, a child at this level has not developed a strong ability to identify objects and pictures when the items are not specifically named (RFFC), or an ability to talk about items or activities when they are not present (conversations).

Ron

General Observations

Ron is a 5-year, 10-month-old boy who has been diagnosed with an autistic disorder. Ron lives with his older sister and natural mother and father. He has recently started attending a special day class at his local school, and has a 1:1 aide for some of the time at school. Ron's parents have concerns about Ron's language delays, his mouthing of items (including his left index finger), and his toileting deficits. Ron is reinforced by a wide variety of items and activities (e.g., music, books, toys, candy, parks, roughhousing), and engages in a fair amount of spontaneous language.

Table 3-4 — Current Communication Skills

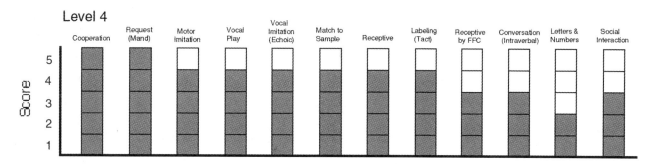

Cooperation with Adults

Ron is cooperative with adults and requests academic work. He will sit at a table and work on language and other related tasks for up to 30 minutes. He rarely engages in negative behavior during this time, except when he gets tired, then he begins to put his fingers in his mouth as well as mouth items on the table.

Requesting (Manding)

Ron can easily ask for numerous reinforcers and does so frequently without prompts and with full sentences (e.g., "I want to go for walk," "I want Frosty (snowman tape)," "Rewind it"). However, he cannot ask simple questions using "Wh" words, nor can he ask for specific items that are missing from a set of materials (e.g., the missing parts of Mr. Potato Head).

Motor Imitation

Ron's ability to imitate others is also fairly strong, especially when doing gross motor activities (e.g., jumping, clapping). He does have difficulty imitating fine motor movements and imitating facial expressions and mouth movements. However, he does not spontaneously imitate others.

Vocal Play

Ron engages in a substantial amount of vocal behavior (especially while playing with toys). He emits a wide variety of words and phrases, some of which are repetitive, or in the form of "delayed echolalia" (e.g., self-reprimands, phrases previously heard on TV).

Vocal Imitation (Echoic) and Articulation

Ron's echoic skills are quite strong; however, when repeating words on request, he often adds an "ah" sound to the end of words.

Receptive Language

Ron's receptive language skills are also quite strong. He can follow simple instructions (e.g., "Go get apple from the refrigerator") and discriminate between a variety of objects. Ron knows 11 body parts and some colors. He can follow several instructions to engage in an action without a model (i.e., clap, jump, stomp, and put arms up). Ron can also select approximately 50 named items from an array of 3 items.

Labeling (Tacting)

Ron can label approximately 40 common objects and actions, and uses some full sentences. However, he cannot use adjectives, pronouns, or prepositions correctly.

Receptive by Function, Feature, and Class

Ron can correctly point to a few specific items when the items are described by their functions (e.g., "Touch the one you eat"), or when given some information about the item (e.g., "Touch the one you play with"). However, he is unable to identify items when given specific features of the items (e.g., "Touch the one that has wheels"), or the class of the item (e.g., "Touch the furniture"). In addition, he cannot correctly select items from a large array of pictures and objects.

Intraverbal

Ron can correctly respond to some fill-in-the-blank questions involving words from familiar songs and common phrases (e.g., "You sleep in your..."), and he can give his name and age upon request. However, he was unable to verbally answer many common "Wh" questions, verbally categorize objects, or verbally sequence activities. For example, he is able to sing parts of the "Happy Birthday" song, but was unable to verbally identify what things he liked to eat, or some kinds of animals, but he could identify those items when shown the corresponding pictures.

Letters and Numbers

Ron could rote count to 4 and identify about 6 different numbers. He was unable to identify any letters or words.

Social Interaction

Ron easily asks his parents and familiar teachers for reinforcers, but he is very shy around unfamiliar people. When around other children Ron plays by himself, often putting his fingers in his mouth when other children approach him.

Language Skills Analysis and Recommendation

The most important areas to focus on for Ron at this time are (1) his weak RFFC skills (Chapter 8), (2) his weak conversation skills (Chapter 9), and (3) his weak problem solving and requesting (with "Wh" questions) skills (Chapter 12). Ron could also benefit from additional training on labeling and receptive identification (Chapter 10). In addition, Ron could benefit from some regular contact with non-handicapped peers in order to facilitate social interaction. Ron has great potential for acquiring more effective language skills, but his rate of acquisition will be directly related to the frequency and type of training provided. Parents and teachers must require a high rate of responding from Ron, especially intraverbal responding (at least several hundred correct responses per day).

Some Suggested IEP Objectives

1. Ron will be able to ask 10 different "Wh" questions.

2. Ron will be able to ask for at least 25 different needed, but missing, items.

3. Ron will be able to request reinforcers from peers at least 5 times per day.

4. Ron will be able to point to 50 different items when given a function, feature, or class of the item (e.g., "Touch the one that you ride").

5. Ron will be able to answer 15 new "Wh" questions (e.g., "Where do you keep the milk?" "Where is your pillow?").

6. Ron will be able to state at least 3 items from at least 5 classes of items/categories (e.g., "Name some animals, toys, things you wear, things that fly, things you ride in").

Level 5 Profile

A child who scores mostly fives on the assessment, but is more than 4 years old and seems to have some type of language problems (Table 3-5), may benefit from the more detailed assessment (Partington & Sundberg, 1998) and the material presented in Section 3 of this book. Often, language deficits are obvious, such as articulation problems, lack of spontaneity or novelty, repetitive topics, or awkward verbal interaction. However, some children may have a sizable vocabulary, but still have clear language deficits. The identification of these deficits may not be completely identified with the current assessment.

Laurie

General Observations

Laurie is a 7-year, 11-month-old girl who has been diagnosed with an expressive language disorder. Laurie lives with her natural mother and father and two younger brothers. She is fully integrated into a 2nd grade class at her local school and has a daily 45-minute pull-out session for speech and language therapy. Laurie's parents have concerns about Laurie's language delays, including her inability to form complete sentences or stay on a topic of conversation for any length of time. Laurie is reinforced by a wide variety of items and activities (e.g., dressing up, music, rides, videos, attention).

Table 3-5 — Current Level of Communication

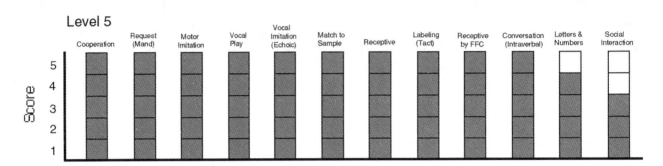

Cooperation with Adults

Laurie is quite cooperative with adults and requests work. She will sit at her desk in her classroom without disrupting the other children, but will also often drift away from attending to the teacher or others who are talking.

Requesting (Manding)

Laurie can easily ask for her reinforcers, but often does so in fragmented phrases and incomplete sentences. She rarely asks questions, but will do so if it is something extremely important to her (e.g., "What happen my new hat?" "When we eat?"). However, she does not spontaneously ask questions seeking other information, such as the names of things (e.g., "What's that?"), or the causes or function of things (e.g., "Why?" and "How?").

Motor Imitation

Laurie's ability to imitate the fine and gross motor movements of others is very strong. In fact, she imitates the behavior of others spontaneously and frequently, often to the embarrassment of her parents.

Vocal Play

Laurie engages in a substantial amount of vocal behavior (especially while watching videos and listening to music).

Vocal Imitation (Echoic) and Articulation

Laurie can easily repeat almost any word or phrase.

Receptive Language

Laurie's receptive language skills are fairly strong. She can easily follow simple instructions (e.g., "Can you get me the car keys") and discriminates between hundreds of objects when asked to do so, but she has trouble responding to instructions involving multiple parts (e.g., "Go to the office and give your note to the secretary"). She also seems to have difficulty understanding complex topics that others her age can follow (e.g., stories, daily problems, current events).

Receptive by Function, Feature, and Class

Laurie can correctly point to a number of specific items when the items are described (e.g., "It has stripes"), or when given some information about the item (e.g., "You drink from it"). But she frequently has trouble (she reports that she "gets mixed up") correctly identifying the class that items belong to (e.g., clothing, furniture, food, toy).

Labeling (Tacting)

Laurie can tact about 200 common objects, actions, adjectives, and prepositions. However, she frequently has trouble with pronouns and constructing complete sentences. Her speech is fragmented, often omitting articles, conjunctions, and the appropriate modifiers. She is typically quiet and does not spontaneously identify items or activities in her daily environment.

Intraverbal

Laurie can correctly respond to a number of specific questions that occur frequently, such as "How are you?" 'Where do you live?" "What do you like to watch on T.V.?" However, she was able to verbally answer only select "Wh" questions, verbally categorize objects, and verbally sequence activities. It is very difficult for her to maintain focus on a specific topic. For example, when asked about her recent trip to the zoo, she quickly changed the topic of conversation to the scarecrow from the Wizard of Oz. She was also unable to answer questions about many current events or topics.

Letters and Numbers

Laurie could count to 10 and read about 15 words. She likes stories and frequently requests that her mother read to her.

Social Interaction

Laurie frequently interacted with her family members but rarely interacted with other children, unless she was heavily prompted to do so. When social interaction with peers was prompted, she often acted very "silly," and the other children would have a hard time responding to her and often lost interest in participating.

General Teaching Recommendations

Laurie has several critical verbal deficits. They appear to mainly be in the areas of conversation (intraverbal) and complex requests (mand). In general, Laurie will benefit from the procedures described in the second part of this book. However, the establishment of specific IEP objectives will require further assessment (see Partington & Sundberg, 1998).

Summary

The initial language assessment is designed to identify major language deficits for children who have clearly limited language skills. The purpose of this assessment is to identify a starting point for a language intervention program, and direct the reader to specific procedures in the training sections of this book. The assessment can also be used as a general tracking system, but the reader is referred to Partington and Sundberg (1998) for a more detailed assessment and tracking system. The following chapter will assist the reader in determining if a child could benefit from augmentative communication, and if so, which type might be the most effective for a given child.

Chapter 4

Augmentative Communication

Most children who fail to learn to talk can learn communication skills through augmentative communication (AC). However, determining which type of AC to use, and how to start and maintain a specific system, is often complicated. For some children, AC may be quite successful and also lead to speech, but for others it may completely fail or not result in any vocal improvement. The success or failure of AC is related to a number of variables, but the first step in using AC successfully involves selecting a system that is the most appropriate for a specific child. This task is often not easy because there are many different choices, and there are not a lot of data or research that support one system over another. The purpose of this chapter is to identify the AC options, and provide the reader with specific guidelines for effective decision making.

Successful communication requires that a child be able to produce words that others can understand. These words can be in the form of speech, but speech is not necessary for effective communication. There are four general options for selecting a form of communication for a specific child: (1) speech, (2) sign language, (3) picture pointing and exchange systems (including computer generated speech), and (4) independent writing, typing, or pointing to words. There is an extensive body of research on each of these alternatives; however, there is relatively little empirical or conceptual research compar-

ing them with each other (for a review of the research that is available see Shafer, 1993). Often, decisions to use one system or another are based on the personal preference of the trainers, rather than on the child's individual abilities and needs or on any empirical evidence supporting a specific system (Reichle, Sigafoos, & Remington, 1991).

Speech as the Primary Goal

Speech is the most desired form of communication for a number of reasons. Perhaps the most significant advantage of speech is the availability of a large speaking community that can easily model, prompt, and reinforce vocal words without special training (this large community is not available for those who use signs and picture systems). Speech also has the advantage of being portable because it is part of the child's musculature. It is therefore always with the child, so words can be spoken quickly and efficiently. In addition, adult speech sounds are often paired with strong reinforcers being delivered to the child (e.g., hugs, food, attention), resulting in specific speech sounds and patterns becoming reinforcers themselves. A child who babbles similar sounds may be "automatically reinforced" for speaking (i.e., they like hearing sounds that are associated with reinforcers), thus the child is more likely to make these sounds without prompts, and this can substantially increase the child's vocal abilities. (Bijou & Baer, 1965; Skinner, 1957; Sundberg, Michael, Partington, & Sundberg, 1996; Vaughan & Michael, 1982).

Because of these unique properties of speech, spoken language can be the easiest form of communication for humans to acquire, as evidenced by the rapid acquisition of speech by most children even though their parents have no special training in linguistics or language development. However, if speech fails to develop in the typical manner, which is often the case for many developmentally disabled children, speech may become an extremely difficult form of communication to establish.

There are many causes for delayed or defective language development, both organic and nonorganic (Drash & Tudor, 1993). However, it is often difficult to determine exactly why language fails for a specific child, but it is clear that the longer a child goes without speaking, the more difficult it becomes to establish speech (Lovaas, 1977; Van Riper, 1978). Direct speech therapy, while often very effective, may not establish speech for some individuals, especially for those who have long histories of failing to communicate. The muscle control required for speech may simply be too difficult for some nonverbal children, especially for those who have a very limited ability to vocally imitate sounds and words. For these individuals an alternative response form may be the most effective way to generate successful communication (Zangari, et al., in press). However, the ultimate objective is still to establish speech as the child's main form of communication.

The three most common types of alternative or augmentative communication are signing, pointing to or exchanging pictures, and writing (or typing). However, there is a substantial amount of disagreement among researchers and practitioners as to which system is the most effective. Unfortunately, there are no easy answers to this problem, but there are several clear advantages and disadvantages of each system. In addition, since each individual child presents special abilities and disabilities, it is important to consider these individual differences when making a decision about an augmentative system. These three alternatives to speech, and the issues involved in their use, will now be examined in terms of their advantages and disadvantages.

Sign Language

Sign language is the main form of communication used by many members of the deaf community (for more information see Moores, 1978). The signs are made by the hands, and like speech, there are different signs (words) for each referent. For example, the sign for ball (curved fingers making the shape of a ball) is different from the sign for book (flat hands touching then opening, as in opening a book). The use of sign language with nonverbal children has repeatedly proven to be an effective way to generate successful communication (e.g., Bonvillian, Nelson, & Rhyne, 1981; Carr, 1979; Clarke, Remington, & Light, 1988; Fristoe & Lloyd, 1977; Partington, Sundberg, Newhouse, & Spengler, 1994; Reichle, York, & Sigafoos, 1991; Sundberg, 1980). Sign language has many advantages as a type of augmentative communication and only a few disadvantages (Tables 4-1 and 4-2).

The Advantages of Sign Language

If attempts to get a child to speak have clearly failed, then sign language may be more effective as an immediate form of communication. There are a number of advantages of using sign language (Table 4-1), but there are some disadvantages as well. However, the advantages of sign language are substantial, and thus they may mitigate the disadvantages of sign language identified later in the chapter.

Sign language training may be easier than speech training because many nonverbal children cannot echo sounds or words, but they can imitate at least some of the fine or gross motor movements of others. These imitative responses can then be used to teach requesting and labeling with signs (Chapters 5 and 7). For example, if a child can imitate a movement to the mouth, it may be easier to teach the child the sign *eat* than it would be to teach him to say the word *eat*. This ease of training occurs because the response (the movement of the hand) is already strong in the child's repertoire, as opposed to the spoken word, which is not available to the child or teacher. However, it should be pointed out that a strong imitative repertoire is not a prerequisite for the use of signs (see Chapter 5).

If a child does not have a strong motor or vocal imitative repertoire, then it probably will be easier to teach him to imitate a motor movement than to echo a sound. Motor imitation is easier to teach because the teacher can use physical prompting and fading procedures. For imitative training, the child's hands can be physically guided by the teacher to the appropriate position, and then these physical prompts can be faded. This physical prompting procedure is impossible with the vocal musculature, because one cannot directly manipulate the parts of the vocal system to produce specific sounds. The use of physical prompting may make the shaping process easier, while also providing clear and unambiguous models of the appropriate sign. This type of training is most effective if conducted in the context of request (mand) training (see Chapter 5).

Table 4-1 — Advantages of Sign Language

❏ Motor imitation may already be strong in the child's repertoire.

❏ The teachers can use, then fade, physical prompts to teach the sign.

❏ The stimulus and the response often resemble, but do not match, each other (an iconic relation), providing a built in prompt.

❏ The deaf community constitutes a natural verbal community that uses sign language, thus materials and trainers are available.

❏ Signs are free from environmental (mechanical) support, like speech.　▶

❑ Sign language constitutes a topography-based language, making it conceptually similar to speech.

❑ Signs may avoid a negative emotional history associated with speech.

❑ Sign language can improve speech.

Sign language training is also facilitated by the fact that many of the signed responses closely resemble the objects that they represent. The sign "pencil," for example, is made by moving the index finger of one hand across the open palm of the other (as if writing on paper). This iconic relation between the object and the response may make sign acquisition easier than vocal acquisition, because there is a built in prompt for the sign. Spoken English has only a few of these iconic, or onomatopoetic relations (e.g., "woof woof," "vum vum"), and they are of little help in early language acquisition. But it is often the case that these are some of the first types of identifiable communication that some children acquire.

There are several other advantages of sign language that parallel some of the advantages of speech as a form of communication. First, signs, like speech, are completely portable (the response is not dependent on auxiliary equipment), so communication can occur under all potential types of circumstances. Also, the deaf population provides a natural verbal community where sign language is the primary form of communication. This community makes sign language a living language in the sense that it is still growing, changing, and affecting a large number of listeners and speakers. This large number of people currently using sign language also ensures the availability of a variety of materials, teachers, videos, research, and other auxiliary support items necessary for teaching sign language to nonverbal children.

In addition, sign language, like speech, constitutes what has been identified as a topography-based language (Michael, 1985; Potter & Brown, 1997; Shafer, 1993; Sundberg & Sundberg, 1990; Wraikat, Sundberg, & Michael, 1991). In a topography-based language there is a different response topography (i.e., a different word or sign) for each referent. In common sense terms, there is a different word for each object, action, etc. This type of language system can be contrasted with a stimuli-selection based language system (Michael, 1985), where the response topography is the same (e.g., a pointing response), but the stimulus identified is different (e.g., as in a picture communication board). While both types of language can be effective as types of augmentative communication, there are several linguistic advantages of a topography-based system. These two types of language will be compared in more detail following the general presentation of picture systems later in this chapter.

Finally, there are several ways in which sign language may facilitate the establishment of vocal responses and improve language acquisition in general. First, sign language may solve the immediate problem of not being able to verbally interact with others. Signs allow the listeners (e.g., parents, teachers, peers) to immediately understand what the person might be trying to say, thereby permitting the delivery of the desired reinforcer. In addition, this successful verbal interaction provides an excellent opportunity to shape articulation. These points could be made for all types of augmentative communication, but sign language, as a topography-based system, is free from environmental support (i.e., no auxiliary equipment is necessary) and has some unique features that may result in substantial vocal improvement.

First, if trainers speak as they sign, and require and reinforce approximations to spoken words, specific words can become associated with specific signs and successful verbal interactions (e.g., reinforced manding). Therefore, not only might specific speech sounds become paired with specific signs, but specific sounds may also become conditioned reinforcers, and even automatic reinforcers as well. These new forms of reinforcement can strengthen vocal behavior in many ways (e.g., Skinner, 1957; Sundberg et al., 1996). For example, in mand training if the spoken word *eat* is consistently paired with the sign *eat* and the delivery of food, the spoken word *eat* may acquire new evocative effects (i.e., the spoken word *eat* may come to, for example, evoke looking at food without any direct training) and reinforcing effects (Michael, 1983). As a result, the spoken word *eat* may make it more likely that the child will sign *eat* and go to where food is normally served (this behavioral effect has been identified as "functional equivalence";

see for example Dougher, 1994; Hall & Chase, 1991). Also, the establishment of echoic stimulus control, and other types of language involving vocal behavior, may now be easier, especially if vocal behavior already occurs to some degree (Clarke, Remington, & Light, 1988).

Sign language may improve articulation for a number of other reasons as well. If signs begin to evoke specific vocalizations, then signs can be used as a new type of prompt to evoke those specific vocalizations. This type of prompting may be more effective than typical echoic prompts that give away the response form (i.e., model for the child the correct word), making it harder to transfer control to the other types of referents. Also, children learn to sequence motor movements that are often easier to sequence than vocal movements. Once the motor movements are learned, specific vocalizations can be matched with the signs. This sign-vocalization prompt can help in other ways as well. A child can use signs to prompt his own vocalizations. That is, if a nonverbal stimulus (e.g., a specific object) can evoke a sign and a child is able to emit a vocalization under the control of a sign, then he can self-prompt his own vocalizations. For example, when a signing child wants a cup, but there is not one present, when he makes the sign for cup the sign may prompt articulation of the word *cup*. This self-prompting may result in more successful vocal-verbal interactions and more reinforcement for attempts to speak.

The Disadvantages of Sign Language

The primary disadvantage of sign language is that the parents and teachers must learn and use sign language (Table 4-2). Learning to sign may require some extra effort on the part of teachers and parents. Also, a signing environment must be established where signs are consistently reinforced, and models of signing are frequently provided and paired with other forms of reinforcement. The establishment of this verbal community is essential for verbal development (Skinner, 1957; Sundberg, Milani, & Partington, 1977), but these barriers may be difficult to overcome because of the lack of available training and resources and frequent staff turnover. However, it should be pointed out that even a small signing repertoire on the part of trainers might be sufficient to begin sign training.

Sign language has other disadvantages as well. First, because sign language is a topography-based system, each response form (sign) must be individually shaped (unless the individual has acquired a generalized imitative repertoire). This requires that staff have special training in shaping, prompting and fading, and in differential reinforcement procedures. Pointing to pictures (discussed later) eliminates this problem by using the same behavior for all language skills. The use of sign language also requires different training procedures than those used with speech and picture systems. For example, physical and imitative prompts can be used along with echoic and intraverbal prompts (e.g., "sign hat"). Learning these training methods may require extra effort on the part of parents and teachers.

Table 4-2 — Disadvantages of Sign Language

❑ Parents and teachers must have special training in sign language.

❑ Parents and teachers need to use sign language when interacting with the child.

❑ Parents and teachers must shape (teach) each individual signs.

Analysis of Signing Using the Concepts From Skinner's Book Verbal Behavior

Sign language is functionally closer to speech than the other types of augmentative communication. This is primarily because sign language constitutes a topography-based language system (i.e., individual signs for each referent), and it is free from environmental support (i.e., no auxiliary equipment is necessary). As a result, the acquisition of language using signs as a response form is similar to the acquisition of language using speech as a response form. Sign language development seems to parallel speech development in every way, providing there exists a consistent reinforcing verbal community. Data show that when a deaf child is raised by deaf parents who sign as a primary response form, the child acquires language similarly to a hearing child raised by speaking parents (Moores, 1978; Vernon & Koh, 1970; Zwiebal, 1987). Therefore, if the critical people in a nonverbal person's environment do not acquire sign language, then the probability is low that verbal repertoires will develop properly. Below is an analysis of how sign language might affect the acquisition of each type of expressive and receptive language.

The mand repertoire: Signs can be equally effective for manding as speech, provided that the people in the child's environment use and reinforce sign language.

The tact repertoire: Tacting in sign language differs in no significant way from tacting with speech. The key issue again is the presence of a reinforcing signing verbal community.

The intraverbal repertoire: The establishment of sophisticated intraverbal behavior primarily depends on contact with a signing verbal community. Limited exposure to signing models and audiences will make it difficult to establish complex intraverbal behavior. However, with a signing verbal community the development of signed intraverbal behavior will parallel that of spoken intraverbal behavior.

Reading and writing: Since there is no point-to-point correspondence between signs and written words, it is unlikely that reading and writing skills would occur via signing (this development would require speaking or finger spelling). However, intraverbal relations between written words and signs can occur (like with picture systems), providing children with a form of literacy.

The receptive repertoire: Responding to a signed verbal stimulus does not differ conceptually from responding to a spoken verbal stimulus. Therefore, all forms of receptive behavior (including RFFC) are possible with sign language, given a reinforcing verbal community.

Why Sign Language Training Programs Often Fail

A common problem with many sign language training programs is that the child fails to acquire a sizable or useful verbal repertoire. For example, it is often that case that, even after extensive training, a child acquires only a few signs and rarely emits them spontaneously or shows reliable generalization. Typically, these failures are blamed on the general inadequacy of sign language as an augmentative communication system, or the child's low cognitive level. For example, in a generally negative review of the sign language literature Poulton and Algozzine (1980) concluded:

> The literature specifically supports the notion that manual signing can facilitate word-object associations. It does not, however, support the contention that retarded persons attain a functional communication system based on manual signing or that manual signing has become a primary mode of communication for nonverbal retarded individuals (p. 51).

It is true that many research studies and training programs for sign language do not generate a complete language repertoire. However, this result may be due to the procedures and methods used rather than an inherent limitation in the use of signs or in a child's ability to learn to communicate (Table 4-3). There are several reasons why sign language programs often fail. First, many programs fail to start with basic mand training (Sundberg, 1980). Rather, the first signs trained are often complex mands such as "more," "please," "yes," "no," "finished," "help," and "toilet." These mands are difficult to acquire because they are often multiply controlled by complicated motivators and stimuli that frequently change.

"More" as a mand, for example, is a type of language where the response should be under the functional control of some motivation for an increase quantity of what was previously given. This is usually not the source of control for more as it occurs with beginning signers. Children who learn to sign "more" do so easily because of its relation to a variety of immediate reinforcers (e.g., delivery of food, drinks, tickles). Typically, however, the sign "more" simply becomes an all-purpose mand, as evidenced by the child signing "more" before any reinforcer has been delivered. This early training will make it more difficult to teach specific responses for specific motivators later, because the response "more" must first be

---

Table 4-3 — Why Sign Language Training May Fail

❑ First signs taught are not mands.

❑ First signs taught are too complex (e.g., please, yes/no, help, toilet, more, thank you).

❑ First signs may resemble each other too closely (e.g., eat and drink).

❑ First signs may involve a complex response form.

❑ Not enough training trials are provided.

❑ Training is conducted under multiple sources of control (e.g., motivation, picture/object prompts, verbal prompts, English prompts, imitative prompts) and prompts are not faded so "spontaneous" responses can occur.

❑ Individual verbal operants are never established (i.e., mands, tacts, intraverbals) and responses remain multiply controlled.

❑ Stuck at one level too long with no progressive curriculum in place.

❑ A single verbal operant is focused on almost extensively (e.g., tacts, but limited intraverbal or mand training).

❑ Failure to establish a signing verbal community.

❑ Failure to require signs outside of the training sessions.

❑ Failure to generalize to novel stimuli, staff, settings, times, etc.

weakened. In addition, "more" as a verbal response is ineffective when the desired item is absent, which means the response must always be multiply controlled by both the motivators and the presence of the desired item. For example, if a child signs "more" while in the car, it is impossible to know what he wants more of (which is a good indicator that the response is not asking for the repeated delivery of a reinforcer, but is an initial delivery of an unspecified reinforcer). This condition may lead to negative behavior (e.g., screaming, tantrumming, self-injury), because it may be impossible for the adult to deliver the appropriate reinforcer.

A similar analysis could be made for "finished," "please," "toilet," "yes/no," "thank you," "help," and many of the other signs often picked for early sign training. The controlling variables are too complicated to establish a strong and functional mand repertoire. The first mands should be related to clear and strong motivators. Signs such as "eat," "music," "swing," "ball," "up," and "tickle" will be much easier to establish and provide the child with a more functional verbal repertoire (see Chapter 5).

Sign language training may also fail because the first signs, even through basic mands, may resemble (rhyme) each other too closely. The signs "eat" and "drink" for example, are often in the first group of signs taught, but these response forms are very similar. This may result in the blending of signs or in emitting a chain of signs until the right sign occurs (guessing). A program that starts out with topographically different signs may avoid this problem. However, it is also important that there be a sufficient number of training trials to establish the discrimination. Sign training three times a week for 30 minutes will not result in the acquisition of an effective sign language repertoire. Lovaas (e.g., 1977) has frequently pointed out the need for a large number of daily trials in early language training. In addition, sign training (like speech training) requires careful prompting, shaping, and differential reinforcement procedures in order to establish the different response forms. Inadequate training procedures can also lead to failure, such as the frequently observed problem of a child becoming imitatively prompt bound.

If the first signs taught to a child are not mands, but are tacts or receptive responses, then the repertoires are less useful to the child. Skinner (1957) makes the point that mands benefit the speaker, while tacts benefit the listener. A child is more motivated to mand because of the strength of the motivation and the specific reinforcement available. In other words, signing gets the child what *he* wants. With tacts the controlling variables are nonverbal stimuli and generalized conditioned reinforcers. The child is asked to do what the *trainer* wants by identifying, for example, items and pictures. While the reinforcers may be similar (e.g., delivery of food) the controlling variables are very different (powerful motivators vs. nonverbal stimuli). A child who does not care about shoes and hats should not be taught the signs "shoe" and "hat" until several other signs (mands) are strong. In fact, early mand training may facilitate later verbal training in a number of ways. For example, mand training often results in a child being more willing to participate, and it also may facilitate the transfer of control in establishing the other verbal operants (Carroll & Hesse, 1987; Sundberg, 1993a).

Sign language programs may also fail if training is always conducted under multiple sources of control. It is common to teach signs under conditions were there are several antecedent variables present, such as a strong EO, the desired item, and verbal and nonverbal prompts. Attention is typically given to fading out physical and imitative prompts, but often not to fading out verbal and nonverbal sources of control. Under these training conditions spontaneous requests (pure mands) may never occur. Appropriate care must be given to fading out all additional sources of control so that pure verbal operants can be established. If a mand is the targeted verbal operant, the verbal and nonverbal stimuli must be faded out. If a tact is the targeted verbal operant, then the EOs, specific reinforcement, and verbal stimuli must be faded out. If an intraverbal is the targeted verbal operant, the nonverbal stimuli, EOs, and specific reinforcement must be faded out. If the training procedures do not involve training under these conditions, it should be no surprise that the signs will only occur when all these controlling variables are present.

Many sign language training programs fail not only because of teaching under multiple control, but also because they do not establish all of the different types of language. It is common to teach only receptive and tact repertoires while neglecting mand, intraverbal, and RFFC training. The research cited by Poulton and Algozzine (1980) used training procedures that taught object and action naming and receptive identification. In addition, the literature review by Sisson and Barrett (1983) also showed that most programs and research projects failed to teach a complete repertoire (all the verbal skills). For example, when the child could produce a sign (unprompted) that corresponded to a specific object of action, he was given credit for "knowing the meaning of the word." Thus, when a particular object was a strong form of reinforcement, the child was expected to "use his memory to recall the sign." Failure to do so was attributed to the child's "defective cognitive system" rather than the inadequacies of the training program. Even most of the procedures described in the behavioral literature on sign training (e.g., Carr, Binkoff, Kologinsky & Eddy, 1978; Kahn, 1981; Kotkin, Simpson, & Desanto, 1978) do not include steps to, for example, teach a person to ask for something when it is absent or missing (manding), or emit a response solely under the control of verbal stimuli (intraverbal).

Poulton and Algozzine (1980) also point out that the children were not using their signs outside of the training sessions. This is a problem of generalization training, and the failure to establish an effective verbal community. Both of these elements are essential to the development of a sign language training program. If the training does not include procedures to bring the signs under the control of different stimuli, people, places, time, etc., then it is likely that the repertoire will be of less functional value to the child. In addition, if attempts are not made to establish a signing community, then opportunities to engage in signing will not be reinforced and models of more complex signing and social interaction involving signing will not be available. If these variables were not present with speech training, we would certainly expect to see language delays, yet there is often no attempt to establish generalization or a verbal community for signers. When signs do not develop in a pattern similar to speech, the blame is typically placed on the use of signs or the limitations of the child.

In conclusion, sign language has several advantages that make it an appealing alternative response form. Especially attractive is the fact that it is a topography-based system that is free from environmental support. In addition, verbal development with sign language appears to closely parallel verbal development with speech, while this is not the case with the other response forms. However, sign programs often fail because of a wide variety of instructor errors. Sign language training also requires that instructors learn how to sign. This barrier alone is often why sign language is not tried, thus children who could make substantial linguistic gains

with sign language may remain nonverbal or may use a less efficient system.

Picture Communication Systems

Pointing to (touching, looking at, exchanging, etc.) pictures, symbols, or pictures on the keyboards of computer-operated devices that electronically produce words has also proven to be an effective type of communication for nonverbal children (e.g., Bondy & Frost, 1993; Hurlbut, Iwata, & Green, 1982; McNaughton, 1976; Mirenda, 1985; Reichle, York, & Sigafoos 1991; Romski & Sevcik, 1988; Shafer, 1993; Vanderheiden & Lloyd, 1986; Zangari, Lloyd, & Vicker, in press). There are several advantages of a picture system that make it an attractive form of augmentative communication. In fact, it is currently the most preferred system used by language intervention specialists (Shafer, 1993). However, there are several disadvantages that must be considered as well. Both the advantages and disadvantages of picture systems will now be considered (Table 4-4).

Table 4-4 — Advantages of Picture Systems

❑ The listener does not need special training because many of the pictures are easy to understand, and the English word typically accompanies the symbols or pictures.

❑ Simple matching-to-sample at first makes initial acquisition easier.

❑ No special shaping required for individual responses, scanning and pointing about the same for each picture.

❑ May avoid negative emotional history involved with speech.

❑ Response is often already strong in the person's repertoire (i.e., pointing).

The Advantages of Picture Systems

Perhaps the main advantage of picture systems is that the listener does not need any special training to understand what the child is saying (as opposed to the special training required for understanding sign language). Most of the pictures are easy to identify, and all of the symbol systems have the English word written on them. This ease of understanding means the response can be emitted in the presence of any attentive listener.

Another major advantage of picture systems is that many of the early pictures or symbols are easy to acquire because they consist of simple matching-to-sample. For example, the picture for *ball* or *cup* may look very much like a real ball or cup, and many children who are nonverbal can easily match similar stimuli (Keogh & Reichle, 1985). This matching-to-sample repertoire may facilitate the early acquisition of correct pointing, much in the same way that a strong echoic repertoire can facilitate speaking, and a strong imitative repertoire can facilitate signing (Sundberg, 1993a).

Picture systems may also be easier for the instructor because the response topography (the child's motor movement) is the same for each word. That is, the child always points to (touches or exchanges) specific pictures, so training differential responding (i.e., to pronounce individuals words or make individual signs) is not necessary. This feature

---

Table 4-5 — Disadvantages of Picture Systems

❑ Requires environmental (auxiliary) support, must have the pictures available to communicate.

❑ There is no existing or natural verbal community that uses picture systems as a form of communication, and there is a limited ability to develop one.

❑ Cannot always emit the response when motivation and stimuli are strong in the natural environment.

❑ Pointer needs an audience close by.

❑ Picture systems constitute stimulus selection-based verbal behavior and may be more difficult to acquire.

❑ The response form involves a complex type of verbal behavior consisting of conditional discriminations (two stimuli to respond) and multiple component response—scan/point.

❑ Symbols and icons become increasingly abstract as the complexity of words increases.

❑ It takes more training trials to teach abstract concepts.

❑ Often there is no improvement in speech.

makes this type of communication especially effective for individuals with muscle control problems, such as those with cerebral palsy (CP) and traumatic brain injury (TBI). Also, there has been substantial progress in the technological development of communication devices, computers, and software that is greatly improving the efficiency of this form of communication (e.g., Zangari et al., in press). These developments may provide some solutions to the many disadvantages of picture systems identified below.

The Disadvantages of Picture Systems

Unfortunately, there are several practical and conceptual limitations with picture systems that may impede verbal development (Table 4-5). These limitations should be considered before designing a language intervention program for a nonverbal child.

Perhaps one of the most significant practical limitations with picture systems is that successful communication is dependent upon auxiliary equipment (or environmental support), such as a picture board. This requirement presents practical problems because, unlike speech and sign language, communication that is dependent on other stimuli and words cannot be emitted when those stimuli are absent. For example, to successfully mand with a picture system, the board must be present. If the board is not available, the response can never occur. Also, many young children with autism are very active, and it may be difficult to get them to carry a communication board. This constraint is significant because communication may be impossible in the child's natural environment when various types of motivation may be strong (e.g., on the bus, in a store, in bed, in the bathroom). These conditions may also lead to negative behavior such as tantrumming or self-injurious behavior (SIB), because of the inability to communicate. The problem of dependence on auxiliary equipment can be ameliorated to some degree with the careful design of a portable system, but even the most efficient systems get left home, lost, or break down (a common problem for computer generated speech devices).

Many other practical limitations of picture systems have been identified in the literature (e.g., Shafer, 1993; Sisson & Barrett, 1983; Sundberg & Sundberg, 1990; Wraikat et al., 1991). Some of these limitations include the difficulties of portraying complex words in symbol form, the space limitation of most boards and books, and the need to always have the listener in close proximity (speaking and signing can be successful even when a listener is across the room). Also, the response of pointing to or exchanging pictures is naturally slower than speaking (or signing) because of the required time to scan the array of stimuli to find the appropriate picture and point or exchange. This problem of a slow response time is a more significant for picture exchange systems because of the need to remove the picture from a Velcro strip, place it in a sentence strip, remove it from another Velcro strip, and hand it to the teacher. However, these problems could be mitigated with substantial training and utilization of the many new technological developments in presenting and arranging stimuli. Lana the chimpanzee (Rumbaugh, 1977), for example, acquired a very rapid rate of verbal responding, using an easily accessible computer-operated response board, strong reinforcers, and careful shaping.

Another limitation with picture systems is the absence of a functioning language community that uses these systems to communicate. Children who learn to use picture systems typically do so without the advantages of observing competent speakers engage in communicative interactions by pointing to or exchanging pictures. Also, these children do not have opportunities to observe competent speakers using more advanced pictures or symbols from the communication system. Rarely is it the case that adults (e.g., teachers, parents, staff) use symbol boards to communicate with each other, nor do they regularly use the boards when verbally interacting with the children; they typically use spoken English. This means that the listener must make a translation from one language to another, in addition to responding to the language task at hand (this problem is also the case for signers who interact with adults who do not sign). This lack of contact with models in the natural environment would seem to make language training more difficult, especially given the fact that exposure to a fluent verbal community is essential for the development of the verbal repertoires (Skinner, 1957). This problem can be overcome if teachers and parents are willing to use picture boards among themselves, and while interacting with the child who uses pictures as a form of communication. However, those who have tried to carry on a conversation with picture systems immediately come in contact with the cumbersome nature of the system.

A major goal of augmentative communication systems should be to eventually move the child to speech as a form of communication. While this is often the case with sign language, it is less common with picture systems. In their review of the literature on picture systems, Sisson and Barrett (1983) note that none of the studies mention vocal behavior or vocal improvement. This lack of vocal improvement may be due to the fact that with pointing there is not a differential response form that can get paired with a specific word. That is, the same pointing response is associated with all words. While it seems plausible that vocalizations could improve due to the effects of successful verbal interaction, the degree of improvement may be small. An exception to this general trend is the picture exchange system (PECS) where the developers of this system have reported substantial improvements in the vocal behavior of a number of children (Bondy & Frost, 1993). PECS will be discussed in more detail later in this chapter.

The conceptual limitations of picture systems present more significant problems not easily ameliorated. A major disadvantage of a language system that is based on the selection of stimuli (as opposed to the use of individual words or signs) is that each response or "word" actually involves two behaviors. The behaviors consist of first scanning the array of pictures to find the correct one (which may take some time as the vocabulary grows) and pointing to or exchanging the picture. This multiple-component response not only slows down the communication process, but all things being equal, is more complicated for a nonverbal person to acquire than a single component response (Sundberg & Sundberg, 1990; Wraikat, et al, 1991).

In addition, unlike speech and sign language, the antecedents involved in picture systems always involve at least two stimuli. For example, to correctly identify a cup by pointing to a picture of a cup, the child must first look at the real cup (stimulus one), then look at (and find) the picture of a cup (stimulus two). A multiple component antecedent is also involved in a mand for cup. The child's motivation for a cup, and the presence of the picture, are required for a successful mand for cup. This type of multiple antecedent for language constitutes what has been identified as a conditional discrimination in the behavioral literature (i.e., the presentation of one stimulus or motivator such as a cup alters the evocative effect of a second stimulus, such as the appropriate symbol for cup or drink). It has been well established that conditional discriminations are more complicated to acquire than discriminations involving a single stimulus and single response (e.g., Catania, 1992).

Therefore, effective communication with a picture system always involves two or more controlling variables and a two-component response. Whereas communication with words and signs involves single stimuli and single responses (of course as language becomes more complicated there are often many stimuli and many responses involved in a single utterance for both systems). These complex features of selection-based language systems make teaching this type of

initial communication more complicated than teaching topography-based language systems (Michael, 1985; Potter & Brown, 1997; Shafer, 1993; Sundberg & Sundberg, 1990; Wraikat, et al., 1991). Unfortunately, these issues are rarely considered when decisions are being made as to which communication systems may be most effective for a given child.

In summary, there are several aspects of a picture system, and stimulus selection-based systems in general, that impede the natural shaping of language that occurs with typical children. Perhaps the main barriers are the dependence on auxiliary equipment, the complexity of the stimuli and responses involved, the lack of a natural verbal community, the slow rate of responding, and the difficulty of portraying complex words in symbol or picture form. Below is an analysis of how these barriers affect the development of each of the different types of expressive language (i.e., the elementary verbal operants), as well as the development of receptive language.

Analysis of Picture Systems/PECS Using Skinner's Analysis of Verbal Behavior

The mand repertoire: Picture systems/ PECS suffer from the fact that successful communication depends on auxiliary equipment. When motivators occur in the natural environment, the child often may not have immediate access to the board or computer. This situation is common for many users of picture systems/PECS who are very mobile (e.g., children with autism) or find carrying a communication device (or board) cumbersome or aversive. The occurrence of motivators in the natural environment, without the picture board (or book) being present, cannot produce manding by pointing to a stimulus, so negative behaviors (e.g., screaming) may occur as mands. In addition, the loss of the opportunity to emit the trained verbal responses under the control of motivators in the natural environment severely limits teaching opportunities, such as those used in incidental teaching (e.g., Hart & Risley, 1975), as well as the development of more complex mands (Michael, 1988, 1993). It may be difficult, for example, to teach mands such as asking *Wh* questions. These problems may not be as serious for children who are wheelchair bound, because their word boards are often attached to their wheelchairs. However, even these children are frequently in situations where they will be unable to mand when motivators are strong (e.g., in bed, on the toilet, on the floor mat).

These problems can be overcome somewhat by ensuring that the board is always available to the child, or devising a system that is highly portable. Picture wallets and picture necklaces have been used successfully for some children, but the number of the responses available are limited, and the rate of emitting a response containing several components is slow. This is a problem because if the response is too slow, the temporal contiguity between specific antecedents, behavior, and consequences will be broken (i.e., searching for the right stimulus takes time and the original controlling variables or the listener's attention can be lost, also the consequences may become too delayed).

The tact repertoire: This type of language would probably be the least affected by the use of picture communication systems. Nonverbal stimuli can easily be presented and responding can be prompted, shaped, and differentially reinforced. However, as the nonverbal stimuli become more complex it becomes increasingly difficult to present these stimuli pictorially or symbolically (e.g., verbs, prepositions, pronouns, adjectives, adverbs, emotions). Colors, for example, are difficult to portray in a picture without using the actual color. If the task is to identify a color and the picture card has the color on it (e.g., a blue cup and a picture of blue), the child may be just matching blue to blue, which is a very different skill than naming blue. This apparent success may lead adults to believe that the child's communications skills are actually higher than they really are, resulting in the neglect of more basic communication skills. An additional problem in using pictures for tacting is that the number of responses available may be limited due to space requirements, and the length of the response may be short due to time and response effort requirements.

Receptive language: This type of communication often seems strong for picture system/PECS users because it is easy to teach. However, a close analysis of the typical teaching procedures may reveal some surprising results. Receptive language with pictures is typically taught by having an adult vocally ask a child to touch a specific picture (just like receptive training for vocal children). Many nonvocal children may be able to quickly acquire this skill because the response can be easily prompted and reinforced. Also, many children already have a number of behaviors under the control of spoken words (often receptive trials occur in the absence of the board). However, a true receptive response with picture systems (one that parallels speech) consists of an adult presenting the child with a picture from the child's board and asking the child to touch the related item. This type of training is common for speech and signs, but is typically not conducted by those using picture systems in a classroom. However, in order to be consistent with the need to develop all the verbal skills with the targeted form of communication (pictures), this must occur. Otherwise there is the potential for the development of major gaps in a child's communication abilities.

The misunderstanding in receptive training results from the fact that in a picture system/PECS the pictures are meant to have the same status as spoken words (or signs). In Skinner's (1957) terms these pictures become "verbal responses," and "verbal stimuli." If spoken words are used in the receptive instruction (e.g., "touch book"), and the response is to touch or exchange the picture on the board (e.g., touching or exchanging the picture for book), then, since both the stimulus and the response are verbal, this type of language is technically intraverbal and not receptive (see the appendix).

Hence, it is probably the case that most of what is assumed to be receptive language training between spoken words and pointing to symbols or pictures is probably intraverbal rather than receptive. On the other hand, what is thought to be intraverbal training may actually be receptive training if the pictures are not established as equiva-

lent to words (i.e., established as verbal stimuli). This problem is discussed in more detail below. In any case, it is cumbersome to conduct true receptive trials consistent with the response form of pointing to or exchanging pictures. As a result, typically spoken English is used, blending two separate language systems.

The intraverbal repertoire: There are several significant difficulties in establishing meaningful conversations with picture systems/PECS. First, in order to be consistent with the established language system of pictures as responses for the child, pictures would need to be presented as verbal stimuli by the adult or peer (like the problem identified above with receptive training). That is, a conversation with pictures would involve both the speaker and listener using pictures to interact with each other (just like signing children who will benefit if adults sign). Adults could use pictures to interact with a child who uses a picture system (and some do), but there are some inherent problems in using pictures as verbal stimuli (a requirement for true intraverbal interactions—see the appendix for more information).

For example, in attempting to teach a child to intraverbally name animals, a teacher could point to a general picture for animals and train the child to point to a number of the pictures for specific animals. However, this type of training is difficult because a general picture for animals may be hard to create (and give it verbal status) without that task actually becoming just matching-to-sample (i.e., the general picture may be a picture of a number of different animals and the child matches this picture to a picture of a specific animal). More causal conversation would also be difficult, but possible. For example, when asking about a field trip, an instructor could point to the pictures for "What did you see on your trip?" However, a correct answer to this question would require that the child be able to correctly respond to pictures for words that are almost impossible to present visually, such as "what" and "you."

This type of conversational training is quite complex and cumbersome, and therefore rarely occurs with children who learn to communicate with picture systems. Instead, teachers and parents typically ask the child questions in spoken English. This may seem just as good as using pictures to interact, and it is actually viewed by many as better than using pictures. However, failing to use pictures in the presence of the child does not allow the child to function as a listener in the language system in which he is expected to function as a speaker. This situation (which is the norm for most who use picture systems) would be analogous to expecting an adult be able to acquire a second spoken language without the benefit of ever hearing people using that language. Also, from the child's point of view, there is an additional linguistic task when spoken words are used exclusively as verbal stimuli in conversations. The child must translate between two language systems, in addition to answering the original question (this is the same problem faced by signing children in an environment where adults do not sign). It would be like someone asking an adult a question in a foreign language. The adult must first translate the question, and then answer the question. Unfortunately, there are no empirical data on the effects of adults failing to use pictures themselves, or the translation required for successful responding on a child's intraverbal development. However, it is not uncommon to see pointing-system users who never reach the level of meaningful conversations with pictures.

Another conceptual problem with picture systems is that typical vocal conversational skills develop, in part, as a function of numerous adult models being available to young children. If adults do not model the language system, it is unlikely that conversational skills will develop in a typical manner. That is, the child never experiences the opportunity to see adults model and use pictures as a main form of communication. The lack of a highly reinforcing natural verbal community means that the pictures are not systematically paired with adults and strong reinforcers in the manner that speech or signs (if adults sign) are paired with such reinforcers. For example, common intraverbal connections (e.g., strings of words, songs, phrases) are often paired with powerful reinforcers such as food, attention, and physical contact. As a result, words become automatically reinforcing to emit because the response products (sensory feedback or what you hear, see or feel when verbally responding) have reinforcing properties. As a result, they have functional control as a consequence (Skinner, 1957; Sundberg, Michael, Partington, & Sundberg, 1996; Vaughan & Michael, 1982). There is a self-shaping process where the response becomes stronger each time it is emitted because the response is automatically reinforcing. This effect may not occur if reinforcing adults do not use the pictures themselves, especially when interacting with the child.

Reading and writing: It is certainly possible that the written word that is paired with the symbol may eventually be able to demonstrate control over the response. However, if English words did come to evoke pointing to specific stimuli, the relation would actually be intraverbal because of the lack of point-to-point correspondence between the verbal stimulus and the verbal response (Skinner, 1957). Thus, it would be impossible to have phonetic reading with pointing, unless it involved pointing to letters to spell out words. Writing skills have no connection to pictures and, as with signs and speech, would have to be taught independently.

Special Consideration of The Picture Exchange Communication System (PECS)

The Picture Exchange Communication System (Bondy & Frost, 1993) presents some unique elements not present in the typical picture systems and warrants some individualized consideration. Perhaps the most unique aspect of PECS is the requirement that the child place the picture in the hands of the listener. This exchange requires that the adult interact with the response form (i.e., they must receive the picture) and thus more actively serve as a listener. A child who points to a picture is not ensured that the adult is attending, but receipt of a picture does ensure attending and more active involvement not only with the child but with the picture. This process may increase the chances of successful communicative inter-

actions, and may result in the pictures becoming conditioned reinforcers more easily. This may mitigate the problem of the adults not using the typical picture board. In addition, it may be that this system avoids the problem of extremely weak echoic or imitation skills, and avoids any negative histories often associated with attempts to speak or sign.

However, the reported success of the system (Bondy & Frost, 1993) is probably due to a number of variables. Most likely it is the use of mand training as the first form of communication that is probably most responsible for the success. Inherent in the mand training procedure is the fact that training is conducted under conditions that involve the child's current motivation for specific reinforcers (i.e., the presence of establishing operations). The use of mands as the first type of communication is typically not the approach suggested by most published language training programs for both speech and augmentative systems (e.g., Carr, Binkoff, Kologinsky, & Eddy, 1978; Guess, Sailor, & Baer, 1976; Lovaas, 1977). However, initial mand training is the approach recommended by the current program, and it has been previously established that mand training is a major element that separates Skinner's (1957) approach to language training from other "behavioral" and traditional approaches (e.g., Sundberg, 1980, 1987, 1990; Sundberg, Milani, & Partington, 1977).

While it likely is the case that other picture systems would greatly benefit from the initial training of mands, they may not be able to replicate the desirable effects of exchanging pictures with a listener. This advantage aside, PECS still suffers for all the other disadvantages of picture systems and could possibly limit verbal development (e.g., dependence on auxiliary equipment, multiple stimuli and multiple responses in each exchange, seemingly higher-level skills, difficulty in teaching advanced labeling and all types of conversations). However, the originators of PECS have reported substantial vocal improvement in their children (Bondy & Frost, 1993), a development not typically seen in other systems. This improvement in vocal behavior is a major advantage of this system, but may be mainly due to starting with mand training and additional echoic training (which could be done with all the systems). In addition, many of the children observed in videos of children who learn to talk using PECS already had some vocal behavior. These issues aside, it is clear that the system is an improvement over typical picture systems, but it is not clear that it is an improvement over the effective use of sign language (which frequently results in improved vocal behavior with the mand training approach). PECS have become extremely popular as a form of augmentative communication for nonverbal children, yet very little research has been conducted on PECS. Given the inherent practical and conceptual limitations identified above, it is quite possible that the enthusiasm for this system may wane as the data become more available.

In conclusion, it appears that there are many disadvantages of picture systems, including several restrictions on the development of more complex types of communication (especially advanced labeling and conversation skills). For some individuals,

there may be no alternatives (see the section below on decision making). Consequently, if pictures are used, then at least they should be used considering the issues raised above. Of all the picture systems, it may be the case that PECs offers the most promise for achieving advanced communication skills. At this point, the final type of augmentative communication, written words, will now be examined.

Spelling, Writing, Typing, and Facilitated Communication

There are a number of nonvocal persons who can effectively communicate by spelling out words. Many disabled individuals have demonstrated the independent use of this form of responding (e.g., LaVingna, 1977). Perhaps most obvious is its value to deaf individuals and persons with cerebral palsy (CP). Also, many individuals with traumatic brain injury (TBI) retain their ability to read and write, even though they are unable to speak. Finally, there are a number of individuals with autism who have limited speech but have demonstrated abilities to read and write (identified as hyperlexia). While less desirable than speech, spelling words or pointing to words as a type of communication can be effective. For example, a person can use written words to ask for reinforcers (mand), identify nonverbal stimuli (tact), and engage in conversations (intraverbal). These skills require a number of prerequisite abilities, such as those involved in literacy. However, this form of communication could be effective for establishing all types of language for a nonvocal person.

The recent technique identified as facilitated communication (FC) makes use of transcription, but differs in many important ways from the independent verbal behavior discussed above. Facilitated communication involves a response consisting of spelled-out words, produced by typing or pointing to letters, with the assistance of a facilitator who guides the learner's arm, hand, or finger (Biklen, 1990; Haskew & Donnellan, 1992). The basic premise is that the facilitation allows a nonverbal person to emit words that he already possessed, but had been unable to emit due to global apraxia (Biklen, 1990).

FC as a form of verbal behavior has produced a substantial amount of attention from the media, due to demonstrations of sophisticated levels of responding being emitted by previously nonverbal children. Proponents of FC have claimed that many previously nonverbal developmentally disabled individuals can demonstrate near normal levels of verbal functioning through facilitation (Biklen, 1990; Haskew & Donnellan, 1992). However, several recent studies have demonstrated that in almost all cases examined, the facilitator was the individual emitting the verbal behavior (e.g., Green & Shane, 1993; Wheeler, Jacobson, Paglieri, & Schwartz, 1993). In a very few cases, it does appear that individuals do have the necessary prerequisite repertoires and could possibly benefit from FC. However, since these applications are very limited, the focus of this section will be on the independent use of written words.

A surprising number of children who are diagnosed with autism have the ability to identify numbers and letters. Some of these children are obsessed with letters and words, and it is for these children that the possible use of written words may actually improve language and speech. In a recent study, Judd, Endicott, and Sundberg (1997) examined a language problem involving a child with autism who could read dozens of words but had only acquired a small vocabulary of spoken words as mand and tacts. This study attempted to determine if written stimuli (a word board) could be used as prompts to increase the child's vocal mand, tact, and intraverbal skills. The first experiment demonstrated the subject's mand skills with and without the word board, and it attempted to determine if new mands could be acquired quicker with the inclusion of the written stimulus in the initial training condition. A second experiment was then conducted to determine if the word board could facilitate the subject's acquisition of tacts and intraverbals.

The results of the study showed that the subject was able to mand more effectively with the written stimuli, and that new mands were incorporated into his previously established word board. It was also shown that the subject was able to correctly tact the action pictures by pointing to the correct written word, and that he failed to acquire any new tacts in the vocal only condition. Also, the subject was able to acquire new intraverbal responses quicker with written words than without the words. These findings suggest that written stimuli can be an effective tool for teaching mands, tacts, and intraverbals to some children with autism, especially those who are strongly reinforced by letters and words. These findings also have several interesting implications and possibilities for future research.

Choosing a Response Form

Speech is obviously the response form of choice. Effort should always be given to developing vocal communication prior to considering an augmentative system. Particular procedures like mand training and automatic reinforcement pairings (see Chapters 5 and 6) may substantially improve vocal behavior, as might a number of other proven speech therapy techniques. In considering speech as a viable response form, one should assess the strength of the person's echoic repertoire. If echoic behavior is moderate or strong, then a vocal response form should be pursued. Even a very small amount of echoic behavior may be enough to immediately get started with vocal mand training. If repeated attempts to establish vocal communication as mands or tacts fail, then an augmentative system should be considered.

Given the three alternative response forms available for nonspeaking individuals, how does one decide which system is most appropriate for a specific individual? First, one must consider the individual and his or her disabling condition. If the nonverbal person is severely motorically involved such as those with CP and TBI, the differential muscle control necessary for speaking, signing, or writing may be impossible. For these individuals, a pointing system or FC may be the only options. However, in order to use FC as the genuine speaker, the person would have to be able to demonstrate literacy. Typing and spelling could conceivably be

taught through facilitation, but it would seem to take a large number of training trials. In addition, the possibility of automatic verbal behavior on the part of the facilitator would have to be ruled out, which would be difficult because it occurs so readily (Hall, 1993). Even if the person is literate, the facilitator could still engage in automatic verbal behavior and control some of the typed messages.

If the nonverbal person is literate, then independent writing or typing may be a reasonable response form to use, especially if echoic and imitative behaviors are weak. Typically, the existence of these verbal operants is accompanied by related mands, tacts, and intraverbals; however, for some individuals the other operants might be quite weak. It is not unreasonable to use the transcriptive mode to establish or further develop these other verbal operants. This may even be possible with facilitation, through an arduous shaping process. But in some cases (e.g., CP and TBI), it is certainly possible that independent verbal operants could be acquired easier or be further developed with facilitation. However, if the person is not literate, or does not have preexisting verbal operants, then FC as a response form will probably not be effective.

When considering a system for nonverbal children who are not literate or severely motorically involved (e.g., most children with autism or other developmental disabilities), the primary choice is between picture systems/PECS and sign language. Given the many advantages of sign language as a topography-based system that parallels and possibly improves speech, and the many disadvantages of picture systems/PECS as a selection-based system requiring environmental support, sign language should be the response form of choice. However, it may be the case that individual differences or histories favor one system over another. In addition, it is possible that a blend of different systems may be beneficial for some individuals (Shafer, 1993).

However, the current trend is to favor picture systems/PECS over sign language (Shafer, 1993), primarily because it is easier for adults (e.g., parents and teachers) to understand what is being pointed to by simply looking at the picture, symbol, or written word that is touched. Sign language requires that the listener receive special training to effectively react as a listener. This practice may be supported by cognitive theory, which focus on what words mean to listeners, thereby placing the emphasis on listener behavior rather than on speaker behavior (Skinner, 1957). This emphasis on the listener would favor picture systems over sign language because of the readily available supply of listeners. Therefore, from this point of view it would not be unreasonable to assume that pointing would be easier to acquire and more functional than sign language. However, behavioral conceptual analyses (Michael, 1985; Shafer, 1993) and empirical analyses (e.g., Sundberg & Sundberg, 1990) show that not only are signs closer to speech, but when all things are equal, sign language is easier for a child to acquire than pointing at stimuli (e.g., Sundberg & Sundberg, 1990; Wraikat et al., 1991).

Summary

Systems of augmentative communication have played a major role in the development of successful verbal skills for nonverbal individuals. The decision as to which type of augmentative system to use is often complicated by an individual's specific needs and the general complexities of the options available. Sign language is conceptually closest to speech and has the most advantages and fewest disadvantages of the various options presented, with picture systems/PECS being the next most preferred. While it is clear that only a small number of nonverbal persons could probably benefit from facilitated communication. There still is a great need for further research on many aspects of augmentative communication systems.

Chapter 5
Beginning Language Intervention

The results of the Behavioral Language Assessment will help determine which aspects of the training program are most relevant for the child being considered for language intervention. The intervention chapters begin with procedures for teaching basic communication skills and progress to more complex language skills. The current chapter is designed for children scoring around Level 1 or 2 in the initial assessment. These are children who do not (or rarely) emit any identifiable words or signs and may be uncooperative. These children may also have strong repertoires of inappropriate behaviors, such as social withdrawal, aggression, and self-abuse. These negative behaviors may occur because a child with ineffective language skills will find other methods of meeting his wants and needs. Unfortunately, these other methods may not be effective in many situations (e.g., a tantrum does not always tell the listener exactly what the child wants). Also, the negative behaviors may be very disruptive to others and result in the use of punishment or medication to control them. Although these children may have learned how to manipulate or change their environment, they typically will not learn appropriate language skills until they are specifically taught those skills.

In order to teach these children language skills, it may first be necessary to get the child to cooperate with the teacher. (If the nonverbal child is somewhat cooperative, then the instructor should immediately begin the mand training procedures (described below) along with the cooperation procedures). There are several ways to teach or increase cooperation. Perhaps the most effective way involves the use of a child's current motivation—the technical behavioral term for motivation is "establishing operation" (Michael, 1988)—and the related reinforcement. For example, if the child wants to watch a video, the instructor should use this establishing operation (motivation) along with the reinforcement of turning on the video to help establish some cooperative behavior.

However, prior to attempting to specifically teach cooperation, it is necessary to consider why the child would want to do what adults ask of him. Ideally, by learning to cooperate, the child should be able to get access to a wider variety of reinforcers and better reinforcers for less effort (i.e., complying with an instruction rather than engaging in disruptive behavior). In order to motivate the child to cooperate with attempts to teach language, he must be shown that by going along with spoken and unspoken requests, he will get access to items or activities he currently desires. If his participation in the instructional process does not easily lead to actual reinforcement, he will probably not continue to participate in the instructional process. Instead, the child may return to the negative methods that have been effective for him in the past.

Establishing Rapport

There are several factors to consider when approaching a nonverbal child who is not readily cooperating or following adult instructions. The first issue is that it is necessary for the child to learn that the sight of the language instructor is desirable. The child will not be easy to teach if he is actively or passively avoiding the instructor. The desired working relationship will be established when the instructor is consistently associated (paired) with the delivery of a child's reinforcing items and events. Therefore, it is important that the instructor acquires and periodically delivers reinforcing items and activities that are effective for that particular child (e.g., food, bubbles, toys, books, cars, video). The instructor should begin to compile a list of these reinforcers, as well as a list of ways to provide access to other reinforcing events (e.g., pushing a swing, opening a door to outside). The main purpose of this procedure is to establish the instructor as a form of conditioned reinforcement for the child. That is, the child should learn to like the instructor, before the instructor begins requiring work from the child.

Furthermore, it is important that the instructor not be associated with the removal of ongoing reinforcing activities. When an instructor initially attempts to gain the cooperation of a child, it is not a desirable practice to stop the child from engaging in enjoyable activities to engage in the learning activities. The child is already

having fun. Why should he stop to work with the instructor? It is best to attempt to approach the child when he is not engaging in some reinforcing activity and allow him to gain access to some highly reinforcing items or activity through the instructor. For example, when the child looks bored, approach him and noncontingently (no response required) deliver his favorite car or tickle him. Alternatively, when the child is engaging in an enjoyable activity, the instructor can make it more fun by participating (e.g., rocking a horse that the child is sitting on). This process of pairing may take several trials (or even sessions) before the instructor is ready to begin to require a response.

Requiring the First Response

When the instructor is ready to start requiring responses, it is very important that the typically non-cooperative child is only required to engage in responses that are clearly known to be easy for that child (many nonverbal children "can" emit certain responses but typically "won't" emit them when asked). In addition, it is best to work with a child when his motivation for a particular reinforcer is strong (e.g., when he is hungry, or when he wants to watch a video or go outside). The child's participation in these easy tasks must result in immediate payoffs for his participation. Over a series of interactions (which can vary considerably in number depending upon the child and the strength of his reinforcers), the child will gradually be taught to be cooperative with more difficult tasks and with a greater number of tasks prior to receiving a reinforcer. At first, however, it is critical that the child learn that the sight of the instructor means that good things are about to occur, and that the instructor will require some responses, but not that too much effort will be required to get those desired items or events.

The ideal teaching situation is for the instructor to have an item or activity that currently has a high reinforcing value for the child (i.e., the child wants it at that exact moment), and access to that item or activity is only available through the instructor. In this situation, the child is usually approaching the instructor in an attempt to get closer to the reinforcer. If the instructor is a careful observer of the child's behavior, it is possible to gradually shape the child's behavior such that the child will do more to gain access to the item or activity over a series of interactions. It is important to note that the key issue is that the child must do something that is specified by the instructor in order to get the reinforcer. In some situations, merely reaching to take a reinforcing item from the instructor's hand when told to do so may be the first response required from the child.

It is important to provide the child with a sufficient amount of an item or activity to result in a strengthening effect on his behavior (i.e., so he will be likely to repeat the required action again), but not to provide him with so much of the item or activity that he no longer desires the item (i.e., satiation occurs). For example, it is possible to provide the child with a few sips of juice in a cup, after the child reaches for a cup when the cup is presented, rather than providing him with a full cup of juice for the same behavior. In this manner, the child will be more likely to immediately repeat that action or engage in a more involved action to receive another sip of juice.

When the instructor has control of a highly desired reinforcer and the child is somewhat cooperative, it is always most advantageous to try to establish a mand (see below). However, some children may not allow the instructor to physically prompt them, or may immediately engage in negative behaviors (e.g., tantrums) when a specific response is required. In this case it may still be possible to get a number of different types of responses from the child. These responses could include (1) getting the child to physically go along with the physical prompts (e.g., allow the instructor to guide them onto a trampoline or manipulate their hand to make a specific ASL sign), (2) matching an item to a corresponding item (e.g., putting a picture of a dog with a matching picture of a dog, putting a puzzle piece in an inset board, putting a shape in a form box), (3) complying with an instruction to do an activity (e.g., "Sit," "Jump," or "Come here," without a model), (4) physically imitating one of the instructors actions (i.e., imitate an action when told "Do this" and an action is modeled), or (5) vocally imitating a sound or a word (e.g., imitate a word or sound when told "Say __").

The main focus at this stage of the intervention is to get the child to do something when the instructor wants him to do it (i.e., follow instructions). It is crucial to go slowly in establishing instructional control. You want to gradually require more responses from the child without going so fast as to result in the child attempting to get out of the teaching situation. It is also important to shape the child's compliance behavior rather than demanding immediate and complete compliance with specific requests. At first, the instructor may be providing many prompts to ensure that the child will be successful at the tasks. As the child learns the task, the prompts should slowly be faded out, allowing the child to do the task with less assistance. Over time, the reinforcers will also be systematically thinned such as to maintain responding without relying on only the most powerful reinforcers to get cooperation.

The main indicator of being successful at this stage of the intervention is that the child comes to the instructor, rather than runs from an approaching instructor. It must be remembered that the instructor's first goal is to establish and maintain an ongoing reinforcing relationship with the child. If the child is required to do too much, is unsuccessful in his attempts, or does not receive items or activities that are important to him at that moment, it will not be possible to maintain the child's participation in the language intervention program. Once the instructor can get the child to engage in a particular response on request, it may be easier to teach him his first mand. Additional compliance training may be necessary and may be an on-going aspect of intervention; however, it is important to move on to mand training as soon as possible (optimally, in the first session).

Dealing with Negative Behavior

There are several specific procedures that can be effective in reducing negative behaviors. Many of these are described in basic texts on behavior modification (e.g., Cooper,

Heron, & Heward, 1987; Malott, Whaley & Malott, 1994; Martin & Paer, 1995) and in texts specifically designed for treating the negative behaviors of developmentally disabled individuals (e.g., O'Neill, Horner, Albin, Sprague, Storey, & Newton, 1997). Readers who are unfamiliar with these techniques should consult one of these books. In general, the instructor should not allow the child to gain access to reinforcers with negative behavior. However, this procedure may result in a substantial burst of negative behavior, especially for children who have long histories of obtaining reinforcers with such behavior. Therefore, it is important to simultaneously teach the child ways to obtain reinforcers through appropriate behaviors. The most effective types of appropriate behaviors are improved communication skills. The purpose of the following section is to describe the basic procedures for teaching these beginning communication skills.

Beginning Language Training (Mand Training)

The first type of language to teach a non-verbal child should be a mand (i.e., a request for a reinforcer). This skill is taught first because the mand is a unique type of language that directly benefits the child by letting his caretakers know exactly what he wants at that particular moment. Mands are typically the first type of communication that humans naturally acquire (Bijou & Baer, 1965; Skinner, 1957). Infants cry when they are hungry and as a result they receive food. They also cry when they are uncomfortable and receive comfort, and cry when they want attention and receive attention. Early in life different forms of crying begin to emerge for each type of motivation; infants even develop "fake crying" to get their needs known (Novak, 1996; Wolff, 1969). The point is that crying quickly becomes a way to communicate with adults, or more specifically, a way to mand (i.e., request reinforcers or to remove aversive stimuli). Most of an infant's first forms of language are mands for reinforcers that are caused by different types of motivation (i.e., establishing operations). Eventually (around 12 months of age), the young child learns to say words to ask for the different things that he does or does not want.

The mand occurs early in language development for typical children because of the direct benefit they receive (e.g., food, comfort). The nonverbal child also desires reinforcers and direct benefits. Regardless of how disabled they are, they still get hungry, need attention, need aversive stimuli removed, and so on. In the early language training for a nonverbal child it is possible to capture these on-going forms of motivation as an opportunity to conduct language trials, and often the child is very willing to participate in this training because of the direct benefit he receives. For example, when a child is hungry (the motivation for food is strong) that is the time to work on teaching the word, sign, or picture point/exchange for "food."

There are several variables that will increase the chances of successfully teaching a nonverbal child to mand. First, strong forms of reinforcement should be used. Most children are reinforced by food, drinks, toys,

attention, and so on. However, each child is different, and individual reinforcement surveys must be conducted. Also, the value of reinforcers may change many times throughout the day, week, or month. Hence, a second tool in developing language is that training should be conducted when the motivation for a particular reinforcer is strong. If a certain toy is being used as a reinforcer, then trials and sessions should be conducted when the motivation for that toy is strong. For example, if a child does not emit any echoic or imitative behavior, but likes to listen to music in the morning before breakfast, then some mand training trials should be conducted at that time. The motivation is strong, and music as reinforcement is the most potent option. Thus at this point in time, an instructor would have the best chances of successfully teaching a mand response. In addition, a variety of prompts can be used (e.g., physical, imitative, verbal) to ensure immediate success.

Before beginning a formal language-training program, the assessment should be conducted (see Chapters 3 and 4) and a decision should be made as to what response form will be used (i.e., speech, signs, or pictures). (It is important to note that this decision can change depending on the child's progress or lack of progress.) Recall that if a child cannot echo a word, or even a close approximation to a word, it will be difficult to immediately teach him vocal language. If a person can imitate some actions, but can't echo sounds or words, then sign language may be the most appropriate response form. If the child cannot imitate any actions, then signs may be difficult, but clearly not out of the question (and perhaps still a better choice than pictures). However, if both echoic (i.e., vocal imitation) and physical imitation are equally weak, then signs should be selected as the initial response form, because it is usually easier to teach someone to imitate actions than to echo words. If the child has severe physical impairments, then a picture system may be most appropriate.

The mand training procedures described below will be divided into four sections based on the child's entry level: (1) procedures for teaching mands to a nonechoic and nonimitative child, (2) procedures for teaching signed mands to a child who has some motor imitation, (3) procedures for teaching vocal mands to a child who has some echoic skills, and (4) procedures for teaching pointing to pictures as mands for a physically involved child who cannot echo sounds or imitate actions.

Mand Training for Children who Cannot Echo or Imitate

If a nonverbal child is somewhat cooperative and has some identifiable reinforcers, but cannot echo or imitate, then procedures to teach the first mand should be implemented. Several variables can be manipulated that will increase the probability of successfully teaching this level of child to mand. The most important teaching tools are the use of strong forms of reinforcement and the

related motivation (specific times when the reinforcers are especially strong) and the behavioral techniques of prompting and fading. In addition, the use of sign language will probably result in faster acquisition of an understandable mand, because the trainer can physically prompt the response that they can not do with speech. This basic training procedure will be described below.

Using Sign Language with Physical Prompts

The teaching procedure for a nonimitative child consists of using physical prompts (along with other prompts) to assist the child in making a successful response. This prompted response will allow the child to immediately come in contact with a reinforcer (e.g., eating a cookie, watching a video). The first step is to select a sign to teach (Table 5-1). This sign should be for a strong reinforcer (e.g., food, book, music) or for a highly desired activity (e.g., a push on a swing, being lifted up), and training should be conducted when the motivation (establishing operation) for the reinforcer is strong. Also, the sign should be physically easy for the child to make, easy for the instructor to physically prompt, and relatively iconic (i.e., it must look like the item or activity it stands for).

Table 5-1 — Issues to Consider When Picking the First Words as Mands

1. Select words that are for reinforcers (existing motivation), especially for those reinforcers that adults can easily control the access to and have the ability to use the items as a reinforcer:

❑ Reinforcers that are consumable (e.g., food, drinks)

❑ Reinforcers that easily allow for short a duration of contact (e.g., bubbles, tickles) reinforcers that are relatively easy to remove from the student (e.g., music, video)

❑ Reinforcers that are easy to deliver (e.g., books, cars, dolls)

❑ Reinforcers that can be delivered on multiple occasions (e.g., small candies, sips of juice)

❑ Reinforcers that always seem strong (e.g., stim toy, outside)

There may be many items that might be reinforcing but are difficult to manage for training purposes, such as car trips, board games, blocks, bike rides, long movies, walks, gum, hard candy, and a bowl of ice cream. These items can still be used as reinforcers, but perhaps for extremely high quality responding or at the end of training sessions.

2. Select words that are already familiar to the child, as demonstrated by an existing receptive, echoic, or imitative skill. For example, when the parent says "Do you want to go outside," the child goes towards the door.

3. For vocal children, select words that involve a relatively short and easy response for the child to make. For example, many speech sounds are easier to produce than others. Sounds such as "aa," "ba," "mm," and "da" may be relatively easy, while "la" and "rrr" may be much harder. Also, words should be selected that match the child's existing echoic repertoire.

4. For signing children, select words that are iconic, that is, the signs look like the objects that they stand for. For example, the sign "book" looks like the action of opening a book, and the sign "eat" looks like putting food in the mouth. Also, signs should be selected that match the child's existing imitative repertoire.

5. Select words that are for salient and relevant items to the child in his daily life. They should be items that the child sees or uses frequently in daily activities. It is also preferable to use items that are stable and clearly identified stimuli, that is, the name of the item is consistent across all variations of the item (e.g., ball), and all adults can agree on what the item is called. The selected words should involve words that occur frequently in the child's day-to-day environment (e.g., "eat" may be heard much more often than "elephant").

6. Select a set of words that will eventually be associated with a variety of motivators. For example, don't select all foods for the first several words or signs or progress will stop when the child is not hungry. Select words for a variety of different motivators (e.g., foods, toys, video, physical play).

7. Avoid selecting words or signs that sound or look alike (rhyme). It will be much harder for the child to differentiate between similar response forms (e.g., don't select the signs "eat" and "drink" as the first two signs because the look very similar).

8. Avoid words and signs that might have a negative or aversive history for the child (e.g., bed, toilet, no).

Mand training is more likely to be successful if the procedure involves the simultaneous use of a number of different prompts and consequences. The top panel of Table 5-2 contains a diagram of nine potential (independent) variables and their relationship to the signed response (the dependent variable). Six of these variables precede the response and are technically referred to as antecedent events, and three follow the response and are termed consequent events. Although this table lists many types of prompts and reinforcers, it should be noted that an instructor should use only the fewest variables necessary to get the response to occur. In addition, it may be that some children have an odd or unique history that makes a specific type of prompt inappropriate for that child. For example, some children are tactilely defensive, so physical prompts would be contraindicated. Other children may have a defective history in relation to specific verbal prompts, such as "What do you want?" so this verbal prompt should not be used. However, the goal of the procedure is unprompted (spontaneous) communication; therefore all prompts and additional reinforcers should be eliminated as soon as possible. Teaching the sign "eat," for example, should begin in the following manner. When the child is hungry (motivated) show him the item of food (nonverbal stimulus) and say "What do you want?" or "Sign eat" (two different verbal prompts) and model the sign "eat" (imitative prompt). It is unlikely that the child will correctly respond at this point (since the child has not been able to imitate in the past), so the instructor (or a second adult) should then physically prompt the child by moving his hand to his mouth (as in making the sign for eat). This fully prompted interaction should then be reinforced with praise, the food (e.g., a piece of a cookie), and physical contact (if such contact is reinforcing for the child). (Note that if the child does sign "eat," or provides an approximation to the sign, without the physical or verbal prompts, he should be immediately reinforced).

Table 5-2 — Quick Transfer Procedure for a Pure Mand Using Sign Language

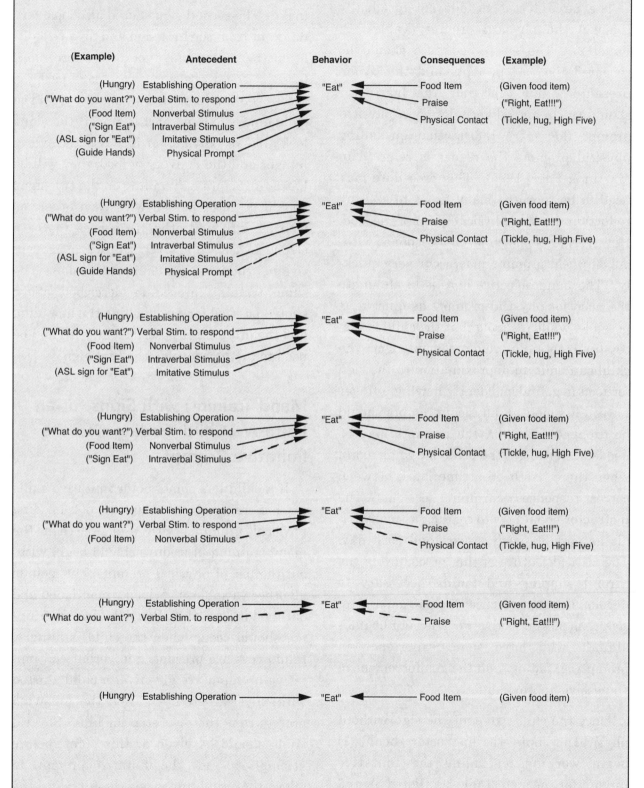

Fading the Physical Prompt

The next step is to fade out (gradually remove) the physical prompt (Table 5-2, Panel 2). The entire sequence should be repeated (i.e., all prompts and the cookie presented), but this time the instructor should try to give slightly less of a physical prompt (for more information on fading physical prompts the reader is referred to Martin & Paer, 1995). This procedure may need to be repeated many times to see any reduction in the physical prompt needed. However, for some children a response without physical prompts may occur very quickly. The main objective here is to eliminate the need for physical prompts as quickly as possible, while insuring that the child is successful in obtaining reinforcement. Once the child can emit an approximation to the sign for food (e.g., independently moving a finger toward his mouth), physical prompts should be dropped (however, the prompts may be needed later to get the behavior going again when there has been a time lapse between correct responses or training sessions). The instructor should try to conduct as many trials as possible each session and each day. The critical feature of this procedure is the careful shaping and fading necessary to develop the sign. Hence this particular procedure is most effectively carried out by individuals who have some experience in prompting, fading, and the reinforcement of successive approximations.

Once the child can emit the sign without physical prompts, the instructor should (1) begin working on fading the imitative prompt for the sign (Table 5-2, Panel 3), and (2) introduce a second sign. The new sign should also be related to a strong form of reinforcement, be iconic, and be easy to make. The second sign should also look very different from the first sign and involve a different motivator and type of reinforcement (e.g., if the first sign was "eat" perhaps "book" could be a second sign, but only if the child enjoys looking at a book). If the signs look alike or "rhyme," or if they both involve hunger and the delivery of food, they will be harder to acquire. Training on the two signs should be interspersed with each other, as well as with and other responses that are strong in the child's repertoire (e.g., receptive instructions, matching-to-sample). The same training procedure described above should be used for establishing the new sign, and the procedures described later should be used to further develop the first sign.

Mand Training with Signs for an Imitative Child: Fading Out the Imitative Prompt

If a child has some motor imitative skills (or has reached the point of not needing physical prompts with a sign), then the mand training procedure should begin without the use of physical prompts, but include all other variables previously mentioned and outlined in Table 5-2, Panel 2. That is, training should occur when the child is hungry, reinforcers are present, and verbal and imitative prompts are given. If a child started with physical prompts, then the following procedure is the next step for him. Several trials should be given at this point (before attempts to fade the imitative prompt) to allow the child to be successful with the training procedures. The instructional task at this point is to teach the child to emit the sign without the imitative prompt (see Table 5-2, Panel 3), and thus "transfer control" to the other variables present (i.e., the motivation, object, and verbal prompts).

The instructor should hold up the food item and ask "What do you want? or "Sign eat." (Note that for some children both verbal stimuli may be unnecessary or simply too much verbal stimuli. If this is the case, use only the "Sign eat" prompt, or even just the specific word eat along with the imitative prompt.) The imitative prompt can be faded out by increasing the delay between the presentation of the question and the delivery of the prompt (Halle, Baer, & Spradlin, 1981; Martin & Paer, 1995). Or, the imitative prompt can be faded out by decreasing the intensity or physical characteristics of the prompt (e.g., only give part of the sign) or a combination of both fading procedures. Correct signs, or approximations, should be immediately reinforced with praise and the food item; hence the next time the food item and the verbal prompt "Sign eat" are presented, the child is more likely to emit the sign without the imitative prompt. Trials on the second sign (e.g., "book") should be interspersed with trials on the first sign. In addition, for some children, it may be beneficial to also intersperse trials with other mastered skills.

The transfer of antecedent control from imitative prompts to the other variables present is the primary objective of this phase of mand training. Transfer may occur in a few trials if the motivators and reinforcers are strong, and the child has a reasonable imitative repertoire. Hence the term "quick transfer procedure" has been used to identify this technique (Sundberg, 1980). Once the behavior occurs without the imitative prompt, the person has emitted a verbal response that is part mand (the motivation variable), part tact (the nonverbal food item is present), and part intraverbal (verbal prompts are present). Eventually, it is important that the person be able to independently (spontaneously) sign eat under the control of each of the above variables when they are presented independently. However, if a previously nonverbal child is able to emit the sign without physical or imitative prompts, this is a major accomplishment for that child.

Adding New Signs and Fading Out the Verbal Prompt

Once the child has been successful with the first two signs, and can emit them without imitative or physical prompts, then the training should proceed with (1) new signs and (2) fading out the verbal prompt (i.e., the verbal prompt "Sign eat," or "Sign book") and bringing back in the general verbal prompt "What do you want?" The selection of new signs should follow the criteria previously described, and the training procedures for the third sign should be similar to those for the previous two signs. Note that the acquired signs need not be perfectly executed or be under each source of control independently to move on to additional signs. However, the responses should be strong under a combination of motivation, nonverbal, and verbal control (i.e., reliably occurring without any imitative or physical prompts).

It is important to make sure that the early signs are strong before adding too many new signs. A common problem with early signers is that new signs are often added to the training program too quickly (imitative prompts are not sufficiently eliminated), and the child's signs become mixed up (the child appears to be guessing). Think of the thousands of times a toddler emits his first few words before other words develop. Instructors need not wait for several months to pass, like for typical early language development; however, they should make sure that a sufficient number of training trials are given to insure that the initial responses will remain strong when new signs are introduced.

In order to further develop the first two signs, the next step with these signs is to carefully begin to fade the verbal prompts, "Sign eat," and "Sign book." The child should be able to emit these signs without physical or imitative prompts, but the other four antecedent variables may still be present (i.e., the motivation, the object, and the two verbal prompts). It is now important to free the response from these multiple sources of control, because they will not always occur together in the natural environment (see Table 5-2, Panel 4). For example, if a child responds only when verbal prompts are given, his verbal abilities will be greatly limited. In order to fade out the verbal prompt "Sign eat," and transfer stimulus control to the motivation, the object, and the verbal prompt "What do you, want?" the instructor should present the child with the object (when the motivation is strong) and say "What do you want" and simply wait a few seconds. If an appropriate response

occurs, immediately reinforce it. If a response fails to occur within 5-10 seconds, give the verbal prompt "Sign eat" and reinforce a correct response. Repeat the trial within a few seconds and wait. Often, after a few trials the child will begin to respond prior to the verbal prompt (i.e., transfer of stimulus control). When he does so for the first time, he should receive extra reinforcement.

Adding More Signs for Reinforcers

New signs can be added at this point, but the instructor should proceed with caution. The number of new signs should not exceed 5 to 10 until the next step in the training (i.e., fading out the object, producing the sign with only the verbal prompt "Sign...") is complete. The child's communication abilities are rather fragile at this point, and too many signs introduced too rapidly can weaken previously established signs. The new signs should also be those for strong forms of reinforcement for the child (e.g., music, ball, book, bubbles, car, boat, cracker, drink, candy, milk), and they should be added one-by-one in the manner described above.

Fading Out the Object

The next step with the previously established signs is to teach the child to ask for the food item in the absence of that item (Table 5-2, Panel 5). The instructor should place the food behind her back, or in a bag, and ask "What do you want?" The instructor should then wait for at least 5 seconds before presenting a prompt, which should consist of bringing the food item out in front of the child. Since the child can already tact "Food," the response should quickly occur. Reinforce the child's response with food and repeat the trial. Place the food item out of sight and ask, "What do you want." Usually, within a few trials, the response will occur under the control of the motivation and the verbal prompt. A second reinforcing object should then be interspersed with the item in order to teach the person to ask for specific reinforcers. Eventually, the verbal prompt also should eventually be faded out (Table 5-2, panel 6) in the same manner as described above. When this occurs, the child has emitted a "pure mand," that is, the response is controlled solely by the motivation (e.g., hunger) and the specific reinforcement (e.g., receiving the desired food item). (Note that the fading procedures need not occur in the order suggested here—fade the two verbal prompts, then the nonverbal prompt. The opposite order may be more effective and appropriate for some individuals; however, it is important at some time to fade out all of these prompts in order to establish "spontaneous" requests. In addition, it is not the case that all signs must occur as pure mands before additional training on the other types of language training are conducted.)

Training in the Natural Environment

It is important to carry over the training procedures from a specific training session to the child's natural environment. These procedures can be easily conducted during the child's normal day, and if this is done, it will most likely increase the speed of acquisition.

The signs selected should be functional for the child in his day-to-day interactions with others in his environment. Parents, staff, and friends should encourage the child to emit the signs when appropriate and reinforce attempts to do so. It is important that these other individuals also provide the child with opportunities to sign when their motivation is strong and watch for satiation (e.g., they are no longer hungry or interested in a certain toy). Language is maintained by the verbal community (i.e., the people around the child who communicate with the child). If a child leaves a training session and goes to an environment where the signs are not used or required, and the previous inappropriate behavior gets reinforced (e.g., whining to get food), progress will probably be much slower. Parents and staff are often concerned about themselves having possible difficulty in learning signs, but in this early stage of training they should be able to learn the signs at least as fast as the child. In addition, if the child is successful, it often motivates the adults to acquire more signs (see Chapter 4 for a further treatment of the need to sign in the presence of signing children).

Mand Training for a Child who has Some Echoic Skills

Speech is the most desired response form (Chapter 4), and if a child has some echoic responses, then efforts should be made to teach him vocal words as mands. There may be some children who have some strong echoic and imitative skills, and they may benefit from a combination of vocal mands and signed mands. The training procedure is diagrammed in Table 5-3 and is essentially the same as that used for the sign language training, except that words rather than signs are used, and there are two less prompt levels available. Like with sign training, the first word should be for a strong form of reinforcement and training should be conducted when the motivation for that reinforcer is strong. The word should also be one that the child can echo (or emit an approximation to the word). For example, if the child can echo "eee," it may be possible to turn this sound into the mand *eat*.

Training should begin with all the antecedent variables present (Table 5-3, Panel 1). Specifically, if the targeted response is "eat," the child should be hungry, and the desired food item should be present. The instructor should hold up the food item and say to the child "What do you want? (verbal prompt), and/or "Say eat" (echoic prompt). If the child emits an approximation to the word "eat," immediately deliver praise and an item of food (in addition, physical contact can be used if it is a reinforcer and is deemed to be necessary to strengthen

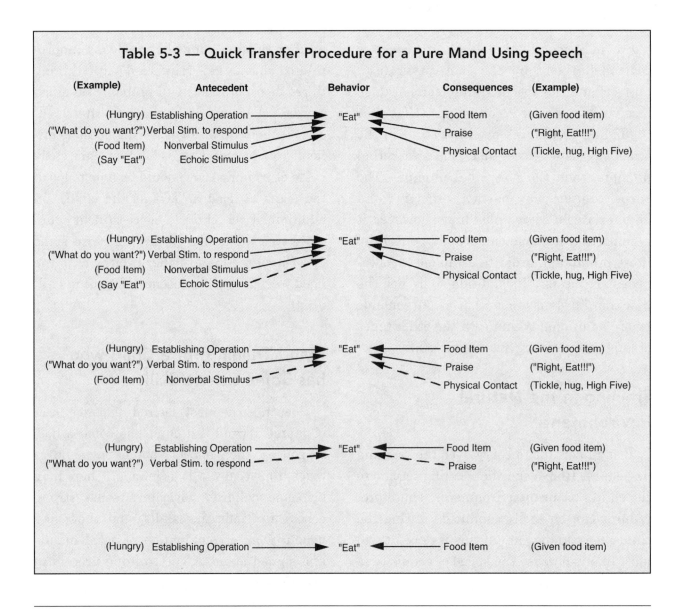

Table 5-3 — Quick Transfer Procedure for a Pure Mand Using Speech

the child's responding). An incorrect response, or no response, should be followed by a re-presentation of the original trial (Panel 1). The child should respond since his echoic skill is strong (at least for the target word), and there is some current motivation for the food item. If the child continues to fail to respond, try a different food item or a different time of day when his motivation may be stronger. If the child continues to fail to respond, consider the procedures described in the cooperation sections above or possibly consider the use of sign language in this early stage of training (only if the child has some motor imitation ability).

The procedure for actual training of a vocal mand begins in Panel 2 of Table 5-3, where the echoic prompt is faded out. The fading procedures are similar to those described above for sign language. The instructor could use a delay procedure or a partial prompt procedure. The combination of these two techniques may also be effective. The objective at this point in the training is to get the child to say "eat" prior to the delivery of the echoic prompt. When this occurs, the child should be immediately reinforced (perhaps with a larger piece of food, if it is the first time, or a high quality response). The next step is to introduce a second word. The criteria for selecting additional words in the early stages of mand training is similar to the criteria recommended for selecting new signs. These first words should be for items that are strong forms of reinforcement and involve sounds that are already strong in the child's echoic repertoire. The words should not rhyme with each other and should be for very different types of reinforcers. Training on the sec-

ond word should be interspersed with the training on the first word, as well as trials on other types of language related skills such as echoic, imitation, and receptive trials (see Chapter 6).

Once the child is successfully manding for two or three items, procedures should be implemented to fade out the object as a source of control (Table 5-3, Panel 3). Procedures to fade out the object are similar to those used to fade out the object for the signer. The object could be placed behind the instructor's back or placed in a box or bag. Correct responses should be immediately followed by the presentation of praise and the object. Incorrect responses should be followed by a repeat of the procedure and only partially hiding the item (e.g., leave it sticking out of the box). It should be noted that eventually it will be important for the child to be able to ask for things when the things are not present (a pure mand). However, for some children the removal of the object may result in the complete loss of interest in manding. While the ultimate goal is to eliminate the object, it is probably best for these children to continue to add new words and to keep the objects in view (the response is technically part mand and part tact). However, this procedure should not last too long (e.g., 10 words) before the child is required to ask for items that are out of view. Otherwise there is a risk of the child becoming prompt bound (i.e., a prompt will always be required to get the response to occur). The last step in the early mand procedure is to fade out the verbal prompt, "What do you want?" (Table 5-3, Panel 5). This last step is less important than the previous three, but if the goal is to obtain spontaneous requesting (a pure mand), then this step must be completed.

Teaching Manding to a Physically Disabled Child who Cannot Echo or Imitate

Some children do not have the manual dexterity to produce signs or the vocal control to emit words. These children may have cerebral palsy or a traumatic brain injury. For these children, the response for mand training should consist of pointing to a picture or an object. There may be other children who cannot echo sounds or imitate actions, but can do exceptionally well on matching-to-sample tasks and may also benefit from a pointing system. (A word of caution is warranted here; many children who cannot imitate or echo can still be taught words or signs with the procedure described in this chapter, and due to the many advantages of speech and signs, every attempt should be made to teach them to communicate with these less restrictive types of communication).

The pointing response in a picture communication can be made in a number of different ways depending on which muscle group the child can control (e.g., a head pointer, a mouth pointer, eye movements, or hand movements). The selection of the first pictures to teach, and the conditions under which the teaching should be conducted, would be exactly the same as those described above for signed and vocal mands. Start with pictures that represent highly reinforcing items or activities, and only conduct training when the motivation for those activities is strong. A correct response, or an approximation to a correct response, should be immediately reinforced with praise and access to the reinforcer (in addition, physical contact should be used if it is a reinforcer).

The types of prompts available for training this type of mand are similar to those described for signs and words. Pointing has some advantages over speech in that physical prompts and imitative prompts can be used (but obviously not echoic prompts). To start training, the instructor should place a single picture representing the reinforcing item on the table or the tray of the child's wheelchair. Then the instructor should hold up the reinforcing item (e.g., a radio) and prompt the child with the verbal prompts, "What do you want? Point to radio," and provide the imitative prompt of pointing to the picture. If the child does not respond, then physical prompts should be used. A fully prompted response should be reinforced with access to the reinforcer (e.g., a minute or two of listening to the radio); the procedure should then be repeated. On the next trial, the instructor should attempt to fade out the physical prompt (like in Table 5-2, Panel 2). Approximations to the correct responses should be successively reinforced (i.e., shaping), with constant effort on the instructor's part to give fewer and fewer physical prompts.

The next step in training is to eliminate the imitative prompt (Table 5-2, Panel 3). The instructor should again present the object, when the motivation is strong, along with the verbal prompts, "What do you want? Point to radio," and the imitative prompt. Approximations should be immediately reinforced and incorrect responses followed by repeating the verbal and imitative prompt. On each successive trial the trainer should attempt to fade out the imitative prompt. Once the child can point to a picture without physical or imitative prompts then new pictures should be introduced. The criteria for introducing new pictures and the fading of verbal prompts are similar to that described for signs and speech. Choose only reinforcing items for the first 5-10 words and intersperse mand responses with each other and with the different types of language trials (i.e., receptive, echoic, imitation).

The picture exchange communication system (PECS) may be more beneficial for some students than a picture pointing system. PECS has the advantage of requiring that the listener interact with the language system by actually receiving the pictures in their hands. This element may have substantial advantages over a pointing system that does not require adult interaction with the communication system. The procedures for the use of PECS also involve early mand training and have been described in detail by Frost and Bondy (1994).

The Need for a Language Based Environment

Teaching language to an essentially non-verbal person is not an easy task, as can be seen from the description of the specific training considerations and procedures presented above. In order to optimize the probability of success, there are several additional aspects of the intervention program that should be considered. A child will make more progress if there is some attempt to create a "language based environment." The

elements of such an environment are complex and involve many components (Table 5-4).

The first step in creating a language based environment is to recognize that language must be viewed by all involved as the key feature of the intervention, and language training must be incorporated into all other activities (e.g., self-care, play, entertainment, motor development, nonverbal tasks). In addition, there must be a large number of daily trials under a variety of stimulus and motivational conditions. Instructors should focus on optimizing any opportunity to get the child to use language by capturing or arranging special opportunities to communicate. It is important to note that it is not necessarily the number of trials that is critical, but rather the type of trials conducted, e.g., imitation, mand, tact, etc. –(these will be discussed later.) A child will acquire language skills quicker if all individuals who interact with the child are trained in language instruction techniques. Specifically, adults may need training in how and when to reinforce, what approximations to accept, what level of prompt to provide, and how to fade those prompts out as quickly as possible. There also needs to be consistency across settings and trainers, and there needs to be several opportunities provided for generalization. A plan (or curriculum) for orderly progression to more complex forms of verbal behavior also needs to be in place. The educational plan (IEP/IPP) must be coordinated with daily activities, and data should be collected on performance.

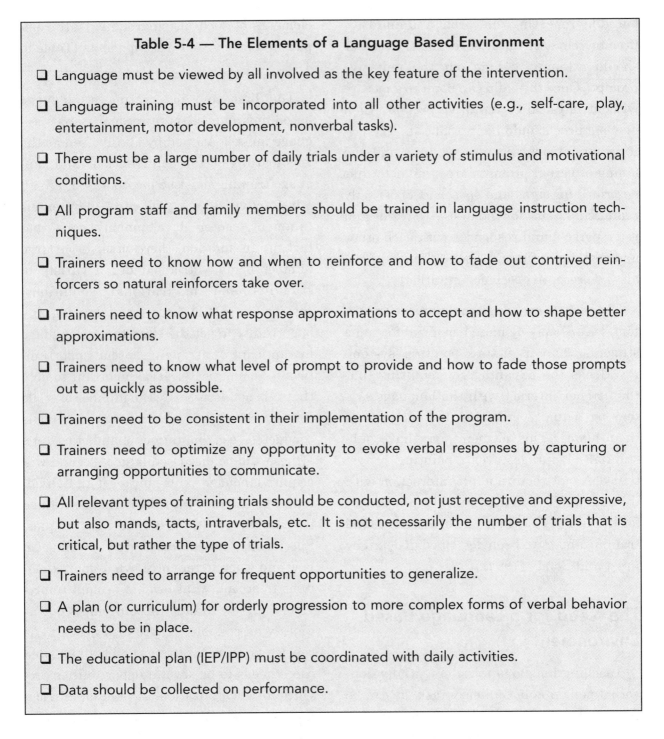

Table 5-4 — The Elements of a Language Based Environment

❏ Language must be viewed by all involved as the key feature of the intervention.

❏ Language training must be incorporated into all other activities (e.g., self-care, play, entertainment, motor development, nonverbal tasks).

❏ There must be a large number of daily trials under a variety of stimulus and motivational conditions.

❏ All program staff and family members should be trained in language instruction techniques.

❏ Trainers need to know how and when to reinforce and how to fade out contrived reinforcers so natural reinforcers take over.

❏ Trainers need to know what response approximations to accept and how to shape better approximations.

❏ Trainers need to know what level of prompt to provide and how to fade those prompts out as quickly as possible.

❏ Trainers need to be consistent in their implementation of the program.

❏ Trainers need to optimize any opportunity to evoke verbal responses by capturing or arranging opportunities to communicate.

❏ All relevant types of training trials should be conducted, not just receptive and expressive, but also mands, tacts, intraverbals, etc. It is not necessarily the number of trials that is critical, but rather the type of trials.

❏ Trainers need to arrange for frequent opportunities to generalize.

❏ A plan (or curriculum) for orderly progression to more complex forms of verbal behavior needs to be in place.

❏ The educational plan (IEP/IPP) must be coordinated with daily activities.

❏ Data should be collected on performance.

When to Conduct Language Trials

Consider how many sounds an infant makes in babbling before words begin to occur. Also consider that typical 3-year-old children emit around 20,000 words a day. This massive number of verbal responses is clearly related to the speed of language development. Quiet toddlers are often language delayed. Many nonverbal and low verbal children receive relatively few language trials. The focus is usually on behavior problems, motor development, self-care, and other nonverbal activities. In order to approximate the language learning patterns of typical children, there must be frequent training trials. These trials should be identified as the primary focus of the treatment plan and should be conducted at every opportunity. It may often take thousands of contrived training trials before verbal behavior occurs unprompted or spontaneously, thus allowing for the natural environment to assist and eventually take over the language training process. Trials should be conducted by everyone involved with the child and should contain a variation of types of trials (depending on the individual's level). Opportunities for language training occur when, for example, the child wants something (mand), or sees something interesting (tact). These natural events however, occur too infrequently to meet the daily number of trials necessary to directly teach language to the child. Therefore, in addition to natural events, opportunities need to be contrived by frequently presenting stimuli that evoke verbal behavior and reinforcing those behaviors immediately. Lovaas (1977) has long maintained that a key to the treatment of children with autism is early intervention and a massive number of daily training trials.

How Far Do You Push?

Language acquisition can be a very fragile process for many children with developmental disabilities. Successful trials need to substantially outnumber unsuccessful ones, and aversive control should be avoided. Language learning should be fun and functional for the child. Early mand training can often accomplish this goal, because the focus is on the child's needs and ways to teach the child to get access to desired reinforcers. If a child begins to avoid or attempt to escape language sessions, then it is likely that it is not fun or directly beneficial to the child. Instructors should watch for signs of escape and avoidance behavior (e.g., falling to the floor, looking away, crying, aggression). As these behaviors begin to occur, try not to let the child get out of the immediate task, and then later intersperse easier tasks (e.g., imitation, echoic, and receptive trials). Always terminate the session after a correct response (without the accompaniment of negative behavior). Never end a session as a result of negative behavior on the child's part. If you do, you will reinforce escape behavior, which will occur earlier and earlier in successive sessions. This escape and avoidance behavior is how many children shape teachers out of making them work. An important element of working with nonverbal children is to always try to get the highest quality response with the least amount of prompting.

Summary

The first type of language to begin teaching a nonverbal child should be the mand. This type of language directly benefits the child by allowing him to gain access to desired reinforcers. The other types of language skills (e.g., labeling, imitation, receptive) do not have this immediate benefit to the child, thus they are often harder to establish as initial forms of communication. Many children can acquire manding quite quickly by using augmentative communication. However, the specific procedures for teaching early mands effectively require a number of important considerations and the careful use of prompts and reinforcement. In addition, mands will be acquired quicker if those working with the child create a language-based environment that fosters the child's language acquisition.

Chapter 6
Teaching Beginning Imitation, Echoic, Receptive, and Matching-to-Sample Skills

Following initial mand training, there are a number of related language skills that should be targeted for early intervention. A nonverbal child needs to learn to imitate motor and vocal models, comply with receptive instructions, and match similar items to each other. Elements of these skills may have been used in the cooperation training and the initial mand training described in Chapter 5, but now they should be further developed and established as independent skills. The primary purpose of these training trials is to strengthen these important skills, but they also can be used to teach the child that some work is going to be required for the opportunity to mand.

Many early manders may be successful at some of these new language tasks, while others may have difficulty with them. For those children who can imitate, match, or comply with receptive instructions, these skills should be interspersed with mand trials. For example, say to the child, "Do this," while clapping. A successful clap should be followed with a mand trial, specifically, "Good. What do you what?" Following the delivery of reinforcement, a different type of trial should be conducted, such as, "Say dog," with a correct response again followed by a

mand trial. The trials should be presented in a mixed order and the instructor should gradually increase the number of trials prior to offering a mand trial (this type of training can be referred to as mixed verbal behavior or "mixed VB"). If the child is having difficulty with these other skills independent of a mand trial, then the following procedures that are designed to specifically develop these skills may be helpful.

Teaching Motor Imitation

The ability to imitate the motor behavior of other people plays an important role in a child's verbal and social development. If a child can imitate the behavior of others, they can acquire a number of skills with only minimal training. However, many nonverbal children cannot imitate even simple behaviors, and special training procedures are required to develop these important skills. Early imitation training can take several forms, but perhaps the most important elements in training involve making it fun for the child, and capitalizing on the child's ongoing motivation for specific reinforcers. For example, training can be fun if the instructor can make it seem like a game, such as playing peek-a-boo, acting like a monster, or making funny faces. Specific motivators and reinforcers can be used if the instructor can identify a strong motivator (e.g., scooping up dried beans in a container), use this activity to encourage imitation by the instructor doing it first, and then encouraging the child to copy her action.

If the child will imitate at least some actions under these circumstances, then further training will probably be easy. However, if the child does not imitate, then more intensive training procedures will be required. The procedure for specifically teaching imitative behavior consists of asking the child to imitate the potentially fun physical movement (e.g., peek-a-boo, scooping beans) with the verbal prompt, "Do this." The instructor should immediately reinforce any correct responses or approximations to the target response. If the child does not respond, or emits an obvious incorrect response, then the instructor should repeat the request and the movement a few more times. If the child still fails to respond, then the procedure should be repeated with the use of physical prompts to guide the child's arms through the correct imitative action (the physical prompt sometimes works better if a second adult does the prompting from behind the child). The child should be reinforced immediately with praise and the desired action (other reinforcers such as food may also be helpful).

The next trial should occur within a few seconds, and the instructor should slightly reduce the physical prompt, and of course, immediately reinforce the child's correct behavior. Other potent reinforcers should be used as well, interspersing them with each

other to avoid satiation. The instructor should try to conduct as many trials as possible each session and each day. The critical feature of this procedure is the use of physical prompts to obtain motor imitation and the gradual reduction of the prompts. For more information on the use of physical prompting, the reader is referred to Martin and Paer (1995).

If a child is learning sign language as a response, his motor imitation can be also be developed by using the newly trained signs. For example, if the child has learned to sign "music" by tapping his arm, present the child with a "Do this" prompt rather than a "What do you want" or a "Sign music" prompt. Immediately reinforce correct responses or approximations with a strong reinforcer. Incorrect responses can be following by a prompt such as holding up the music box. This procedure uses the variables that control mands (i.e., motivation) and tacts (i.e., the object) as prompts to teach imitation, and is often an immediately successful procedure if the child has already learned to mand with signs. The procedure can be repeated with the other signs that the child has learned.

Some children may have more success at imitating an action when the instructor uses an object with the action—for example, using a drumstick to pound a drum. The instructor should say "Do this" and then hit the drum with the stick. If the child imitates (or provides an approximation to imitation), he should be immediately reinforced. If he fails to respond, then the physical prompting procedure, like the one described above, should be implemented. There are a number of other types of imitation tasks with objects that could be tried, such as placing objects in containers, racing cars, throwing or pushing balls, pouring water or sand, or opening and closing doors. Gross motor imitation tasks should also be tried, such as jumping, sitting, dancing, running, or turning in circles. Some children may be more successful with this type of imitation. The objective of this training is to teach the child to copy the instructor's behavior. If he can copy one or two behaviors, these imitative responses should be reinforced and interspersed with mand trials (i.e., conduct one imitation trial and then follow it with a mand trial). Gradually introduce new imitative behaviors while trying to keep the child as successful as possible by making it fun, using physical prompts, and providing strong reinforcers.

Additional Variables for Developing Imitation

Motivation (establishing operations) will weaken if the reinforcement being used can be freely obtained (i.e., without responding) outside the session. For example, if music is obtained free throughout the day, then its value may not be so strong when some response effort is required to obtain it. Also, its removal (under circumstances where the individual always has it) may be an aversive event that evokes aggressive behavior. Martin and Paer (1995) have identified several other factors that can contribute to the development of imitative behavior. These factors should be taken into consideration, especially when attempts at developing imitative skills have failed.

First, a trial should be presented only when the child is attending to the instructor. The model that an instructor uses should be presented clearly and concisely, and it should not be accompanied with complicated verbal instructions. For example, the verbal prompt should simply be "Do this," while modeling a clap. The instructor should avoid saying additional words such as "Come on Fred. Do this. You can do it Fred. Look at me Fred." For some children, no verbal prompts should be given; the instructor should just perform the action. Or, for some children, the instructor should present the clap in exactly the same manner each trial (e.g., same force, position, number of claps) and avoid emitting additional physical behaviors such as head and body movements. It should be noted that each child is different, and these additional verbal and physical stimuli may actually help teach imitation to some children.

Martin and Pear (1995) also suggest that imitative "control can be developed much more effectively when the teacher attempts to minimize the possibility of errors on the part of the student" (p. 121). This suggestion of using "errorless learning" is derived from the work of Terrace (1963) and Touchette (1971), as well as several other basic behavioral researchers. The skillful use of prompts, and the fading of those prompts, can help minimize errors. A child who cannot emit any imitative behavior has obviously had a long history of failure. If no response typically occurs after the "Do this" prompt, then the instructor should simultaneously give the student a physical and verbal prompt and immediately reinforce the behavior. The instructor should then gradually delay the delivery of the physical prompt. A teacher who skillfully uses prompts (by adjusting the delivery and removal of the prompts) and reinforces closer approximations can greatly reduce a student's errors, thereby increasing the probability that the child will learn to imitate.

A final point presented by Martin and Pear (1995) is to maximize the number of training trials. Training should be conducted every day with as many trials as possible each session. Some students may need several hundred trials every day in order to show improvement, others may require less intensive training. However, it is clear that sporadic training is not very effective for a child who cannot imitate motor behaviors. Finally, it is important to remember that training should be as fun as possible. If the child is forced to imitate, it is less likely that spontaneous or unprompted imitation will occur in the future.

Increasing Vocal Play and Teaching Vocal (Echoic) Imitation

Recall that speech is the most desired response form for a nonverbal child (see Chapter 4), and every effort should be made to achieve this goal. In general, the objective of vocal training is to increase the child's spontaneous vocal play and to bring specific vocalizations under imitative (echoic) control. There are several techniques that can help accomplish these goals. The first procedure involves the use of direct reinforcement for any vocalizations that the child emits. That is, when the child makes some identifiable speech sounds, the instructor should directly reinforce this behavior with atten-

tion, physical contact, or other effective reinforcers. The goal is to increase the frequency of vocalizations, and reinforcement is the main way to accomplish this objective. The intensity of this program depends on the individual child. If a child almost never makes sounds, every effort to reinforce a sound should be made. If the child makes a variety of sounds, these different sounds should be reinforced.

The second technique for increasing vocalizations is to take every opportunity to pair (associate) adult vocalizations with naturally occurring reinforcers. For example, just prior to delivering tickles to a child, the adult should say a sound such as "baba" and then tickle the child (the sound should always slightly precede the delivery of the reinforcer by about 1 to 2 seconds). Repeat this pairing several times. If tickles are reinforcers, soon the sound may become a reinforcer because it is associated with tickles. Repeat this procedure with a variety of different reinforcers and eventually with a variety of different sounds.

If sounds become reinforcers to the child, then it is possible for these sounds to become automatically strengthened when accidentally emitted by the child. That is, some sounds may sound different to the child because of this pairing and appear fun for the child—fun in the sense that they have become reinforcing. Skinner (1957) has identified this effect as "automatic reinforcement," and he and others have suggested that it plays a critical role in the early establishment of speech in typical children (e.g., Bijou & Bear, 1965; Mowrer, 1950; Osgood, 1953; Vaughan & Michael, 1982). The use of this procedure has also been effective for increasing speech for children with language delays (Sundberg, Michael, Partington, & Sundberg, 1996).

The purpose of increasing a child's vocal play is to strengthen his vocal cords and increase the probability of establishing echoic skills (vocal imitation). Echoic skills play a major role in the teaching of new words, because if a child can repeat a word on command, then the transfer of control procedures described in Chapter 5 can be used to not only teach mands but to teach other types of language as well (e.g., tacts, intraverbals). The procedures for strengthening a child's ability to echo an instructor are similar to those used for motor imitation, except that vocal behavior is used and physical prompts are impossible. The procedure consists of presenting the child with the verbal prompt "Say..." and reinforcing a correct response or an approximation to a correct response. Training may be most successful if instruction begins with a sound that the child has emitted frequently in the past. The objective is to get the child to emit the specific sound on command. Many children can emit a wide variety of sounds, but cannot emit them when specifically asked to do so. Catching a sound that the child is emitting and asking the child to repeat it may also work for some children. These procedures should be used in addition to the shaping procedures described above and, when combined with the direct and automatic reinforcement procedures, may result in an increase of vocal behavior.

Teaching Beginning Receptive Language

Many nonverbal children have at least some receptive behavior under stimulus control (e.g., they can successfully follow instructions such as "Look at me," "Sit down"). These skills are important because the child must be able to both attend to and respond to the language of others. He must also eventually learn to follow a wide variety of instructions, some of which require multiple and complex discriminations. Some of the earliest instructions require the child to engage in a single specified action (e.g., "Stand-up," "Come here," "Jump"), while others require the child to attend to others (e.g., "Go with Bill") or discriminate between a selection of items or pictures (e.g., "Give me the red ball").

The main goal in the development of receptive skills is to teach the child to correctly respond to the language of others. It must be remembered that all children have had exposure to the language of other individuals, and they may enter the teaching process with a competing negative history. If a child has not been successful in acquiring receptive skills, it is important that the initial attempts to develop these skills involve responses that are relatively easy for the child, and correct responses should be immediately reinforced.

Many of the first receptive responses naturally acquired by typical children involve those that occur in the context of ongoing reinforcing events in their daily lives. For example, some nonverbal children learn to get their coat when they see other children getting their coat, and a teacher provides a verbal prompt to get their coat. Teaching may be more successful if it occurs under reinforcement conditions, rather than under conditions where the child must give up something in order to respond correctly to the parent's verbal instruction. For example, parents and teachers are often anxious to teach children to comply with an instruction to come when called. Unfortunately, children are frequently called at a time when they are already engaging in some reinforcing activity, or when the requested activity is undesirable by the child. Hence, coming when called frequently does not result in a reinforcing situation.

In order to teach a child to come when called, it is critical to consider what behavior is expected on the part of the child. Specifically, the child should walk to the instructor when he hears the words "Come here." Many children will walk to take a reinforcer that is in view or held-out by another person (i.e., offered), and it is often relatively easy to teach the child to come under these circumstances. It is also possible to provide a gentle physical prompt (e.g., take the child's hand and lightly lead them closer) or to provide a beckoning hand gesture while repeating the instruction. As soon as the child moves to the instructor, it is important to immediately deliver the reinforcer and pair the delivery of the reinforcer with praise. Once the child has been successful in responding to the instruction and multiple prompts, the prompts should be reduced as soon as possible. However, the physical and gestural prompts should not be faded so quickly that the child no longer comes when called.

Once the child is approaching when the reinforcer is clearly present and the instructor is only a few feet away, the instructor should slightly increase the distance that the child must travel to get the reinforcer. The next step is to gradually reduce the visual presence of the reinforcer. For example, if the reinforcer is a food or drink item, it is possible to briefly show the child the item, give the instruction, and then partially hide the item behind the instructor's back. When the child arrives, the item is immediately given to the child along with praise for coming. As the item is being placed behind the instructor's back, it might be necessary to once again use the gestural prompt to help get the child to come. Eventually, it should be possible to get the child to come when called and when given a gestural prompt to come while the reinforcer is completely hidden behind the instructor's back.

Next, the child should learn to come to a variety of individuals, in a variety of situations (e.g., different locations inside each room and different places outside) for a variety of hidden reinforcers. Varying these conditions is important because if coming when called is only taught by one person, in one situation, using one reinforcer, the behavior may not occur when any of these conditions change. For example, if the child is not interested in a specific item or event that is characteristically used, he may not respond. Rather than only giving a specific item as the reinforcer for coming, events such as being picked-up or tickled can be used as reinforcers. However, since the activity may not have an item that can be used as a visual prompt to get the behavior to occur, it will probably be necessary to use some specific hand motion to signal that the activity is likely to occur upon the child's arrival. For example, if the child likes to be tickled, the instructor should first get the child's attention in some manner, and then while approaching the child, make a motion with her fingers (as if she were tickling the child's torso) immediately prior to tickling the child for a few seconds. After repeating this sequence a few times, the instructor could back away a few feet from the child and say "Come here" while making the tickling motion, and tickle and praise the child when he steps forward to the instructor. Training trials should be spaced throughout the day to avoid satiation and to make use of the varying conditions during a child's day.

A number of additional receptive responses can be taught by using the context of ongoing routines and reinforcing situations. Many children are simply led to the table to get food that has been placed on the table for them, or are guided into a sitting position so that their shoes can be put on prior to being allowed to go outside in the backyard. If these regular events are reinforcing to the child, it is possible to build in a response requirement into these routines. For example, prior to the parent giving a plate of food (usually a reinforcer) to the child, with the plate in one of the parent's hands, the parent could lead (i.e., gently physically guide) the child to the table with the other hand. When standing next to the chair, the parent can give the instruction to "Sit down," gently physically prompting the child to sit and then placing the plate in front of the child. In this example, the key response is the child sitting down on the chair. Physical prompts to assist in teaching

the child to sit when given the instruction must be gradually eliminated (usually over a series of trials), while the child does more of the work of getting into the sitting position.

If the child has acquired some imitative behavior, it is possible to use these skills to help teach a variety of receptive skills. For example, a child who can imitate clapping or jumping can also learn to do these same actions when asked to "Clap" or "Jump" without the imitative model. In this situation, the instructor could get the child to clap imitatively, and then reinforce his imitative clapping. On the next trial the instructor could say "Clap hands" (instead of saying "Do this") and present an imitative model of clapping. If the child claps, immediately reinforce the behavior and present the trial again with a slight delay in the imitative prompt (i.e., begin to fade the prompt). If the child does not immediately begin to clap following the imitative model, a slight physical prompt could be used to get the clapping to occur, and the child's clapping should be followed with the delivery of a reinforcer and a repeat of the trial. After the first response is acquired, repeat this process with a second response (e.g., "Jump") and then teach the child to discriminate between the two verbal stimuli by intermixing the two receptive commands. Once these two responses are acquired, additional commands should be used.

Eventually, the child must learn to touch or point to specifically named items. Although receptive identification of items usually results in considerable recognition and praise for the typically developing child, this outcome may not be a sufficient reinforcer for many children with language delays. The child with language delays often does not know what response is expected of him and may not know the name of the item. In order to increase the motivation for the child to participate in this type of learning activity, it is often helpful to use a reinforcing item as the one to be touched, because the child usually has a tendency to reach for reinforcers. The critical response to teach the child is to touch the item when given the instruction to "Touch (reinforcer)" a shown item. At first, it may be necessary for the instructor to hold the item (e.g., a cookie) in one hand and, after having presented the instruction "Touch cookie," use the other hand to physically guide the child's hand to touch the cookie. The child should be presented with praise for touching the cookie (e.g., "Yes! That's the cookie!) and be allowed to eat some of the cookie.

On subsequent trials, the goal is to fade all of the prompts used to teach the child to reach and touch the named item. Note that in this task the child is not being required to discriminate between items, which is a much more difficult task for the child. In order to fade the physical prompt to touch the item, it is often necessary to use a subtler gestural prompt to get the response to occur. Moving the item slightly closer to the child and/or tapping the top of the item with one of the fingers holding the item often serve as an effective prompt to get the touching to occur. As these types of receptive trials are being conducted, it is important to generalize the reach and touch response to include reaching to a variety of positions in front of the child (i.e., on the right and left sides, above and below eye level). The child should also be

taught to touch a variety of other reinforcing items (only one at a time). The outcome of this procedure is that the child will be able to reliably touch a named item on request. This skill will ultimately facilitate the child's ability to learn to receptively discriminate between a variety of items.

The next step in the procedure is to introduce a distracter stimulus. Often an empty hand can provide such a stimulus. The instructor should hold up the targeted item along with her empty and open hand and say "Touch..." There are several ways to increase the probability of success during this initial discrimination training. The item can be placed closer to the child, tapped on, or wiggled. Attempts to touch the open hand should result in the instructor moving her hand away from the child and moving the object closer to the child. Once the child can successfully touch a specific item on command, additional objects (reinforcers) should be used along with the empty hand. If the child can discriminate between these two stimuli without errors, then additional objects should be slowly introduced. The initial presentation of additional items can be done in a manner similar to the introduction of the hand as a distracter (i.e., errorless if possible).

Teaching Matching-to-Sample

One of the skills that can be used to develop instructional control is that of matching identical objects or pictures to samples of those items. Although many children with language delays have difficulty learning to attend to words used by others, these same children can be taught to attend to and match visual stimuli. For some children, the task can begin with matching a single object or picture to a single sample stimulus. However, a common method used to teach this skill involves placing two different items on a table, handing the child a third item that matches one of the items on the table, and having the child place this third item next to or on the matching item on the table.

To teach this matching-to-sample skill, the instructor should sit next to a child at a table and place two items about a foot apart from each other. Then, show the child the third item and model the task by placing that item with the matching item. After the task is modeled by the instructor, the third item should be given to the child. The child should be provided with prompts to complete that same matching task. The prompts can include physical prompts to place and release the item in the correct location, gestural prompts (e.g., pointing to the correct item on the table), verbal prompts (e.g., "Put with same," "Match"), or a prompt involving placing the matching item closer to the child. Reinforcement should then be provided following correct responding. As the task is repeated, the placement of the target item should be randomly switched between the left and right sides so that the child learns to attend to the position of the target item. Through this process, instructional control is established, and the child learns to match similar items together.

Although this task can be taught by modeling the response and using only physical and gestural prompts, it is more typical to use a verbal instruction to start the task. The words spoken to the child as he is given the item to match (e.g., "Put with same," "Match") can acquire some instructional control over the child's responding. The child learns that the particular verbal instruction indicates that a specific type of response is being requested, and that successful completion of that matching response will result in the delivery of reinforcement. Thus by participating in this type of learning task, the child learns to respond receptively to the verbal instruction used in the task.

Another type of teaching activity that can help with the development of general instructional control, and also specific receptive language skills, involves the use of simple puzzles and form boxes. Simple, one-piece inset puzzle pieces or pieces that fit into holes in a form box can be handed to a child along with a particular verbal instruction (e.g., "Put in"). As with the matching procedure described above, a variety of prompts can be used to help the child learn to successfully complete the task. Eventually, the extra prompts can be eliminated and the child should be able to complete the task with only the initial verbal instruction, and the actual item to place in the puzzle board or form box. Once again, these types of tasks, which are often easy to teach because they capitalize on child's visual discrimination skills, can be instrumental in teaching a child to respond to specific requests.

Summary

At this point the child should be able to mand for some reinforcers, imitate some actions, echo some sounds and words, follow a number of verbal commands, discriminate between a few objects, and match items to corresponding samples.   Trials on these skills should be interspersed with each other (mixed VB) in order to not only teach these important skills, but to teach the child that some work (responding) will be required to obtain the opportunity to mand. It should be kept in mind that every child is different, and these procedures may vary substantially for individual children. It is hoped that this general presentation of the procedures will assist the instructor in establishing a program that meets the needs of an individual child.

Chapter 7

Teaching Tact and Receptive Skills

Following the successful acquisition of a few mands for reinforcers, and some success on echoic, imitation, compliance, and matching-to-sample, training should begin on naming (i.e., tacting) and receptively identifying common objects. It is important to note that training on the other skills (i.e., mand, echoic, imitation, early receptive, and matching-to-sample) should be continued daily both in formal sessions and in the natural environment. These other types of trials should be interspersed with the newly targeted tact and receptive trials (i.e., mixed VB). The only prerequisite skills necessary for beginning tact and receptive training are that the child has some responses under echoic or imitative control, and that the child has some mands that occur without imitative or echoic prompts.

Once the child has developed a minimal echoic or imitative repertoire (i.e., he can imitate new words or signs without much training) the transfer of control procedures (described in Chapter 5) can be used to teach the child to label objects. At the same time (within the same session) procedures to teach the child to receptively discriminate between these same objects should also occur. The procedures for teaching tacts and receptive responses will be described independently, but the reader should keep in mind that both procedures should be con-

ducted concurrently for each new word introduced. In addition, the procedures for teaching tact and receptive responses involving speech, signs, and pictures will also be described separately.

Beginning Tact Training Using Speech as the Response

There are two general approaches to starting initial tact training. The first is to begin with the same words that were used for mand training, and the second is to select new words. Eventually, the child will need to be able to do both, but some children may learn to name the items that they initially learned to mand quicker than learning to emit new words (this often depends on the strength of their echoic repertoire). The procedures for both types of training will be described below, and both could be conducted concurrently with an individual child in order to determine which approach will be the most desirable for the child.

Children typically learn to ask for items they want fairly quickly because it results in them getting those items. However, it is also important for children to be able to identify those items even when they don't want the item or the item itself is not forthcoming (e.g., saying "TV" because the child sees the "TV" not because he wants the TV). In this situation, the child would be reinforced (praise, or some other item or event) for being correct in his labeling of the item, but would not receive the item that he had previously learned to request. Although he would say the same word as when he was requesting the item, he would be saying the word for different reasons. When the word is said as a mand for the item, certain motivational variables make the receipt of those items reinforcing. In order to teach that same response to occur as a tact of those items, it is necessary to transfer the response from the control of the motivational variables to the control of the (nonverbal) item itself and to other reinforcers (that do not include that item) that typically follow a correct tact response.

The procedure to establish tacts is very similar to the procedure to teach initial mands, except the verbal stimulus should be "What is that?" instead of "What do you want?", and the reinforcer should be praise (or some other reinforcer) rather than the delivery of the specific item. For example, if the child learned to say "car" when he wanted a toy car (mand), he could be taught to tact car by presenting the verbal prompt "What is that?" and by following a correct response with praise and a different reinforcer (e.g., a tickle). The first objective in this training is to fade out the specific reinforcer (the delivery of the toy car) and to transfer control from motivation to the object (Table 7-1, Panel 2). The procedure may work quicker if the instructor tries it when the child is not very interested in a car (i.e., he does not have a strong establishing operation for a car), or the instructor uses a picture of a car rather than a real car. The process of fading out the elements of the mand (i.e., the establishing operation and specific reinforcement) may occur quite quickly for some children. The primary objective is to free the response from establishing operation (EO) control, and transfer it to nonverbal control by changing from specific reinforcement to nonspecific reinforcement. That is, the child must learn to identify an item, but not expect to receive the item. Eventually, the verbal stimuli "What is that?" versus "What do you want?" can help the child to discriminate between these two different conditions.

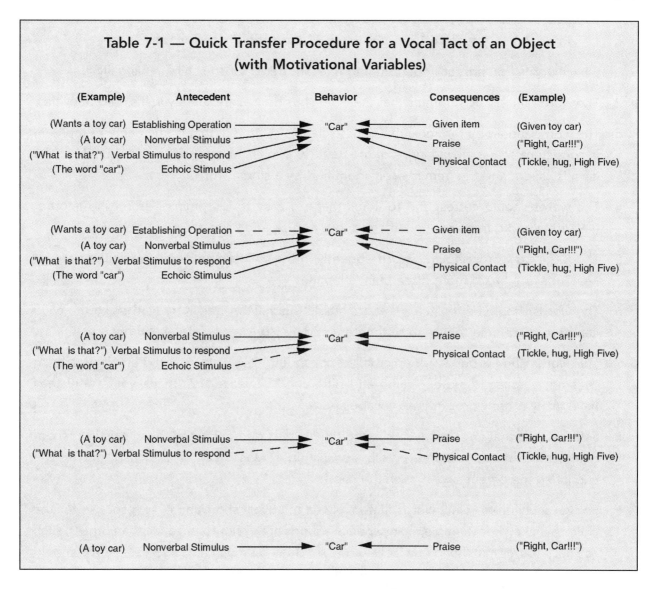

Table 7-1 — Quick Transfer Procedure for a Vocal Tact of an Object (with Motivational Variables)

The second approach to tact training involves the establishment of a new response that is not directly related to strong reinforcers. The selection of these words requires some careful consideration (Table 7-2). The words chosen should be nouns, and they should be for those items that the child comes in contact with on a regular basis. Real objects should be used, but for some children pictures can be used (real objects may be more effective in developing tacting because they are three dimensional and are present in the child's daily environment).

The objects should be easy to identify, clearly defined, and talked about frequently in the child's environment (e.g., shoes, socks, hat, shirt, pants, pen, paper, car, table, chair, door, window, bus, tree, water). There are several additional issues presented in Table 7-2 that the instructor should consider before selecting specific words for training.

Fading Out the Echoic Prompt

The teaching procedure for a vocal tact without an EO (motivation) consists of presenting the object in front of the child along

Table 7-2 — Issues to Consider when Picking the First Words as Tacts*

1. Select words that are for important and relevant items for the child in his daily life.

2. The words should be for items that the child sees or uses frequently in his daily activities.

3. The words should be for items that can be clearly identified; that is, the name of the item is consistent across all variations of the item (e.g., ball), all adults can agree on what the item is called, and the item is easily identified by a single word.

4. The words should correspond to items that are easy to discriminate from one another (i.e., a hat and a tree are very different, but a truck and a car are quite similar).

5. The targeted words should occur frequently in the child's day-to-day environment (e.g., "eat" may be heard more often than "elephant").

6. The words should be for items that are stable (nouns) not transitory (verbs), so the child can have more time to attend to the item and also physically interact with it.

7. The words should be developmentally appropriate (e.g., typical children do not learn "yes/no," "toilet," "more" "same and different," "please," or "thank you," until they have many other words in their vocabulary.

8. Select words that are already familiar to the child as demonstrated by an existing receptive, echoic, mand, or imitative skill. For example, teach "cup" if the child touches the cup when the parent says "Touch the cup."

9. For vocal children, select words that involve a relatively short and easy response for the child to make. For example, many speech sounds are easier to produce than others, such as "aa," "ba," "mm," and "da"; "la" and "rrr" may be much harder. Also, words should be selected that match the child's existing echoic repertoire.

10. For signing children, select words that are iconic; that is, the signs look like the objects that they stand for, as in the sign for "book" looks like the action of opening a book, or the sign for "food" looks like putting food in the mouth. Also, signs should be selected that match the child's existing imitative repertoire.

11. Avoid words and signs that might have a negative or aversive history for the child (e.g., bed, toilet, bath, no).

*Note the many similarities to the issues raised for selecting initial mands for a child.

with the verbal prompt "What is that?" and an echoic prompt (Table 7-3). For example, while holding up a shoe the instructor says "What is that? Shoe. Say shoe." Correct responses (or approximations) should be reinforced with praise and, if reinforcing, physical contact (eventually the praise alone should follow the response, and the physical reinforcement—assuming it is reinforcement—should be faded out).

Beginning with the next trial, the instructor should start to fade out the echoic prompt (Table 7-3, Panel 2), while keeping in the verbal prompt "What is that?" The fading of the echoic prompt can be accomplished by using the delay procedure previously described or by fading from full echoic prompts to partial echoic prompts. For example, in teaching the tact "shoe" the instructor should first try to delay the prompt a few seconds. If no response occurs, then the instructor should provide a partial prompt such as "Sh..." This prompt should

be continuously reduced until the child's response "Shoe" occurs in the absence of the prompt. If errors occur while fading the prompts, the instructor should back up to more full prompts, and then attempt to reduce the prompts again. An echoic prompt can also be faded by decreasing the auditory level of the prompt. The instructor should systematically (over several trials) decrease the volume of the prompt until the response occurs in its absence. If errors occur, the volume of the prompt should be increased slightly, and then reduced again on the next trial. A combination of these fading procedures may produce quicker results for some children. The main purpose of these procedures is to transfer control from an echoic prompt to the object itself, while reducing the possibility of errors. It is important in early training to keep errors low and success high (this can also be accomplished by interspersing known responses with the newly trained responses).

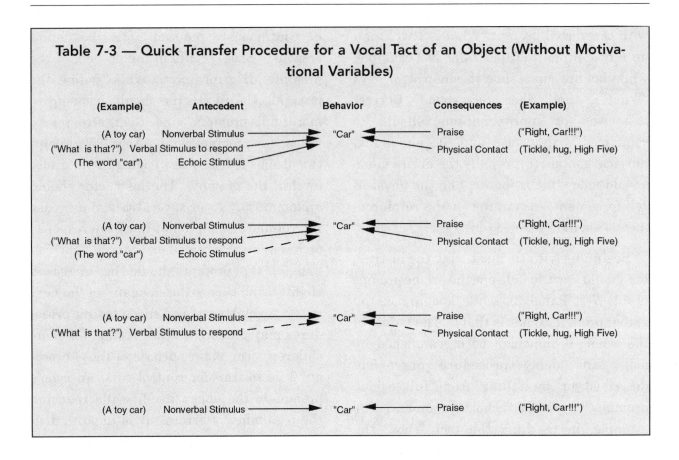

Table 7-3 — Quick Transfer Procedure for a Vocal Tact of an Object (Without Motivational Variables)

Fading Out the Verbal Prompt

The prompt "What is that?" should also be eventually faded out if the goal is to obtain spontaneous tacting. That is, the child needs to learn to identify at least some objects without being verbally prompts to do so (Table 7-3, Panels 3 & 4). A spontaneous, or "pure tact," is a verbal response controlled only by a nonverbal stimulus (and nonspecific reinforcement). For example, a child looks up in the sky and says "airplane" without an adult prompting him in any way. The sight and sound of the airplane alone should evoke the correct word. However, spontaneity is a complicated issue, because the child still needs to be able to tact when asked to do so, therefore the verbal stimulus should not be completely faded out. Rather, training should be given both ways so the child can emit tacts independent of verbal prompts, but also when asked to tact.

Spontaneous Manding and Tacting

Once a child has acquired a few verbal responses, it is not uncommon for the child to spontaneously initiate an interaction. These initial spontaneous responses are usually mands for a particular item or event, but they may also include a tact of an item or action. It is important to ensure that spontaneous verbal responses are reinforced as often as possible with the child's most powerful reinforcers. The reinforcement of the spontaneous verbal responses will result in the child using his new skills more often, which will greatly expedite the child's acquisition of additional language skills.

Beginning Tact Training Using Sign Language as the Response Form

The procedures for teaching tacts using sign language are very similar to those used for teaching vocal tacts, except there are some additional prompt available (Table 7-4). The training can begin with new signs or by using the signs acquired as mands and transferring them to tact control. The deci-

sion on which approach to take should be based, in part, on the child's ability to imitate. If the child's imitative skills are strong, then it may be possible to teach him new tacts quickly. If his imitation skills are weak, then early tact training may be more successful using some of his known signs to develop tacting skills.

The procedure to teach tacts using known signs previously established as mands

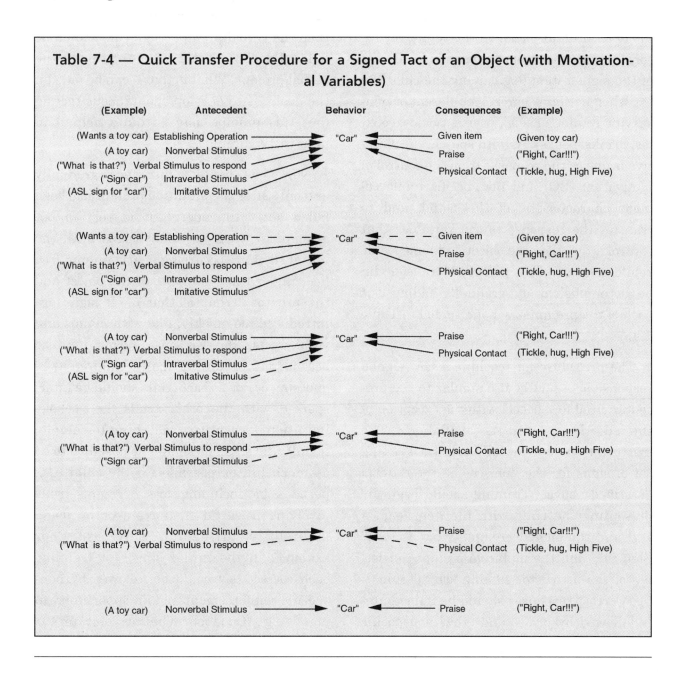

Table 7-4 — Quick Transfer Procedure for a Signed Tact of an Object (with Motivational Variables)

involves the same elements as described above for speech, except a physical prompt can be used at the beginning of training, (but only if necessary). Also, an intraverbal prompt such as "Sign..." can be used in the process of transferring control from the EO (motivation) to the object. It may be best to begin training when the EO for the specific item is not very strong (although this may not be possible). Also, the use of pictures may reduce the child's tendency to expect a specific reinforcer. The task for the instructor is to gradually change the reinforcer for correct responses from the specific reinforcer of the signed item (e.g., giving the child the car when he signs "car") to a different or non-specific reinforcer (e.g., praise, tickles, cookies, drinks, books). As with speech, the objective is to free the response from the control of motivation (EO) and the specific reinforcement characteristic of the mand, and to transfer the response to the variables that control a tact (i.e., the object and nonspecific reinforcement). This process of transfer can be accomplished by gradually fading out each of the prompts as diagrammed in Table 7-4.

The procedure for teaching a new signed response as a tact is also similar to the procedure used for speech, with the exception of the additional prompts available. The instructor should carefully select a starting set of signs for the items using the criteria described above. Training should begin by presenting the child with the item (e.g., a car) and the signed prompt "What is that? Sign car" and the imitative prompt consisting of the instructor signing "car" (Table 7-5). Correct responses should be immediately followed by praise and other nonspecific

reinforcers (e.g., tickles, food). If the child is unsuccessful in responding, the instructor should drop back to the use of a physical prompt, but should also work on eliminating this prompt as soon as possible. The primary objective at this point is to fade out the additional prompts, beginning with the physical prompt, if used, and the imitative prompt (Panel 2, Table 7-5). The procedures for fading these prompts are similar to the ones previously described. Once the child is successful without the imitative prompt, then the verbal prompt "Sign car" should be faded (Panel 3 of Table 7-5). And finally, the verbal prompt "What is that?" can be faded if the desire is to develop spontaneous tacting (but this prompt may be quite helpful in later tact training).

New signs should be introduced gradually and only after the imitative prompt has been faded out. In general, it is best to not attempt to teach too many signs until the initial signs are occurring nearly prompt free (i.e., under the conditions of the object and the prompt "What is that"). If signs are introduced too quickly, like with mands and vocal tacts, the response forms tend to become mixed up for many children (i.e., guessing occurs). Tact trials should be interspersed with the other trials (i.e., echoic, imitation, receptive, matching-to-sample, mand), and sessions should be designed to be as much fun as possible for the child (i.e., perhaps by including lots of mand trials involving powerful reinforcers or by using naturally occurring fun activities). For example, in the initial stages of training, each correct tact could be followed by non-specific reinforcement and an opportunity to mand (e.g., "Good job. What do you want?").

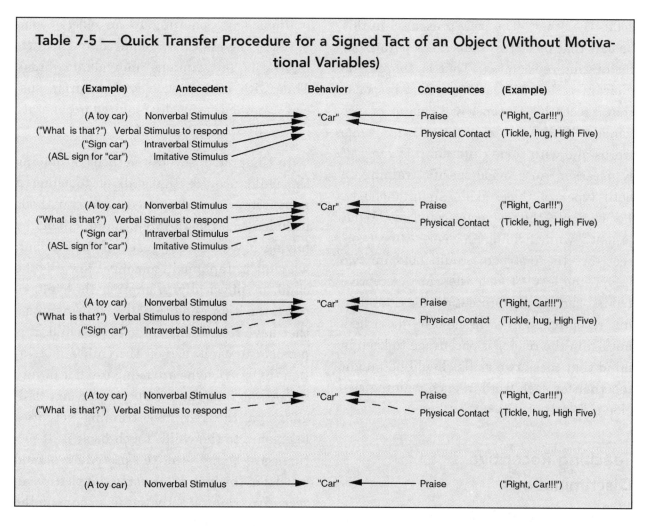

Table 7-5 — Quick Transfer Procedure for a Signed Tact of an Object (Without Motivational Variables)

Tacting Using a Picture Pointing or Exchange Response

The procedures for teaching pointing to pictures (or an exchange) as tacts differs in several ways from tact training with words and signs. Perhaps the most significant way is the need to teach a scan response along with a pointing to/exchange response. However, in the early stages of pointing to/exchanging pictures, the procedure is quite easy because it is matching-to-sample. That is, the child is shown, for example, a ball and asked to point to/exchange a picture of a ball. The closer the similarity of the picture to the object, the closer it is to matching.

This early type of tacting can be quite successful for some individuals, but the long-term issues involved in using pictures as a communication system are complicated, and the reader is referred to the points raised in Chapter 4.

Teaching Receptive Responses Along with Tacts

There is a long-standing controversy in the language acquisition literature concerning the relation between receptive and expressive (tacting) language (e.g., Bloom, 1974; Spradlin, 1974). Typically, the arguments concern which form of language precedes the other. The view presented in this book is that these two skills are separate but facilitating repertoires. That is, there is no guarantee that by teaching a tact response that a receptive response will emerge or vice versa. While this may occur with some words and with some children, it is generally necessary to provide specific training on both types of these skills simultaneously. For example, the instructor could say "What is that?" while holding up a car. After a correct tact the instructor could hold up two items and say "Touch the car" (receptive trial). The specific procedures for establishing receptive skills will now be described, but again the reader is encourage to keep in mind that these two skills should be taught together for each word in each training session (i.e., mixed VB).

Teaching Receptive Discriminations

Children frequently do learn to receptively identify many items prior to being able to tact the item (however, as previously stated, this is not always the case). They are also more likely to be able to follow instructions to perform a specified action before they learn to tact a particular action. However, with typically developing children, the receptive skills frequently occur close in time with the acquisition of the tacting skills such that both skills appear to occur almost simultaneously. With many children with language delays however, the receptive skills are often more clearly seen to precede the tacting skills. The difference in the rates of acquisition may be due to the ease of the responses required for the receptive discrim-

inations (e.g., pointing to an object) compared to the responses required for the tacting skills (i.e., unique individual words). Thus with language delayed children, special training is typically required to generate both repertoires.

In Chapter 6, several methods of helping the child acquire the skill of touching a named item were discussed. Those methods included making the item more salient by having it within easy reach of the student, wiggling or tapping it, moving it towards the child, or physically prompting the child to touch the item. Additionally, by using items that have reinforcing value to the child, it is possible to capitalize on the child's motivation (EOs). If signs are being used, it is very important that the instructor use sign language in the receptive training activities (e.g., sign to the child "touch book"). If pictures are being used, the procedure should consist of the instructor using the pictures in receptive training activities (e.g., hold up the picture of a book while saying "Touch the book" and have the child touch the actual object).

Once a child is able to touch a named item that is held within easy reach, and is able to touch that item when an empty hand is presented as a distracter, it is possible to begin the process of teaching the child to discriminate between several items. The next step in the teaching process is to conduct discrimination training between a reinforcing item and a non-reinforcing item (two nonreinforcing items can be used for children who may acquire this skill quickly). For example, if the child enjoys playing with bubbles, but doesn't particularly enjoy using pencils, it may be possible for the instructor to use a pencil as a distracter item. The instructor should hold up the two items in separate hands (the bubbles being positioned slightly closer to the child than the pencil) and present the instruction "Touch bubbles." Reinforcement in the form of praise, access to other reinforcing items or activities, or even playing with the bubbles should be delivered following the child's correct discrimination and touching response (it should be noted that although playing with the bubbles would probably serve as a reinforcer for the requested response, eventually this particular (specific) reinforcer would need to be eliminated).

It is also desirable to teach the child to touch the one reinforcing item (i.e., the bubbles) when it is held in a variety of positions with a variety of distracters. For example, the instructor should request that the item be touched when it is located in either the instructor's right or left hand, or when it is held at the instructor's eye level or chest level. The item should also be positioned above or below the non-reinforcing item, and the child should be able to locate and touch the named item. One of the main aspects of teaching the child to discriminate between objects is to ensure that the child visually scans the selection of items being presented. As with any other instruction that is presented to the child, it is best to give the instruction when the child is attending to the instructor, and to present a simple and clearly stated instruction at a time when the instructor has a potent reinforcer available to deliver to the child for engaging in the specified action.

Once the child is consistently able to touch the first (reinforcing) item used in the discrimination training procedure, a second reinforcing item (e.g., music) should be substituted for the first item (i.e., the bubbles). The non-reinforcing item that was used as a distracter when teaching the original discrimination should be used in this second phase of the discrimination training. After the child is consistently able to discriminate and touch the new item (i.e., the music) from the non-reinforcing item, then re-present the original reinforcing item (i.e., the bubbles) with the non-reinforcing item (i.e., the pencil). Once the child can successfully locate and touch the specified reinforcing item when presented with a non-reinforcing distracter, it is then possible to begin teaching the child to discriminate between the reinforcing items (i.e., bubbles versus music).

In order to teach the child to discriminate between the two reinforcing items, the instructor should run a series of trials in which one of the reinforcing items (e.g., the bubbles) is used as the primary item to touch, while the second reinforcing item (i.e., the music) is used as the distracter item. At first, it may be necessary to use the various prompts described in the initial discrimination procedure (i.e., the bubbles and the pencil). Once the child is consistently able to touch the item (i.e., the bubbles) without prompts, the instructor should then request that the learner touch the other reinforcing item (i.e., the music) while the other reinforcing item (i.e., the bubbles) is now used as a distracter. After the child consistently responds correctly to this second item, the first item should become the primary item to be touched. The number of trials prior to switching the target item should gradually be decreased as the child is able to quickly locate the named item. This portion of the discrimination training will be complete when the learner is able to select either of the two items requested by the instructor in a random order.

Following this initial discrimination training, additional items can be taught in a similar manner. For example, a third reinforcing item (e.g., the Winnie the Pooh character) can be added to the other items used. After the child can readily discriminate between several reinforcing items, the instructor can begin to introduce other items that may not have as strong of a reinforcing value for the child (e.g., items from the tact list). Receptive trials should be interspersed with tact trials, as well as trials on the other language related activities described thus far (mixed VB).

Once the child has learned to touch one of two items held in front of him, training should be given on learning to touch one of two items placed on a table. The procedure is similar, but this type of trial is often a little more difficult for a child because it eliminates most inadvertent prompts (e.g., slight position, movement, or eye prompts). Eventually, it may be possible to teach the child to pick up one of the two items placed on a table, and even give the selected item to the instructor. The items should be placed on the table about 12 inches apart, and the child given the instruction "Give me the ___." The same prompting and reinforcement procedures could then be used to teach the child to use this new response in the discrimination task. The two instructions (touch and give me) should be interspersed with each other to teach the child to attend to different instructions.

Another variation of the receptive discrimination task is to use pictures of the objects. If the child has learned to match objects to identical objects as described in Chapter 6, the child could also be taught to match objects to pictures of those same objects. The matching task could also include the variation of matching pictures to identical pictures, and matching pictures of objects to the actual objects. The additional skill of being able to match objects and pictures may prove to be helpful in teaching the child to discriminate the pictures of items that had previously been used in the discrimination training.

Generalization and Data Collection

Following training on a small set of tact and receptive responses, it is important to introduce objects and pictures that vary from the original training stimuli. For example, if the student learns to tact "car" in the presence of a model red Thunderbird, then training should be give on a blue Thunderbird, a red Corvette, a white Honda, and so on. Training should also be given on pictures of cars and real cars out on the street. To teach this behavior, the student should be presented with the new (untrained) stimulus and be asked "What is this?" The instructor should also use the prompt and fade procedures described earlier. Training should also occur across the day with different instructors in different environments. This training should be conducted with every tact and receptive response acquired before the child's vocabulary becomes too large.

Another form of generalization involves the use of different "carrier phrases" that surround a target word. In tact training, for example, the instructor should vary the way the child is asked to name an object by using phrases such as "What do you see?" "Can you tell me the name of this?" "This is a..." or "That is called a..." The instructor should also vary her volume, pitch, prosody, and other dynamic properties of speech. The point of this type of training is to teach the child to tact an item given a variety of phrases and speech patterns more like those he may encounter in his natural environment. A sample of a data collection and tracking sheet is presented in Table 7-6.

Expanding the Tact and Receptive Vocabulary

Early language training programs can fail for a number of reasons (Chapter 4). Perhaps one of the most common problems is the general haphazard way in which new vocabulary words are selected to teach a specific child. Typically, there is no organized plan as to what words to teach a child and in what order to teach them; so words are randomly added to the vocabulary without consideration of their ease of acquisition or relevance to the individual child. There are a number of important factors to consider when selecting new words, and the probability of success is related to this decision (Table 7-2).

Table 7-6 — Tact/Receptive List

	WORD	Receptive						Tact					
		Object	Pict 1	Pict 2	Pict 3	B&W	Dif P	Object	Pict 1	Pict 2	Pict 3	B&W	Dif P
1													
2													
3													
4													
5													
6													
7													
8													
9													
10													
11													
12													
13													
14													
15													
16													
17													
18													
19													
20													
21													
22													
23													
24													
25													
26													
27													
28													
29													
30													
31													
32													
33													
34													
35													
36													
37													
38													
39													
40													
41													
42													
43													
44													

A suggested list of the first 240 words to teach a child is presented in Table 7-7. It should be noted that these are only suggestions based on the criteria presented in Table 7-2, and since every child is different, these words may not be right for some children. Readers are encouraged to individualize each training program by selecting words most relevant to the specific child.

Summary

A typical child first learns to mand for strong reinforcers in his daily environment. Then, he learns receptive, echoic, imitation, and matching responses. Eventually the child learns to label (tact) common objects, actions, and pictures in his every day life and to receptively discriminate between those objects, actions, and pictures. The training sequence for the nonverbal child should follow this same general order. The quick transfer procedure can be very effective in teaching a person to tact the nonverbal stimuli in his environment, and can be done almost errorlessly, which can make learning more reinforcing.

Tact training can occur with the words taught as mands or with new words. Training should begin with real objects or actions, and pictures should be used for generalization purposes and expanding tacting skills. Receptive discriminations should also be taught along with tacting. A child must also learn to tact in the presence of other people and in other environments, as well as with stimuli that differ slightly from the training stimuli. Tacting should also be freed from verbal and motivational control in order to develop pure tacts. During training sessions, tact trials should be interspersed with trials on the other repertoires discussed thus far (i.e., mand, echoic, imitative, receptive), especially if learning is slow and it takes several trials and strong reinforcers to develop tacts. And finally, data should be taken on the acquisition of tact and receptive responses in order to determine if the child is acquiring the targeted skills.

Student: _____   **Table 7-7**
First 240 Words List   Date: _____

Group 1

WORD	CATEGORY	Receptive	Generalized Receptive	Tact	Generalized Tact
Cat	Animal				
Dog	Animal				
Cake	Food				
Candy	Food				
Chips	Food				
Cookies	Food				
Crackers	Food				
Ice Cream	Food				
Juice	Food				
Milk	Food				
Popcorn	Food				
Soda	Food				
Water	Food				
Movie	Miscellaneous				
Music	Miscellaneous				
Books	School Item				
Computer	School Item				
Up	Special Word Group				
Balls	Toy				
Bubbles	Toy				
Dolls	Toy				
Play dough	Toy				
Puppets	Toy				
Puzzles	Toy				
Swing (object)	Toy				
Top (toy)	Toy				
Airplane	Transportation				
Boat	Transportation				
Car	Transportation				
Train	Transportation				
Drink	Verb				
Hugs	Verb				
Jump	Verb				
Open	Verb				
Run	Verb				
Tickle	Verb				
Walk	Verb				

Data Collection Instructions

When completing this form for the first time, place a "+" in each collumn in which the student has acquired the skill. Leave the remaining cells blank. When updating the form, place the date in the column when the skill is known to be acquired (i.e., the date the form is updated).

Receptive = The student has demonstrated the ability to receptively identify at least one example of the item or action.
Generalized Receptive = The student can receptively identify at least five examples of the item or action that have specifically been taught, or can identify at least one example that had not previously been taught.
Tact = The student has demonstrated the ability to tact (i.e., label) at least one example of the item or action.
GeneralizedTact = The student can tact (i.e., label) at least five examples of the item or action that have specifically been taught, or can tact at least one example that had not previously been taught.

Student: _____   **Table 7-7**   Date: _____
First 240 Words List

Group 2

WORD	CATEGORY	Receptive	Generalized Receptive	Tact	Generalized Tact
Bird	Animal				
Fish	Animal				
Coat	Clothing				
Hat	Clothing				
Jacket	Clothing				
Shirt	Clothing				
Shoes	Clothing				
Socks	Clothing				
Apples	Food				
Bananas	Food				
Fries	Food				
Hamburger	Food				
Hot Dog	Food				
Oranges	Food				
Sandwich	Food				
Bed	Household				
Chair	Household				
Cup	Household				
Door	Household				
Fork	Household				
Garbage Can	Household				
Pillow	Household				
Plate-Dish	Household				
Refrigerator	Household				
Sink	Household				
Sofa-Couch	Household				
Spoon	Household				
Table	Household				
Toilet/Potty	Household				
TV	Household				
Window	Household				
Bowl	Miscellaneous				
Phone	Miscellaneous				
Flower	Outside				
House	Outside				
Tree	Outside				
Brush-Hairbrush	Personal Item				
Comb	Personal Item				
Keys	Personal Item				
Paper	School Item				
Pencil	School Item				
Scissors	School Item				
Balloons	Toy				
Bike	Toy				
Slide	Toy				
Bus/School bus	Transportation				
Truck	Transportation				

Student: _____   **Table 7-7**   Date: _____
First 240 Words List

Group 3

WORD	CATEGORY	Receptive	Generalized Receptive	Tact	Generalized Tact
Bear	Animal				
Cow	Animal				
Duck	Animal				
Tiger	Animal				
Turtle	Animal				
Eyes	Body Part				
Feet	Body Part				
Mouth	Body Part				
Nose	Body Part				
Button	Clothing				
Pants	Clothing				
Bagels	Food				
Bread	Food				
Cereal	Food				
Grapes	Food				
Pizza	Food				
Pudding	Food				
Raisins	Food				
Soup	Food				
Spaghetti	Food				
Yogurt	Food				
Bathtub-Tub	Household				
Blanket	Household				
Lamp-Light	Household				
Soap	Household				
Stove	Household				
Toothbrush	Household				
Towels	Household				
Bell	Miscellaneous				
Broken	Miscellaneous				
Camera	Miscellaneous				
Candle	Miscellaneous				
Clown	Miscellaneous				
Fire	Miscellaneous				
Wheel	Miscellaneous				
Moon	Outside				
Rain	Outside				
Stars	Outside				
Sun	Outside				
Barn	Outside				
Glasses-Eyeglasses	Personal Item				
Umbrella	Personal Item				
Crayons	School Item				
Broom	Tool				
Drum	Toy				
Wagon	Toy				
Fire truck	Transportation				
Close	Verb				
Cut	Verb				
Eat	Verb				
Jump	Verb				
Pour	Verb				
Shut	Verb				
Throw	Verb				

Student: _____   **Table 7-7**   Date: _____
First 240 Words List

Group 4

WORD	CATEGORY	Receptive	Generalized Receptive	Tact	Generalized Tact
Chicken	Animal				
Elephant	Animal				
Frog	Animal				
Horse	Animal				
Lion	Animal				
Monkey	Animal				
Pig	Animal				
Rabbit	Animal				
Sheep	Animal				
Squirrel	Animal				
Ankle	Body Part				
Arm	Body Part				
Ear	Body Part				
Elbow	Body Part				
Fingers	Body Part				
Hair	Body Part				
Hands	Body Part				
Head	Body Part				
Hips	Body Part				
Knee	Body Part				
Leg	Body Part				
Shoulders	Body Part				
Teeth	Body Part				
Toes	Body Part				
Tummy	Body Part				
Baby Bop	Character				
Barney	Character				
Bert	Character				
Big Bird	Character				
Cookie Monster	Character				
Donald Duck	Character				
Elmo	Character				
Ernie	Character				
Grover	Character				
Mickey Mouse	Character				
Minney Mouse	Character				
Oscar	Character				
Tigger	Character				
Winnie The Pooh	Character				
Belt	Clothing				
Blue Jeans	Clothing				
Boots	Clothing				
Diaper	Clothing				
Dress	Clothing				
Pajamas	Clothing				
Panties	Clothing				
Shorts	Clothing				
Sweater	Clothing				
Underpants	Clothing				
Carrots	Food				
Cheese	Food				
Eggs	Food				
Goldfish (Crackers)	Food				
Icee	Food				
Meat- Steak-Beef	Food				

Student: _____   **Table 7-7**   Date: _____
First 240 Words List

Group 4 (Continued)

WORD	CATEGORY	Receptive	Generalized Receptive	Tact	Generalized Tact
Peas	Food				
Potatoes	Food				
Strawberries	Food				
Tomatoes	Food				
Knife	Household				
Napkin	Household				
Paper Towels	Household				
Pot-Pan	Household				
Toilet Paper	Household				
Washcloth	Household				
Box	Miscellaneous				
Clock	Miscellaneous				
Radio-Music	Miscellaneous				
Stereo-Record Player	Miscellaneous				
Bridge	Outside				
Grass	Outside				
Leaf	Outside				
Watch	Personal Item				
Paints	School Item				
Student's Desk	School Item				
Hammer	Tool				
Ladder	Tool				
Blocks	Toy				
Coloring Book	Toy				
Horn	Toy				
Teddy Bear	Toy				
Video Tape	Toy				
Helicopter	Transportation				
Brush	Verb				
Clap	Verb				
Cry	Verb				
Draw	Verb				
Kick	Verb				
Play	Verb				
Push	Verb				
Read	Verb				
Sing	Verb				
Sit	Verb				
Swim	Verb				
Swing (verb)	Verb				
Wash	Verb				
Write	Verb				
All done	Special Word Group				
Bye Bye	Special Word Group				
Hi	Special Word Group				
No	Special Word Group				
Want	Special Word Group				

Student: _____   **Table 7-7**   Date: _____
First 240 Words List

Special Words

WORD	CATEGORY	Receptive	Generalized Receptive	Tact	Generalized Tact

Chapter 8

Receptive by Function, Feature, and Class (RFFC)

The language training procedures presented in this book thus far have focused on teaching a child to request reinforcers (mand), copy sounds (echoic) and actions (imitation), identify objects (matching-to-sample), and label aspects of the physical environment (tact). Also, procedures have been presented for teaching a child to correctly respond to the words used by others in his daily environment (receptive language). The next two chapters present procedures to further develop a child's ability to correctly respond to the words (or signs or pictures) used by others. This chapter will describe techniques for expanding a child's receptive skills, while the next chapter will focus on teaching the rudiments of conversation (intraverbal) skills. The common link between these two skills is that they both involve teaching a child to respond to words rather than to nonverbal objects, personal desires (EOs), or modeled stimuli (imitation). The difference between the two types of verbal stimulus control is that one involves a nonverbal response to words (receptive, or behaving as a listener), while the other involves a verbal response to words (intraverbal, or behaving as a speaker).

Many children with language delays have difficulty understanding and reacting to the words used by others. These children may range from being quiet and non-interactive to children who engage in a substantial amount of inappropriate and disruptive behaviors. Even though these children may have extensive tact and receptive vocabularies, they may not be able to correctly respond to the wide range of constantly changing verbal stimuli that they hear in their everyday environment. Most people never say the same thing in the exact same way or use the exact same words when talking about an item or activity. Teaching children with language delays to correctly respond to this wide variety of verbal stimuli in their everyday environment is a complicated task. This chapter will describe several procedures specifically designed to teach a child to receptive identify an item when told something about the item (e.g., its function) but not given the name of the item.

Standard Receptive Training Versus RFFC

The difference between standard receptive training and receptive by function, feature, and class (RFFC) is that in standard receptive training the verbal stimulus is specific to the action or discrimination requested, whereas in RFFC the name of the specific action or item is absent. For example, in standard receptive training the instructor may say "Touch the *book*," whereas in RFFC the instructor may say "Touch the one that you *read*." In RFFC training the child is asked to identify something based on the functions of the item, its features, or its categorical class. Functions are the things that one can do with the object (e.g., bounce it, drink it, read it, play with it, pet it). Features may be descriptions or common characteristics of objects such as its parts (e.g., tail, wheels, leaves, legs), shape or size (round, big, tiny), or texture (e.g., soft, rough, comfortable). And finally, classes are the general categories that many items can be grouped together in (e.g., animals, foods, clothing, kitchen items, vehicles, toys, things that fly).

Procedures for teaching standard receptive language skills were described in earlier sections of this book, and there are many additional training procedures for standard receptive language available in the literature (e.g., Kent, 1974; Lovaas, 1977; Guess, Sailor, & Baer, 1976). All of these procedures focus on the important skills of being able to correctly respond to the specific words (e.g., instructions, commands, requests) of others. Standard receptive training typically begins by teaching the child to respond to specific verbal instructions (e.g., "Stand up," "Jump,"), and then progresses to receptive discriminations where the child is asked to distinguish between different items shown to him (e.g., "Touch the shoe"). Eventually, training should move on to more complex verbal stimuli involving multiple commands (e.g., "Go to the table and get the book and give it to Mary"). These skills are important for a child to learn, but they may not adequately prepare the child to correctly respond to the

wide range of verbal stimuli that he will encounter in the natural environment. These verbal stimuli occurring outside of the training session may differ substantially from the verbal stimuli used in training, and may be partly responsible for the difficulty that many autistic and developmentally disabled individuals have in generalizing formally trained skills to natural environment settings. However, even if training was conducted solely in the natural environment, the child may still not learn to respond to the wide variety of complex verbal stimuli that they will regularly encounter.

In standard receptive training the child hears the exact name of the action or object (e.g., "Stand," or "Touch the book"). Thus upon hearing a specific word, the child learns to emit a specific response. While this learning to respond to the name of a specific action or object is an important skill, it may not result in the child being able to emit the same response when the verbal stimulus does not include the specific name of the action or object but describes it in some way. For example, a child who can successfully touch a picture of a car when given the instruction "Touch the car" may not be able to touch the car when given instructions such as "Touch the one that mommy drives," or "Touch the one your ride in," or "Touch the one that has wheels," etc. These discriminations are, of course, more difficult but must be specifically trained. However, the teaching procedures are more complicated to implement for a number of reasons.

Perhaps the most complicated aspect of this advanced receptive language training involves the teacher's ability to generate the wide variety of potential verbal stimuli that may exist in the natural environment. The teacher must be able to present these verbal stimuli in an organized manner ranging from simple to complex, while providing enough variation in the training to avoid the establishment of rote stimulus-response relations. In addition, this training must be incorporated into the existing procedures previously described for receptive, mand, and tact types of language (mixed VB). These special requirements are in addition to the general issues for effective language training, such as appropriate use of prompting, fading, shaping, reinforcement delivery, generalization, etc. The successful implementation of RFFC training requires that all of these general issues be considered in the design of a program for an individual child.

Prerequisites for RFFC Training

Most children with verbal deficits seem to be ready for RFFC training following the acquisition of approximately 50 words, signs, or pictures as mands, tacts, or receptive discriminations. These words should be strong as measured by a high percentage of correct responses and a short response latency (the time between the question and the child's answer). The tact and receptive responses should also be generalized in that they can easily occur under a variety of different conditions (i.e., different pictures of the same object, different instructors, different settings, etc.). Finally, the child should be able to maintain this high level of responding when different carrier phrases are used for tacts (e.g., "Can you tell me what this is?" or "What do you see here?" instead of just "What is that?") and for receptive discrimi-

nations (e.g., "Show me the____," or "Can you find the____," instead of just "Touch the____"). If a child is able to meet these criteria, then training on RFFC should be added to the daily language instruction program (and included in the mixed VB format).

Beginning RFFC Training

The first set of words to target for RFFC training should come from the above-mentioned list of acquired responses. Training should begin with a two-component discrimination consisting of the presentation of two known items. The items should be very different from each other and should be from a different categorical class (e.g., a food item versus an animal). The instructor may want to begin training by having the child tact and receptively discriminate between the two items. This activity will serve as a warm-up trial and ensure that the child has not forgotten those items. The easiest types of RFFC responses appear to be synonyms, animal sounds, common phrases, or common associations, and it is suggested the initial training begin with these simpler tasks.

Once it is clear that the child can correctly tact and receptively identify the target items, the instructor should present two items and ask the child to touch a specific item when given, for example, a synonym (e.g., "Touch the kitty," instead of the previously acquired "Touch the cat"). A correct response should be immediately be followed by praise, a pause, and then the presentation of the next trial, which could be an RFFC trial with the other item or the introduction of a new item. An incorrect response should be followed by a correction procedure similar to the procedure described for standard receptive training (i.e., represent the question with a prompt such a slight shaking of the correct item). A high rate of failure may indicate that the child is not ready for this type of training, or he has been overtrained with the specific names of each item.

Once the child is successful at responding to simple RFFC instructions with the initial two objects or pictures presented, additional items should be gradually introduced and be interspersed with the known items and commands. (Note that it is probably not necessary to always have the child tact or receptively select each new picture, especially since the chosen pictures should come from his known list of words.) Again, the selection of the specific items used is quite important (only use items that the child can already tact and receptively discriminate). Also, additional verbal phrases should be introduced for each item presented. A list of approximately 70 words and sample verbal stimuli are presented in Table 8-1. They are mostly the same words that were in the list of suggested first mands and tacts presented in the previous chapters. The table also contains suggestions for different verbal stimuli to present along with each item and a data sheet for tracking acquisition. The potential size of an RFFC repertoire can become quite large, hence it is probable that in order to effectively acquire this skill, there must be a large number of daily trials. In addition, data should be collected on the acquisition of the skills to provide the instructor with feedback as to the effectiveness of her procedures. Finally, it should be pointed out that the child should still be acquiring more tacts

and receptive responses, in addition to new RFFC responses. Therefore, by the time a child reaches some classes, or detailed features of items, he may have hundreds of tact and receptive responses.

The verbal stimuli for each item presented in Table 8-1 are divided into three groups. Group A is viewed as the verbal stimuli that have the highest probability of evoking a correct receptive response from a learner with a very limited verbal repertoire. These phrases were chosen because they are commonly associated with the targeted items (e.g., "Where do you sleep" when given a picture of a bed). Group A phrases might also involve animal sounds (e.g., "Touch the one that goes meow"), synonyms (e.g., "Touch the juice" after being taught to tact and receptively respond to the item as "drink"), or words describing the function of known items (e.g., "Touch the one you ride"). Once a child is successful at several of these verbal instructions, the instructor should move on to Group B and C verbal phrases.

Group B phrases are somewhat more difficult than Group A phrases in that they typically involve a description of the item or some specific feature of the item. For example, when shown a picture of the dog, the instruction "Touch the one that has a tail" could be given. This may be more complicated because it involves a word (i.e., tail) that might not be in the child's repertoire. However, it may be that this use of the word in the RFFC task is an effective way to expand a child's receptive skills. Group C phrases are viewed as even more difficult to respond to because they involve the class, category, or location of the item. For example, when shown a picture of a dog (along with a second picture) the child is asked to "Touch the animal." It should be pointed out that these levels are not always mutually exclusive (specific phrases may be members of different groups), and that the phrases be viewed as only suggestive and not as hard-and-fast distinctions. Every child with language delays is different and has been exposed to an individualized verbal environment; hence, it may be that some children are successful with C items before A or B items. In Table 8-1 each set of phrases is followed by blank lines in order for the instructor to write in additional, or child specific, phrases that may have been frequently paired with those items for a particular child.

Further Development of the RFFC Repertoire

Following the successful discrimination of a number of pictures and objects, there are several ways to increase the complexity of this task, thereby further developing the repertoire. Perhaps one of the simplest ways is to begin to increase the array from which the correct item can be selected. The increase may begin with 3-4 items, then gradually be moved up to 10-20 items on a table. The instructor can then ask the child to give her one specific item with any number of RFFC phrases. In addition, the instructor should begin to use different carrier phrases (e.g., "Can you show me...," "Which one do you...," "Where is the one you..."), in order to teach the child to respond to a variety of verbal instructions. This variation is important and should be included as

soon as possible. (It should be noted, however, that some children may benefit more from the use of the same verbal carrier phrase.) Also, the instructor can begin asking for different types of specific motor behaviors in relation to RFFC discriminations (e.g. "Pick up..." versus "Point to...").

There are several critical behaviors to look for in order to determine if the child is ready to increase the array and complexity of the RFFC task. Success with the simpler stimulus configuration is the main indicator. However, the child's careful scan of the array, a short response latency, and a quick rejection of incorrect items are also good indicators that the array can be increased in size and complexity. In addition, the absence of any negative behavior or attempts to escape from the task are positive signs that the instruction is appropriate for the child.

There are a number of other ways to increase the complexity of the array of visual stimuli used in this task. A wide variety of both objects and items can be placed in the array. In addition, picture books with multiple items on one page or a complex scene can be very useful for the further development of this repertoire. For example, a book that has a picture of a playground scene can be shown to the child, and the child can be asked to show the instructor the item that "spins around in circles." Also, items in the natural environment can and should be used as often as possible in the day-to-day interactions with the child. This type of training can often be easily accomplished in a game like format (e.g., "Run to the thing that has leaves") and may more closely resemble many of the receptive skills that the child should ultimately acquire.

The instructor can also make the discrimination more complicated by using items that are very similar but differ in some specific way—perhaps only indicated by the verbal stimulus. For example, give the child a picture of a dog and a cat and ask the child to give you the one that has claws. The instructor can also ask for several items from a specific category (e.g., "Can you find all the animals?"). All of these activities have the common element of teaching the child to receptively discriminate between items, even when they are not provided with the specific name of the item.

Verbal Modules: Incorporating RFFC Trials into Other Verbal Trials

In order to maximize the effects of the RFFC procedure, it is important to eventually incorporate these skills into the other verbal skills that the child has learned (mixed VB). Specifically, at this point the child should be able to tact and receptively respond to a number of items, mand for them if he wants them, and easily be able to echo and/or imitate an instructor. RFFC trials should be connected to these known skills and interspersed with them. The concept of a "verbal module" perhaps best describes this cluster of activities. A verbal module might be thought of as a conversation about a specific topic. Once the child has the basic skills outlined above, they should all be brought together. For example, while sitting with a child who has an array of pictures and items in front of him the following interaction might occur:

Instructor:	"Can you give me an animal?"
Child:	Gives the instructor a dog.
Instructor:	"Right! What animal is this?"
Child:	"Dog."
Instructor:	"Good! Do you see another animal?"
Child:	Gives instructor a cat.
Instructor:	"Right! What animal is this?"
Child:	"Cat"
Instructor:	"You got it! Can you touch the cat."
Child:	Touches cat.
Instructor:	"Yes! Can you say 'cat'" (instructor attempting to improve the child's articulation).
Child:	"Cat"
Instructor:	"Good! Which animal goes woof, woof?"
Child:	Touches dog.

Instructor:	"All right! Say woof."
Child:	Says "woof."
Instructor:	"Good! Which animal goes meow?"
Child:	Touches cat.
Instructor:	"Yes! What do you want"
Child:	"Cat"
Instructor:	"Great job! Let's go outside and see the cat."

This interaction involved the following types of trials related to dog and cat: (1) RFFC, (2) tact, (3) receptive, (4) echoic, and (5) mand. If the session were to continue, the instructor could have introduced other RFFC instructions involving dog and cat and worked them into similar modules. They could have also added other pictures of dogs and cats and expanded the questions to other animals as well. This blend of trials may help establish the concept of dogs, cats, and animals, as well as begin to establish the rudiments of the extremely important ability to engage in intraverbal conversations (this topic will be presented in more detail in Chapter 9). It is important that the interaction be as natural as possible, and not be the same script each time. The natural environment rarely contains exactly the same arrangement of verbal stimuli, and the child's new skills will more likely generalize to these other important conditions if they include such variation.

Success in the Natural Environment

An important aspect of teaching language to children with autism or other develop-mental disabilities is to teach skills that will be useful to the children in their natural environment. This goal is important because once it is reached, or approximated, language training can occur outside of formal sessions. That is, the same elements that operate for the expansion of the language abilities of typically developing children can now operate for children with language delays. For example, it may take several trials of formal training to teach a child to mand for reinforcers, but once the skill is acquired, it may be maintained, and even advanced, by its successful use in the child's natural environment. Therefore, it is important to include elements in a language-training program that closely resemble the contingencies in the natural environment. It is important to note that some children may require repetitive trials, specific training stimuli and prompts, and immediate and powerful reinforcers in order to acquire the initial responses in this repertoire. However, once the initial skills are acquired, it is important to begin developing variation as soon as possible, and that is one of the main effects of the RFFC procedure on the development of receptive language.

Summary

There are many ways to verbally refer to the same thing. Therefore, it is important that a language-delayed child receive some training on how to respond to the wide range of words that he might hear in his natural environment. Often, receptive training focuses exclusively on teaching a child to respond to specific words, in a specific verbal frame (e.g., "Touch the book"), but a child may not always hear the item referred to in this manner. The purpose of RFFC training is to teach the child to be able to correctly respond to a wide variety of words that all may refer to the same item. A variety of procedures were presented to both establish and strengthen this skill. In addition, procedures to increase both the visual array and number of different verbal stimuli associated with individual items were presented. Also, ways were suggested to incorporate RFFC trials into the previously established types of language and events occurring in the child's natural environment.

Receptive By Function, Feature & Class

Staff: _____   Student: _____

DATE

Object	Verbal Stimulus	Rank
Cake	You eat it	A
Cake	Is food	B
Cake	Eat at birthday parties	B
Cake	Put candles on it	B
Cake	Is sweet	C
Cake	Eat for dessert	C
Cake	Put frosting on	C
Candy	You it eat	A
Candy	Food	B
Candy	M & M's	B
Candy	Gummi bears	B
Candy	Tastes good	B
Candy	Snack	C
Candy	Sweet	C
Candy	Chocolate	C
Chips (potato)	You eat them	A
Chips (potato)	Is food	B
Chips (potato)	Something salty	C
Chips (potato)	Made from a potato	C
Chips (potato)	Something that is crispy	C
Chips (potato)	Something that is a snack food	C
Chips (potato)	Something that you dip	C
Chips (potato)	They come in a bag	C
Cookie	You eat it	A
Cookie	Is food	B
Cookie	Something that is round	C
Cookie	Something that is sweet	C
Cookie	You bake them	C
Cookie	Dessert	C
Cookie	As a snack	C

Note: Vary the verbal SD "Show me _____," "Where is _____," "Point to _____," etc.

© 1998 Behavior Analysts, Inc.   STARS School

Student: _____

Staff: _____

Receptive By Function, Feature & Class

Item	Code	Description
Crackers	A	You eat it
Crackers	B	Is food
Crackers	C	They crumble
Crackers	C	Eat for a snack
Crackers	C	put cheese on
Ice cream	A	You eat it
Ice cream	B	Is food
Ice cream	B	Eat in a cone
Ice cream	C	It is cold
Ice cream	C	Keep in the freezer
Ice cream	C	Sometimes it is chocolate…
Ice cream	C	Is sweet
Ice cream	C	It melts
Ice cream	C	Eat with a spoon
Ice cream	C	Put it in a bowl
Ice cream	C	Scoop it
Ice cream	C	Dessert
Juice	A	You drink it
Juice	C	Keep in the refrigerator
Juice	C	You pour it
Juice	C	Goes in a cup
Juice	C	Made from fruit
Juice	C	Sweet drink
Milk	A	You drink it
Milk	B	You pour it
Milk	C	Comes from cows
Milk	C	Keep in the refrigerator
Milk	C	Is white drink
Milk	C	Dairy product

Note: Vary the verbal SD "Show me ____," "Point to ____," etc.

STARS School

Staff: _____   Receptive By Function, Feature & Class   Student: _____

Popcorn	You eat it	A
Popcorn	Is food	B
Popcorn	You pop it	B
Popcorn	Eat for snack	C
Popcorn	Cook in microwave	C
Popcorn	Comes from corn	C
Soda	Drink	A
Soda	You pour	B
Soda	Comes in a can	C
Soda	Has bubbles	C
Soda	Coke	C
Soda	7-up	C
Soda	Pepsi	C
Soda	Slice	C
Water	You drink it	A
Water	Your pour it	B
Water	Goes in a cup	B
Water	Get at sink	B
Water	Wash hands in it	B
Water	Go swimming in it	B
Water	Boat goes in	C
Video (tape)	Movie	A
Video (tape)	Watch movies	B
Video (tape)	On TV	B
Video (tape)	Use in a VCR	C
Video (tape)	Lion King	C
Video (tape)	Winnie the Pooh	C

© 1998 Behavior Analysts, Inc.   Note: Vary the verbal SD "Show me ____," "Where is ____," "Point to ____," etc.   STARS School

Staff: _____

Student: _____

Receptive By Function, Feature & Class

Item		Code
Music	Song	A
Music	Sing	A
Music	Listen to it	B
Music	Hear music	B
Music	Stereo	C
Music	Cassette	C
Music	Radio	C
Music	Drum	C
Music	Guitar	C
Music	Piano	C
Books	Read them	A
Books	Tells a story	B
Books	Has pages	C
Books	Has pictures	C
Books	Has words	C
Books	Magazine	C
Computer	Play games on	A
Computer	Like a TV	C
Computer	Has a mouse	C
Computer	Has keyboard	C
Balls	Throw them	A
Balls	Bounce	A
Balls	Roll them	B
Balls	Catch them	B
Balls	Kick them	B
Balls	Is round	C
Balls	Toy	C

Note: Vary the verbal SD "Show me _____," "Where is _____," "Point to _____," etc.

STARS School

Staff: _____   Receptive By Function, Feature & Class   Student: _____

Item	Description	Code
Bubbles	Pop them	A
Bubbles	Blow them	A
Bubbles	Toy	C
Bubbles	use a wand	C
Bubbles	Soapy	C
Dolls	Play with it	A
Dolls	Toy	C
Dolls	Dress them	C
Dolls	Feed them	C
Dolls	Put to bed	C
Dolls	Has legs	C
Dolls	Has eyes	C
Dolls	Has hair	C
Dolls	Has arms	C
Play Dough	Play with it	A
Play Dough	Roll into a ball	B
Play Dough	Comes in a can	C
Puppets	Play with them	A
Puppets	Toy	C
Puppets	Put on hand	C
Puppets	Has legs	C
Puppets	Has eyes	C
Puppets	Has arms	C
Puppets	Has hair	C
Puppets	Has mouth	C

© 1998 Behavior Analysts, Inc.   Note: Vary the verbal SD "Show me ___," "Where is ___," "Point to ___," etc.   STARS School

Receptive By Function, Feature & Class

Staff: _____   Student: _____

Item	Cue	Code
Puzzles	Play with it	A
Puzzles	Has many pieces	B
Puzzles	Put it together	B
Puzzles	Makes a picture	C
Puzzles	Toy	C
Swing	Play on it	A
Swing	Get a push	B
Swing	Find outside	C
Swing	Toy	C
Swing	At a playground	C
Top	Play with it	A
Top	You spin it	B
Top	Toy	C
Airplane	Something that flies in the air	A
Airplane	Something that has wings	B
Airplane	That takes you places	B
Airplane	You ride in	B
Airplane	Something you find at a airport	C
Airplane	Has a pilot	C
Airplane	Has a propeller	C
Airplane	Has an engine	C
Airplane	It is a vehicle	C
Airplane	Lands on a runway	C
Boat	Floats on water	A
Boat	Take a ride in it	B
Boat	Vehicle	C
Boat	Takes you places	C
Boat	Ski behind it	C
Boat	Go fishing on it	C

STARS School

© 1998 Behavior Analysts, Inc.   Note: Vary the verbal SD "Show me _____," "Where is _____," "Point to _____," etc.

Staff: _____   Student: _____

Receptive By Function, Feature & Class

Car	Something you drive	A
Car	Go for a ride in	A
Car	You go places in	B
Car	It is a vehicle	C
Car	Something that has four tires	C
Car	Has a horn that honks	C
Car	Has wheels	C
Train	Says "choo-choo"	A
Train	Runs on tracks	B
Train	Stops at a station	C
Train	Has a conductor	C
Train	Has a engineer	C
Train	Has a caboose	C

Note: Vary the verbal SD "Show me ____," "Where is ____," "Point to ____," etc.   STARS School

Staff: _____

Student: _____

Receptive By Function, Feature & Class

Cat	Says meow	A
Cat	Kitty	A
Cat	Kitten	A
Cat	Kitty cat	A
Cat	Something that has whiskers	B
Cat	Something that has a tail	B
Cat	Something that purrs	B
Cat	Is an animal	C
Cat	Something that is fury	C
Cat	Something that scratches	C
Cat	Something that climbs a tree	C
Cat	Something that chases birds	C
Cat	Something that eats mice	C
Cat	Has 4 legs	C
Cat	Is a pet	C
Dog	Says woof-woof	A
Dog	Barks	A
Dog	Puppy	A
Dog	Wags his tail	B
Dog	Has a tail	B
Dog	Something that chases cats	C
Dog	Guards places	C
Dog	Is a pet	C
Dog	Has fur	C
Dog	Has paws	C
Dog	Has four legs	C
Dog	Eats bones	C
Dog	Take on a leash	C
Dog	You walk a dog	C
Dog	Is an animal	C

Note: Vary the verbal SD "Show me _____," "Where is _____," "Point to _____," etc.

STARS School

Receptive By Function, Feature & Class

Staff: _____   Student: _____

Bird	Says "Tweet tweet"	A
Bird	Has wings	B
Bird	Has feathers	B
Bird	Flies in the air	C
Bird	Lives in a nest	C
Bird	Has a beak	C
Fish	Swims in water	B
Fish	Has gills	C
Fish	Has a tail	C
Fish	Fisherman catch them	C
Fish	Has scales	C
Coat	You wear it	A
Coat	Put on when cold	B
Coat	You wear it outside	B
Coat	Clothing	C
Hat	You wear it	A
Hat	Wear on head	A
Hat	Keeps head warm	B
Hat	Clothing	C
Jacket	You wear it	A
Jacket	Wear over shirts	B
Jacket	Wear when cold	B
Jacket	Clothing	C

Note: Vary the verbal SD "Show me ____," "Where is ____," "Point to ____," etc.   STARS School

Staff: _____

Student: _____

Receptive By Function, Feature & Class

Shirt	Wear it	A
Shirt	Has buttons	B
Shirt	Clothing	C
Shirt	Clothing	C
Shoes	Wear on your feet	A
Shoes	Wear with socks	B
Shoes	Tie them	C
Shoes	Protects your feet	C
Shoes	Clothing	C
Socks	Wear on feet	A
Socks	Put on before shoes	C
Socks	Clothing	C
Apple	You eat it	A
Apple	Is food	B
Apple	Is a fruit	C
Apple	Grows on a tree	C
Apple	Is red	C
Apple	Is round	C
Apple	Has a stem	C
Banana	You eat it	A
Banana	Is food	B
Banana	Something a monkey eats	B
Banana	Something you peel	C
Banana	Something that is yellow	C
Banana	A fruit	C
Banana	Something that is long	C

Note: Vary the verbal SD "Show me ____," "Where is ____," "Point to ____," etc.   STARS School

Staff: _____   Student: _____

Receptive By Function, Feature & Class

Item	Descriptor	
Fries	You eat them	A
Fries	Is food	B
Fries	Get at Mc Donald's	B
Fries	Get at Burger King	B
Fries	Made from potatoes	C
Fries	Eat with Hamburgers	C
Fries	Put ketchup on them	C
Hamburger	You eat it	A
Hamburger	Is food	B
Hamburger	Has a bun	B
Hamburger	Get at McDonald's	B
Hamburger	Get at Burger King	B
Hamburger	Meat	C
Hamburger	Can cook on a grill	C
Hamburger	Put mustard on it	C
Hamburger	put ketchup on it	C
Hot dog	You eat it	A
Hot dog	Is food	B
Hot dog	Can put it on a bun	B
Hot dog	Can cook on a grill	C
Hot dog	Has meat	C
Hot dog	Put mustard on	C
Hot dog	Put ketchup on	C
Oranges	You eat it	A
Oranges	Is food	B
Oranges	Is fruit	C
Oranges	Grows on a tree	C
Oranges	Round fruit	C

STARS School

Note: Vary the verbal SD "Show me ____," "Where is ____," "Point to ____," etc.

Staff: _____   Receptive By Function, Feature & Class   Student: _____

Item	Prompt	Code
Sandwich	You eat it	A
Sandwich	Food	B
Sandwich	Made with bread	C
Sandwich	Peanut butter & jelly	C
Sandwich	Eat for lunch	C
Bed	Something you sleep on	A
Bed	Put your pillow on	A
Bed	You sleep in	A
Bed	Has blankets	B
Bed	Has sheets	B
Bed	Has covers	C
Bed	Where you go at night time	C
Bed	Where go when you are tired	C
Bed	It's in a bedroom	C
Bed	Is furniture	C
Chair	You sit on	A
Chair	Has four legs	C
Chair	Has a back	C
Chair	Is furniture	C
Cup	Drink from	A
Cup	Drink juice from	A
Cup	Pour juice into	B
Cup	Find in a kitchen	C

© 1998 Behavior Analysts, Inc.   Note: Vary the verbal SD "Show me ____," "Where is ____," "Point to ____," etc.   STARS School

Receptive By Function, Feature & Class

Staff: _____   Student: _____

Item	Task	Code
Door	Open it	A
Door	Close it	A
Door	Go through it	B
Door	Use a key to open it	C
Door	Has a handle to open it	C
Fork	Use it to eat	A
Fork	Utensil	C
Fork	Find in a kitchen	C
Garbage can	Put trash in it	B
Garbage can	Throw garbage in it	B
Pillow	Lay head on it	A
Pillow	On your bed	B
Pillow	Find in a bedroom	C
Pillow	Use when go to sleep	C
Plate	Use when eating	B
Plate	Put food on it	B
Plate	Find in a kitchen	C
Refrigerator	Put milk in it	A
Refrigerator	Put food in it	B
Refrigerator	Find in a kitchen	C
Refrigerator	Keeps food cold	C
Sink	Wash hands in it	A
Sink	Wash dishes in it	B
Sink	Can get water from it	B
Sink	Put dirty dishes in it	B
Sink	Find in kitchen	C

STARS School

Note: Vary the verbal SD "Show me ____," "Where is ____," "Point to ____," etc.

Student: _____

Staff: _____

Receptive By Function, Feature & Class

Item	Description	Code							
Sofa-couch	Sit on it	A							
Sofa-couch	Furniture	C							
Sofa-couch	Find in livingroom	C							
Spoon	Use it to eat	A							
Spoon	Scoops food	B							
Spoon	Find in a kitchen	C							
Spoon	Utensil	C							
Table	Eat at it	B							
Table	Sit at it when eating	B							
Table	Find in a kitchen	C							
Toilet	Potty	A							
Toilet	Go pee in it	A							
Toilet	Flush it	B							
Toilet	Find in the bathroom	C							
TV	Watch it	A							
TV	See movies	B							
Window	Open it	A							
Window	Close it	A							
Window	Look out it	B							
Window	Can see outside	B							
Window	Made from glass	C							
Bowl	Eat from it	A							
Bowl	Put food in it	B							
Bowl	Put cereal in it	B							
Bowl	Put ice cream in it	B							
Bowl	Dish	C							

Note: Vary the verbal SD "Show me ____," "Where is ____," "Point to ____," etc.   STARS School

Receptive By Function, Feature & Class

Staff: _____   Student: _____

Phone	Say "Hello"	A
Phone	Say "Good-Bye"	A
Phone	Rings	B
Phone	Call on it	B
Phone	Talk on it	B
Flower	Pretty	A
Flower	You water them	B
Flower	Smell it	B
Flower	A plant	C
Flower	It grows	C
Flower	Find them outside	C
House	Where you live	A
House	Where you sleep	B
House	Has a roof	C
House	Has windows	C
House	Has doors	C
Tree	Has leaves	A
Tree	Has trunk	B
Tree	Has bark	B
Tree	Can climb it	B
Tree	Has branches	B
Tree	Gives us shade	C
Tree	Has roots	C
Tree	Grows outside	C
Brush	Use on hair	A
Brush	Makes hair nice	C

© 1998 Behavior Analysts, Inc.   Note: Vary the verbal SD "Show me ____," "Where is ____," "Point to ____," etc.   STARS School

Receptive By Function, Feature & Class

Staff: _____   Student: _____

Item	Function	Code		
Comb	Use on hair	A		
Comb	Fix hair with it			
	Opens doors	C		
Keys	Opens doors	A		
Keys	Opens locks	B		
Keys	Locks doors	B		
Keys	Keep on a ring	C		
Paper	Use with a pencil	A		
Paper	Write on it	B		
Paper	Draw on it	C		
Paper	Paint on it	C		
Pencil	Write with it	A		
Pencil	Write on paper	B		
Pencil	Sharpen it	C		
Scissors	Cut with them	A		
Scissors	Cut paper	B		
Scissors	Sharp	C		
Balloons	Blow them up	A		
Balloons	Play with them	B		
Balloons	Find at parties	C		

Note: Vary the verbal SD "Show me ____," "Where is ____," "Point to ____," etc.

STARS School

Receptive By Function, Feature & Class

Staff: _____ 　　　　　Student: _____

Bike	You ride on it	A
Bike	Something that has 2 wheels	B
Bike	Has handle bars	C
Bike	Has pedals	C
Bike	Has tires	C
Bike	Something you pedal	C
Slide	Find on the playground	A
Slide	Play on it	A
Slide	Climb the ladder	B
Slide	Go down fast	B
Bus	You ride on it	A
Bus	Has a horn that honks	B
Bus	Takes you to school	B
Bus	A yellow vehicle	C
Bus	You wear seat belts	C
Bus	Has a driver	C
Bus	Carries other students	C
Bus	It is a vehicle	C
Truck	You ride in it	A
Truck	A vehicle	C
Truck	Takes things places	C
Truck	Has a driver	C
Truck	Has big wheels	C

Chapter 9
Teaching Beginning Intraverbal Skills

A significant part of a typically developing child's language consists of responding to the words (or signs) of others. These responses can be nonverbal, as in the examples of receptive language described earlier, or they can be verbal, which would then be classified as intraverbal behavior. Intraverbal behavior is a type of expressive language where a word or phrase evokes another word or phrase, but the two do not match each other (if they did, this would be an example of echoic language). For example, a child's tendency to say "farm" when someone else says "Old MacDonald had a..." is an intraverbal relation. The first phrase, "Old MacDonald had a..." evokes, but does not match, the second response "farm."

Other examples of intraverbal behavior consist of word associations, such as a tendency to say "mouse" when someone says "Mickey," or a tendency to say "computers" when someone says "IBM." Responses to fill-in-the-blank items also exemplify intraverbal behavior, such as a tendency to say "hill" upon hearing "Jack and Jill went up the...," or "earned" upon hearing "A penny saved is a penny...." In fact, much of a child's early language development involves intraverbal relations such as singing songs, reciting nursery rhymes, counting, telling stories, answering questions, and so on.

Intraverbal behavior also plays a major role in adolescent and adult behavior as well. Social interactions and conversations between individuals primarily involve intraverbal behavior. For example, conversations about sporting events, TV shows, newspaper articles, current events, community projects, political activities, and so on, all involve intraverbal behavior. Much of the field of education has the goal (although not stated as such) of developing effective intraverbal repertoires on the part of their students. The standard high school topics of history, literature, science, political science, and mathematics all rely on intraverbal behavior (as do most other academic topics such as drama and debate, biology, chemistry, physics, philosophy, religion, anthropology, and psychology). Classroom activities of lectures, discussion, reading, and multimedia presentations are designed to establish an intraverbal repertoire regarding the subject matter. That is, the student should be able to talk about and explain the subject matter. This newly acquired repertoire is then assessed by exams that are often purely intraverbal (e.g., closed book exams, no copying or cheating). For example, a student's ability to recall the basic events that led to the Great Depression on an essay exam is dependent on the strength of his intraverbal repertoire regarding the great depression. If the student fails to provide correct answers, then remedial activities involving a further strengthening of his intraverbal behavior is required.

The intraverbal is different from the mand and the tact in that it involves verbal responses that are controlled by non-matching verbal stimuli. This type of control is very different from the motivational (EO) control of the mand and the nonverbal control of the tact. Verbal stimuli are not only a completely new class of variables that control verbal behavior, but they vary significantly, and can become extremely complicated. For example, a typically-developing child can answer the same question in many different ways, using a variety of words, carrier phrases, synonyms, intonations, etc. It may be very difficult for a child with language delays to learn to even respond to verbal stimuli, let alone respond with such variation.

Given the importance of intraverbal behavior, it is necessary to begin generating the rudimentary elements of this repertoire as soon as possible for a child with language delays. In general, intraverbal training should begin after a child has acquired about 50 mands and tacts, and about the same time RFFC training begins. However, some children may be able to be successful with intraverbal training much sooner, while others may need further development of their basic mand, tact, and receptive repertoires. The objective for this type of language training is to teach a child to say a word that goes with, but does not match, the word or phrase presented to him.

There are many simple types of intraverbal behavior that can be targeted for a specific child, such as filling in the blanks for well-known and favorite songs. For example, if the child enjoys the song and characters from Winnie the Pooh, the instructor could sing the song a few times, with the child copying her (echoic behavior), and then leave off the last (and prominent) word as in "Winnie the..." A correct response (the child says "Pooh") should be immediately reinforced, perhaps by repeating the song, presenting the Pooh character, or whatever else might function as reinforcement. An incorrect response, or no response, should be followed by the use of echoic prompts, and then the careful fading of those prompts as in saying "Winnie the Poo...," "Winnie the P...."

There are many different ways to begin to develop the intraverbal repertoire. In early intraverbal training, the focus should be on simply establishing the child's ability to respond intraverbally to the verbal behavior of others. The focus need not be on attempting to teach the child specific intraverbal behavior, such as giving his name or address or the names of animals. The first types of intraverbals may be very unique to the child and may often seem quite meaningless, as in the Winnie the Pooh example or other simple word associations. But they do begin to establish the child's ability to emit verbal responses that do not echoically match the verbal behavior of others.

The first general rule for early intraverbal training is to focus on what interests the child (the child's EO). The fill-in-the-blank intraverbals should be fun and directly relevant to the child's ongoing interests and contain words he hears in his daily environment. These intraverbals might include not only songs but rhymes (e.g., "One two buckle my..."), commonly heard and spoken phrases (e.g., "I love..."), animal sounds (e.g., "The kitty says..."), object sounds (e.g., "The train goes..."), common associations (e.g., "Mommy and..."), specific daily activities (e.g., "Put on your shoes and..."). The procedure for using these phrases is similar to the fill-in-the-blank procedure described above

for the use of songs. The basic objective is to get the child to emit the second part of the verbal phrase upon hearing the first part of the phrase.

The same prompting and fading procedures that were described for mand and tact training can be used for intraverbal training. For example, a child who can easily mand and tact "cracker" should be presented with the cracker (when he wants one) along with

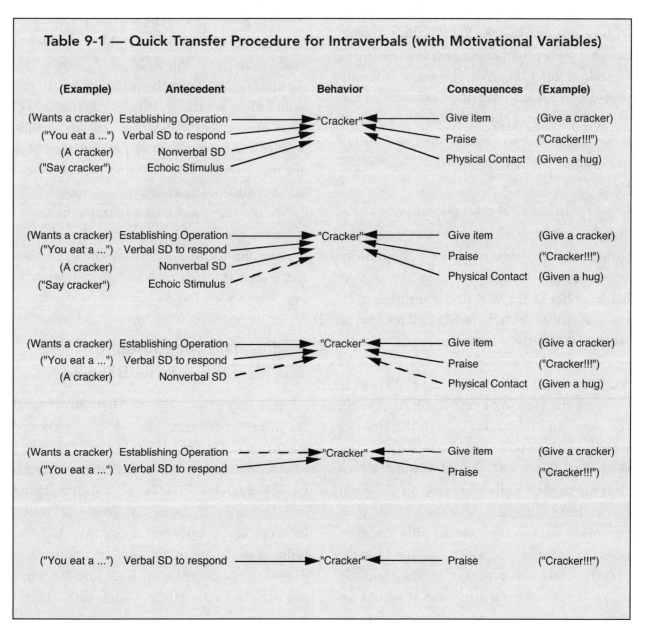

Table 9-1 — Quick Transfer Procedure for Intraverbals (with Motivational Variables)

the verbal stimulus "You eat..." (Table 9-1). A correct response should be followed by the delivery of a small cracker. On the next trial the instructor should cover up the cracker (remove the nonverbal stimulus) and repeat the verbal stimulus "You eat..." Then the instructor should wait several seconds (delay procedure) for a response. If no response occurs within 5 seconds, then the instructor should slightly uncover the cracker. If this evokes the response "cracker," then the instructor should reinforce the response with praise and the cracker. If the response does not occur, completely uncover the cracker and reinforce a correct response with only praise and repeat the trial. Transfer to the verbal statement should occur in a few of these trials; hence a multiply controlled intraverbal response has been successfully trained.

Perhaps one of the best ways to teach a beginning intraverbal repertoire is in the child's natural environment. Especially since much of the early training in intraverbal behavior is actually under multiple control (i.e., there is often an EO and nonverbal stimulus jointly controlling the child's responses). For example, when the child is watching a video of Winnie the Pooh and is enjoying the video and perhaps even echoing the song, an instructor can join the child in watching the video and start singing the song but leave out the last word as in "Winnie the...," while encouraging the child to continue singing. Another variation of this procedure is to conduct this training prior to putting the video in the cassette player. Here the response would certainly be multiply controlled in that it would be comprised of mostly mands (an EO for the video), partly tacts (the video is visually present), and partly intraverbals (the first part of the phrase). This type of training in the natural environment may not seem like training to the child, but may result in the quick establishment of simple intraverbal behavior.

The natural environment can also be used to teach other intraverbals as well. For example, when a child is about to go to the sink and wash his hands, the instructor could present a prompt for an intraverbal response by saying to the child "You need to wash your..." If the child says "hands," he should be immediately reinforced. If the child fails to correctly respond, then a correction procedure consisting of an echoic prompt can be used. It is possible that this natural environment training, where teaching is conducted in an environmental context in which the response might be likely to occur in the future, may actually increase the probability that next time the child goes to the sink there may be a slight tendency to say "Wash your hands."

Additional Procedures for Teaching Intraverbal Behavior

It is important to note that intraverbal training procedures should be conducted simultaneously with training on the other repertoires (and even mixed together with the other trials). That is, don't stop teaching new mands or tacts in order to teach intraverbals, simply add the intraverbal procedures to the other language training procedures discussed thus far. A child who has acquired sign language along with speech may already have acquired some simple intraverbal in the form of translations. That is, when the instructor says "ball" the child signs "ball" (or vice versa), this is intraverbal behavior and may be very useful in early language training. This repertoire can be used to help transfer stimulus control to other variables, or to intersperse with training on new verbal relations.

The transfer of stimulus control procedures can also be used by fading out the echoic or imitative prompt. This procedure is essentially the same as that described above, but the echoic prompt "cracker" is faded out rather than the object. This procedure can be equally effective (as it appears to be in mand training, cf. Hall & Sundberg, 1987), but it gives away the word that the child should say. It may be more desirable for the child to say the word without echoic prompts.

Once the echoic (or imitative) or tact prompts are eliminated, the next step is to fade out the EO and the specific reinforcement (Table 9-1). Both of these sources of control can be eliminated by fading from specific reinforcement to nonspecific reinforcement (same as the tact procedures described previously). The procedure described above should be repeated, but use only praise as a reinforcer and don't deliver the cracker. If the response quickly weakens, then fade out the cracker by using a variable ratio reinforcement schedule (i.e., reinforce on an average of every other correct response, then an average of every three responses, then four responses, and so on). This move to nonspecific reinforcement should help to free control from the EO and bring the response

solely under the control of the verbal stimulus (Skinner, 1957).

Pure Intraverbals

A pure intraverbal occurs when a child can provide a correct word or phrase to a question without any nonverbal or echoic prompts (Table 9-2, bottom intraverbal). "Spontaneous" participation in conversations may be pure intraverbal behavior, in that a speaker's words evoke an appropriate intraverbal response from the child without any prompting (i.e., verbal prompts to speak or sign, nonverbal stimuli present, or EO in effect). This language skill must be directly trained for most children with language delays, and it is a mistake to assume that it will develop as a function of receptive or tact training, cognitive processing, cognitive awareness, perception, or any other indirect activity. When it fails to develop for a child, the blame is traditionally placed on these cognitive difficulties, or the child's "retardation," rather than the failure to directly teach this language skill. It may take several trials (and sessions) to completely free control from all the different prompts. However, training should begin with additional intraverbals after some success with the first verbal relation.

The next several intraverbal responses to be trained should also be linked to strong establishing operations and specific reinforcement to maximize the child's probability of success. Also, the responses should already be in the child's repertoire as an echoic (imitative), mand, or tact. At this early stage of training, avoid teaching common social intraverbals such as "How are you? I am fine," rather keep the intraverbals relevant to the individual child and observable stimuli (e.g., eat... raisin, drink... juice, mommy... daddy, dog... cat, bounce... ball, ride... bike, sleep... bed). It is important to note that the main point of Skinner's analysis is that the same response can occur for different reasons or "meanings." These meanings or reasons are simply different types of control (i.e., echoic, mand, tact, intraverbal, written), and it is essential that all the "meanings" are taught to the child. Therefore, additional intraverbal responses targeted for training should be drawn from the list of acquired echoics, mands, and tacts, and these words/signs should be brought under intraverbal control.

Using RFFC Trials as a Bridge to Intraverbal Responding

Another effective way to teach some early intraverbal responding is to use a variation of the basic technique of RFFC described in the previous chapter. Recall that RFFC training consisted of presenting the child with nonverbal stimuli (e.g., a picture of a cookie and a ball) and asking him to touch one based on the instructor's description of a function, feature, or class of the item (e.g., "Touch the one you eat."). Many of the children who are successful in this RFFC task begin to tact the item as they touch it (i.e., saying "cookie" as they touch the cookie). This verbal responding, along with the action of pointing when given a picture and a verbal instruction, contains the basic elements of an intraverbal response, with the exception of the presence of the picture and pointing (e.g., the intraverbal relation "you

eat... cookie"). This effect suggests that RFFC can be a bridge to the development of some types of intraverbal responding if some adjustments are made to the procedure.

The basic elements of the procedure consists of fading out the picture following a correct RFFC response and slightly changing the verbal stimulus to a question format. Specifically, the instructor should present an RFFC trial (e.g., "Touch the one you eat" with an array containing several pictures including a food item such as a cookie), then the instructor should represent the verbal stimulus, but drop the words "touch the one" and remove the pictures. This "transfer trial" should immediately follow the RFFC trial and should consist of the instructor saying "You eat..." and the child saying "Cookie." If the child responds correctly, immediately reinforce this behavior with praise (or even with a cookie—making the response part mand—if the child is having difficulty with the transfer training). Incorrect responses should be followed by a new trial (correction procedure), but only slightly cover (or partially hide) the target picture. In a minute or two ask the question again without the picture. The process of fading the picture may occur quite quickly for some children, or it may require careful and systematic fading for other children.

This type of intraverbal training can be conducted in addition to the other types suggested above. There are several elements of the training (in addition to reinforcement and fading) that can increase the chances of the child acquiring functional intraverbal behavior. First, the word chosen should come from the child's list of known tacts and receptive responses. That is, this procedure is not meant to teach new words but rather to bring old words under a new type of stimulus control (verbal stimulus control). The words and verbal relations should be relevant to the child (rather than to adults or elements of the environment that do not concern the child). Training should also be conducted on a daily basis with several opportunities to respond each day. Finally, training should also be conducted in the natural environment when the relevant conditions occur (e.g., when the child is about to eat a cookie after dinner) and with variation (i.e., different food items) in order to promote generalization.

If a child begins to acquire intraverbal responses, at least one new word or sign should be added each day. As mentioned above, these new intraverbal skills should be worked on both in the formal sessions and in the natural environment. Often, the point is made that the child will become confused with all of these procedures and new words; however, the strength of these repertoires depend on the stimulus control developed by daily training and the use of these language skills in the natural environment. If training does not occur, and verbal behavior is not carefully reinforced, then stimulus control will be weak and the child's communication will be less effective. If language training is only conducted in formal sessions a few times a week, then the repertoires will be slow in developing and stimulus control may become defective (this point is relevant for all the verbal skills). On the other hand, if training is conducted on a regular basis throughout the day—at home and in school, in formal and informal sessions, with different instructors, parents, and materials—then a child's verbal repertoires will have a much greater probability of improvement, and even perhaps match the development of a typical child's verbal behavior (Sundberg, 1980).

A training session with a child with language delays should contain trials on all of the different verbal skills. By interspersing receptive language with the mand, tact, and intraverbal, verbal interactions between a child and an instructor more closely approximate typical interactions between speakers and listeners. Speakers don't, for example, just tact things or point to things when asked to do so, or speakers don't just mand for reinforcers or just emit intraverbal behavior. Rather, speakers do all of these at different times in a conversation, and a more typical language repertoire will develop if the training sessions contain trials on these different repertoires. While conducting intraverbal trials, for example, the instructor should intersperse a few mand and tact trials (mixed VB, or "intraverbal modules").

These suggestions for language training may sound overwhelming, but it should be pointed out that they do not require that all individuals involved with a child drop everything for the language program. Instead, they simply can incorporate the procedures into the child's daily activities. Formal sessions should be used to teach new words/signs; however, natural events in the environment are often some of the best circumstances to use for training and they should incorporated into the program. The careful attention to opportunities to conduct the quick transfer procedure in the natural environment may produce relatively rapid language development. An instructor's careful arrangement of the environment can increase the frequency of such opportunities, for example, by requiring a child to mand for reinforcers during the day and using the opportunity to mand for a reinforcer (and getting it) as a consequence of a few correct intraverbal responses. Training language in the natural environment is essential for the success of this program. If a child is never required to emit the verbal responses under these contingencies, then a very atypical verbal repertoire will develop, and other behavior that may function as language (e.g., aggression) may not decrease.

The Effects of Intraverbal Training

The results of successful intraverbal training become obvious in many ways. The main objective is to free verbal behavior from exclusive control of echoic and nonverbal stimuli (the EO) and bring the response under the control of a different type of antecedent—a verbal stimulus that lacks point-to-point correspondence to the response. Not only will the child be able to verbal classify objects and events when they are not physically present (e.g., naming some animals), but the child may (and should) begin to intraverbally respond to the verbal behavior of others. That is, prior to intraverbal training a child may emit pure echoic behavior (i.e., copying the verbal behavior of others without any prompts to do so). The pure echoic repertoire plays an important role in language development; however, in many respects echoics are trivial when compared to pure intraverbal behavior.

With the development of intraverbal behavior, a child may be observed to respond to the content of another speaker's verbal behavior, rather than its form. For example, a toddler emits pure echoic behavior when he immediately repeats some of the sounds or words made by his parents. His tendency to say "Bye, bye" when a parent says "Get your shoes and we'll go bye, bye" is controlled by the parent's words (i.e., "Bye, bye") and is thus echoic. Later, a parent says "Get your shoes" and the toddler says "Bye, bye." Here the toddler's response is controlled by a verbal stimulus that lacks point-to-point correspondence, and thus it is intraverbal (it may also be part mand in that the toddler has a strong EO to go bye, bye). Under these circumstances we could say that the toddler is responding to the content of the adults verbal behavior, which is often taken as a demonstration of "higher cognitive processes." Behaviorally speaking, when this effect occurs, we have observed the transfer of stimulus control from echoic (or EO) to intraverbal sources of control.

Summary

At this point the child should have received training on the basic aspects of language. The child should be able to mand for several reinforcers, even in the absence of these reinforcers. The child should also be able to tact several common objects and actions in his environment and be able to do so without specific reinforcement. The child should be able to nonverbally respond to a wide variety of verbal stimuli, both when the specific name of the items or action is provided (standard receptive training) or when the items and activities are described in some way but not specifically named (RFFC). And finally, as a result of the intraverbal training presented in this chapter, the child should also be able to correctly emit several responses that are intraverbally controlled by the verbal behavior of others (or possibly himself). Once an individual has a basic echoic, imitative, mand, tact, receptive, and intraverbal repertoire, the language instruction task becomes easier in some respects but much more complicated in other respects. The following chapters consist of suggestions for the further development of each of the verbal operants, as well as some other more complex forms of verbal behavior.

Chapter 10
Advanced Tact and Receptive Training

Once a child has acquired a basic vocabulary of mands, tacts, intraverbals, and receptive responses (including RFFC), training should progress to the more advanced aspects of each of these different language skills. This chapter will focus on teaching advanced tact and receptive responses. In the previous chapters several different procedures were presented to teach tact and receptive responses for known reinforcers and common objects and actions. Children must also learn to identify other aspects of the physical environment, such as less common objects and actions (nouns and verbs), properties of objects and actions (adjectives and adverbs), relations between objects and actions (prepositions), and words for persons (pronouns). They must also learn to identify elements of the environment through their other senses (e.g., auditory, olfactory, gustatory, tactile) and to identify events occurring within their own body (e.g., pain, emotions). Finally, they must be able to combine these responses into meaningful sentences and be able to correctly react to these sentences when spoken by others.

The training program provided in this book approaches the task of deciding which words to teach by conducting an analysis of the complexity of the stimulus and the complexity of the response. The stimulus can be a very simple nonverbal stimulus such as a shoe, or it can be a highly complicated stimulus like a cancer cell (although both are nouns). The stimulus can have one part (e.g., a spoon) or many parts (e.g., a playground); it may affect one sense mode (e.g., light) or several sense modes (e.g., cake); it can be fixed (e.g., a crayon) or transient (e.g., a clap); it can be observable (e.g., red) or unobservable (e.g., stomach ache). These are just some of the distinctions that can be made between types of nonverbal stimuli when considering what order to introduce new words to a child with language delays.

The tact repertoire can also be enhanced by increasing the complexity of the response. A successful tact may be a single phoneme, a morpheme, a word, a sentence, or even a whole paragraph. Linguists have studied this aspect of verbal behavior extensively and use the concepts of phoneme, morpheme, syntax, grammar, and "mean –length –of –utterance" (MLU) to describe the nature of responses in language. In general, the response can increase in complexity by including more words to describe events in the environment. For example, when shown a ball a child might initially say "ball" and be reinforced. Eventually, they may learn to say "my ball," "big ball," or "bouncing ball." Carrier phrases soon are attached to the words such as "I see... my ball," "There's... my ball." Ultimately, nouns, verbs, adjectives, pronouns, and carrier phrases are combined into meaningful sentences (e.g., There's my big bouncing ball").

Receptive responses can also increase in complexity, but much of the complexity is related to the stimuli involved rather than the response. That is, as receptive tasks become more complicated the child must learn to discriminate between increasingly complex verbal stimuli in conjunction with increasingly complex nonverbal stimuli. For example, early receptive responding may consist of touching a hat when an instructor says "Touch the hat." Later, the child might be asked to find Waldo (from the book *Where's Waldo*) wearing a small red hat. The response is the same pointing response, but correctness is dependent on the child's ability to discriminate between a wide array of complicated visual stimuli when given a particular set of verbal stimuli. This type of discrimination task is often quite difficult for many children with autism. Responses can become more complicated by requiring more difficult behavior or behavior involving several parts (e.g., "Clean your room," "Go to the store and get some wheat bread")

.The quick transfer procedure was described as a teaching strategy that often allowed for the errorless acquisition of new types of verbal behavior. That same general strategy can be used to teach these more advanced types of verbal behavior. As previously stated, tact and receptive training should begin with real objects and actions and use pictures for generalization purposes. However, soon it becomes much more convenient to use pictures for training, and real events in the natural environment can be used for generalization. It is important to remember that stimulus and response generalization is critical throughout the language training process. The child must also learn to respond to other people, in other environments, and to stimuli that differ from the original training stimuli.

Teaching Verbs

After a child has learned a number of tacts and receptive responses for common objects and pictures (perhaps 20-30), then training should begin on some actions (verbs). Actions are a little more complicated to teach because the stimulus for a verb is a fleeting or transitory stimulus. That is, the stimulus is only temporary, as in a push or jump, whereas the stimulus for a noun is constant, as in the physical presence of a pen. For tact training, the actions used should be performed by the instructor (or another student) rather than presented in pictures (pictures may be used for generalization trials after the response becomes strong). The instructor should pick a few common actions (e.g., roll, stand, jump, bounce, walk, run, dance) and teach the student the tact by using the quick transfer procedure (Table 10-1). However, the intraverbal prompt "What am I doing?" (or "What is s/he doing?") should be substituted for the prompt "What's that?" used in noun training. Initially the stimulus conditions will involve three types of control (echoic, tact, and intraverbal), and the instructor's task is to fade out the imitative prompt and eventually the intraverbal prompt. However, the transfer of stimulus control can be observed when the action and verbal intraverbal prompt alone evoke a correct response.

Receptive training should be conducted simultaneously with tact training. For example, after a tact trial on jump, the instructor can say "Show me jumping?" or, when shown an array of pictures, the instructor can ask the child to "Touch the girl jumping." Tact and receptive trials should be interspersed with trials on the other language skills discussed thus far (i.e., mand, echoic, imitative, RFFC, intraverbal), and training should also be conducted in other settings and in the child's natural environment.

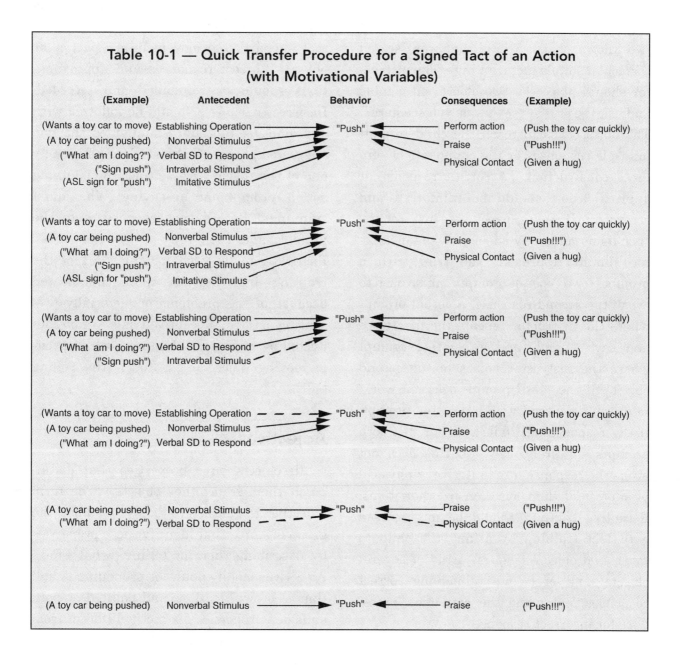

Table 10-1 — Quick Transfer Procedure for a Signed Tact of an Action (with Motivational Variables)

Noun-noun Combinations

Following training on individual nouns and verbs, the instructor should begin to develop the child's ability to tact and receptively respond to multiple objects (for some children the noun-verb combinations presented below may be easier). For tact training, the first set of items should consist of two known objects (those that were scored correct on simple tact training). The instructor should place the two objects on a table and ask the student "What do you see here?" The objective is to teach the child to emit multiple responses or the rudiments of sentence construction. A correct response or approximation should be reinforced and recorded. If an incorrect response occurs, such as naming only one object, the instructor should re-present the trial with a prompt. Two types of prompts can be used to evoke the second response, a verbal prompt where the instructor repeats the first word and says "...and" and a pointing prompt where the instructor points to the second object. If the "and" prompt does not work, re-present the trial with a pointing prompt. If the response still fails to occur, try both prompts simultaneously. If this does not evoke the response, use imitative or physical prompts and then move on to other items. Receptive training should be interspersed with tact training by asking the child to touch two objects from an array of several objects (and of course reinforcing correct responses and using the correction procedure for incorrect responses).

Noun-verb Combinations

Next, known nouns and verbs should be presented in combination with each other. For example, a bouncing ball, a spinning top, or a running dog. For tact training, the instructor should present the stimuli and say "What am I doing? The objective of this aspect of the program is to teach the child to tact the particular movement of a particular object. Correct responses and approximations should be reinforced and recorded. Incorrect responses should be followed with a prompting procedure similar to the one suggested above. If the student emits only one of the responses, say, just the spinning action, prompt him by saying "What am I spinning?" Record the response, note the prompt, and then present the next trial. Pictures can be used for this part of the training, but they are more complicated because of the problems of pictorially presenting actions. Receptive trials can be conducted by asking the child to touch a specific moving object (e.g., "touch the rolling ball")

Adjectives

All objects have properties that distinguish them from other objects. The term adjective is characteristically used for the group of words that identify these properties by describing them or telling "what kind." Adjectives modify nouns or pronouns. A ball that is brown, leather, and pointed at both ends has properties distinctly different from a red, round, plastic ball. However, the properties of objects are not restricted to specific objects, rather, many objects share the same properties such as color, shape, weight, and size. "Any property of a stimulus present when a verbal response is reinforced acquires some degree of control over that response, and this control continues to be exerted when the property appears in other combinations" (Skinner, 1957, p. 107). This makes the discrimination rather complicated when a property of an object, such as its color, acquires control over a verbal response, rather then the defining stimulus features of the object. For example, if a child, learns to say "wagon" under the control of a red wagon, then later calls a red ball a wagon, the property of the wagon acquired more control than the defining features of a wagon (e.g., four wheels, a base, a handle). A similar problem with acquiring tacts for properties may occur when a child learns to identify an object by one of its properties, for example, calling a wagon a "red." This child may face some difficulty when encountering other red objects or wagons that are not red.

Another complexity in acquiring tacts of properties is that many of the properties of objects are relative to the properties of other objects. A box might be heavy compared to empty boxes, but light when compared to larger and heavier boxes; or a pencil might be long compared to a shorter one, but that same "long" pencil will become short when compared to a baseball bat. This complicates the acquisition of adjectives because the child must abstract the critical features from the stimulus configuration, which may be very difficult because of the problem of shared properties (i.e., many different things are red, long, or sharp).

As a result of these complexities, adjectives are typically more difficult to acquire

than nouns and verbs. In order to teach tacts of adjectives, the instructor should present the child with a known object and request that the child identify a property of the object. For example, the instructor should hold up a ball and say "What color is this?" A correct response or approximation should be reinforced and recorded. An incorrect response should be followed by the correction procedure. Receptive trials should be interspersed with tact trials. A receptive trial would consist of presenting the child with two colors and asking him to touch one of the colors.

A Single Word May Have Several Different Functions

It is important to note that the same word can be a noun, verb, or adjective; just like the same word can be a mand, tact, or intraverbal. For example, consider the following uses of the word "farm."

1. Did John farm all last summer? (A verb.)
2. His farm is in Oregon. (A noun.)
3. John enjoys farm life. (An adjective.)
4. That is a farm. (A tact controlled by nonverbal stimuli.)
5. Can we go to the farm? (A mand controlled by an establishing operation.)
6. Cows live on a farm. (An intraverbal controlled by the verbal stimulus "Where do cows live?")

This exercise demonstrates the point that the form of the response (what is said, signed, written, etc.) can be the same word but have different "meanings" when there are different controlling variables. The current training program is designed to establish verbal responses under all of these different types of control.

Combinations of Nouns, Verbs, and Adjectives

A good way to determine if the task might be appropriate for a specific child is to identify the complexity and the components of the nonverbal stimulus configuration. A tact that includes a simple object, a property of that object, and an action has three separate stimulus functions and represents the most complex multiple tact presented thus far. The correct tact "Bouncing red ball," for example, is a verb-adjective-noun combination that demonstrates that the child's words are controlled by all three nonverbal stimuli. The strength of the stimulus control can be more completely assessed by separating the elements and presenting them in different arrays (e.g., present a rolling blue ball or a spinning red top). In order to teach multiple tacts, the instructor should present the child with the multiple stimulus and say "What do you see here?" Correct responses and approximations should be reinforced and recorded. If a child emits an incorrect response, the instructor should conduct the correction procedure. Receptive trials should be interspersed with tact trails and training in a manner similar to that described above.

Adverbs

Adverbs typically serve as modifiers for verbs, adjectives, other adverbs, or prepositions. A particular action may have proper-

ties that distinguish it from other actions. These properties can be in terms of manner (how), place (where), time (when), degree (how much), and number (how many), as well as others such as opposition, affirmation, and denial. For example, the sentence, "He quickly jumped down," contains two modifiers for the verb jump; quickly (how he jumped) and down (where he jumped). The stimulus control involved in tacting adverbs may be somewhat more complicated than that of tacting properties of objects (adjectives), because of the transitory nature of the primary action. This is not to say that the acquisition of adjectives always precedes the acquisition of adverbs, but rather to simply note that one is more complicated than the other and, all other things being equal, usually takes more time (and trials) to acquire.

In order to teach a child to tact adverbs the instructor should present the nonverbal action (quickly jump down from a chair) and should ask the student to describe the properties of the action by using a question such as "How did I jump?" An array of trials should be presented. As always, correct responses and approximations should be reinforced and recorded. Incorrect responses should be followed by a correction procedure. Receptive trials should be interspersed with tact trials and training in a manner similar to that described above.

Prepositions

Prepositions are also more complicated than simple nouns and verbs. They are tacts of relations that exist between a noun, or a pronoun, and some other aspect of the nonverbal situation. For example, the tact

"Book on table" identifies the relation between the book and the table. The book and the table are tangible objects that have clear and individual stimulus features. But what about the word "on"? It cannot be touched or picked up because it is a nonverbal spatial relation between two objects. The acquisition of tacts and receptive responses for these relations often requires more training than is required for nouns and verbs. Receptive and tact trials should be interspersed with each other. Contrasting prepositions such as "in" and "out" might be the simplest place to start training. For receptive training, the instructor should present the child with two known objects, such as a toy car and a bowl. Put one bowl upside down and place the other near by. Ask the child to put the car "in" the bowl. Follow correct responses with reinforcement and incorrect responses with the correction procedure. Repeat the trial but with the word "on" and alternate between the two words.

Following success on this discrimination task, add tact training by placing the car in one of the positions and ask the child "Where is the car?" Reinforce correct responses and follow incorrect responses with the correction procedures. Following success on these trials, begin to intersperse receptive trials with expressive trials. Then focus on generalization for these two prepositions by changing the items, the location of the work area, and the staff member who conducts the trials. Also, conduct preposition training in the child's natural environment. Introduce new prepositions slowly and in a similar way. Try and use contrasting prepositions (e.g., above and below, in front and behind, near and far, on and off) and begin to inter-

sperse the prepositions with each other and with both tact and receptive trials.

Pronouns

A pronoun is a word that stands for a noun, or a group of words used as nouns, and refers to persons or things named or understood in a specific context. For example, the sentence "The boy broke the train, but he fixed it," contains the two pronouns "he" and "it." Both pronouns are irrelevant unless "he" and "it" have been previously identified as they are in the first part of the sentence. In addition, many pronouns have a problem of reversibility as in "your" and "my." For example, when working with a child the instructor might say "Whose shoe is that?" If the child responds "My shoe," there is a tendency to say "Right, it's your shoe." These two factors make the acquisition of pronouns somewhat complicated, and often present a substantial problem for children with autism.

An effective way to teach pronouns is to begin with receptive trials first, using the pronouns "my/mine" and "your/yours" (avoid pronouns such as "he," "she," "her," "his," until some others are well acquired). Select a stimulus that is clearly possessed by each individual, such as a clothing items or a body part (make sure the child can easily tact and receptively identify the item). Ask the child to "Touch your shirt" and reinforce correct responses. Follow incorrect responses with the appropriate correction procedure (e.g., prompting, fading, and differential reinforcement). Next, ask the child to "Touch my shirt" and consequate appropriately. Intersperse the two trials to establish a discrimination and then add other items, including reinforcing items such as "My cookie" and "Your cookie."

The move to tacting pronouns should be done carefully because of the pronoun reversal problem. In order to reduce this problem, introduce only one pronoun (e.g., my) in a play or game format and don't reverse it when the child is correct. For example, after the child successfully touches "My cookie" say "Whose cookie is it?" and reinforce the response "My." If an incorrect response occurs, provide an echoic prompt while touching the cookie and reinforce the correct echoic response, then re-present the trial. Pretend to take the cookie while asking "Whose cookie is it?" and return it when the child says "my" (here "my" is also part mand). Next play the game with other reinforcing items. Remember don't reinforce with the words "Right, it's *your* cookie."

Following success on several items, repeat the procedure in a group of other children (who already know pronouns). The other children can be used to introduce "your" to the target child by having them hand the child reinforcers and say, for example, "Here is your cookie" and have the children take turns. The target child should then be prompted to hand other children cookies while saying "Here is your cookie." As this becomes strong, return to the original one-to-one setting and conduct some "my" trials. Gradually bring the two situations closer together and, if successful, reintroduce receptive pronouns. If the child begins to reverse the pronouns and does not seem to be able to make the discrimination, it may be best to drop pronouns for a month or so and

work on other language areas in need of intervention.

More Complicated Combinations and Grammatical Sentences

A complex tact can involve any combination of nouns, verbs, adjectives, adverbs, prepositions, pronouns, conjunctions, and articles. For example, "The small rabbit quickly hopped up on the table." If the student has been successful on several of the tact items presented thus far, then the instructor should attempt to train these more complicated responses. Stimuli can be combined in a variety of ways, and the natural environment may be the best place for this type of training.

Auditory Tacts

The tacts discussed thus far all consist of responses controlled by visual nonverbal stimuli. However, a large part of an effective speaker's repertoire consists of tacts that are controlled by stimuli affecting any one of the other four major senses. Auditory tacts are verbal responses that are controlled by an auditory nonverbal stimulus and reinforced by some form of generalized conditioned reinforcement. Auditory stimuli are certainly not as ubiquitous as visual stimuli, but they occur at a high rate and play an important role in day-to-day behavior. The tendency to say "telephone" when one hears a ring, or "dog" upon hearing a bark, exemplifies the auditory tact. There are many different sounds in the environment that a speaker learns to identify.

A person who is blind acquires a very strong auditory tact repertoire. He learns to identify people by their voices, by their sounds, and many other auditory stimuli that go completely unnoticed by the seeing person. Children learn to tact the auditory sounds produced by animals, toys, parents, moving objects, dangerous events, entertaining events, and so on. A skilled adult acquires many complex auditory tacts. For example, some individuals can instantly identify a musical note or a slight tone difference. These auditory discriminations, like visual discriminations, are behaviors learned by contact with the environment. This type of tact repertoire is obviously important for the typical speaker, as evidenced by the problems faced by individuals who lose their hearing, or were never able to hear (Moore, 1978).

Auditory tact training in the child's natural environment can be a very effective way to strengthen this repertoire. Especially since many of the sounds are difficult to reproduce in a formal teaching situation. However, some sounds may never occur naturally in the presence of the instructor and must be presented in a more formal manner. The formal teaching procedure consists of presenting auditory stimuli on a cassette tape or in removing the visual properties of the stimulus (blindfolding the student or turning out the lights). The instructor should say "What do you hear?" and reinforce correct responses and approximations. Incorrect responses should be followed by repeating the correction procedures. The use of games can be an effective way to teach children to identify sounds that they hear.

Tactile Tacts

An effective speaker can also tact nonverbal stimuli that affect his sense of touch. There are many objects that can easily be identified by touching them (e.g., ball, pen, cup, light bulb). A person who is blind acquires a very strong tactile (and auditory) tact repertoire, and learns these discriminations because of the environmental contingencies in his day-to-day living. A person who is blind may quickly learn to identify the rooms and obstacles in a house because it allows him to move around successfully without being hurt. It is often important that even sighted people be able to identify things without the benefit of seeing them. For example, if the lights go out, it is useful for a person to be able to identify a candle by touch alone.

The training procedures for this repertoire are very similar to those of the auditory tact repertoire. Training in the natural environment and in formal teaching environments can be used to establish tactile tacts. The instructor should block the visual and auditory components of the stimuli (e.g., have the student reach into a bag or box) and should ask "What do you feel?" The standard procedures for consequating and recording the response should be employed.

Olfactory Tacts

Olfactory stimuli (smells) can also control verbal responses. These tacts make up a smaller part of a typical speaker's verbal repertoire, but they can be essential to survival. The ability to identify the smells produced by smoke, gas, or other harmful chemicals may save a person's life. There are several pleasant smells that a child may learn to identify such as the odor produced by certain foods, flowers, and fragrances. The olfactory tact repertoire can be trained in basically the same manner as the auditory and tactile tacts. The training should include natural environment trials as well as formal training trials. In formal training the instructor should block off the other senses and ask the student "What do you smell?" Responses should be appropriately consequated and recorded.

Gustatory Tacts

The last of the more common sensory systems that can control tacts is the gustatory (taste) repertoire. These tacts, like olfactory tacts, comprise only a small portion of a typical speaking repertoire, but they still represent an important skill. Consumption of some poisons or harmful substances may be prevented if the taste can be identified. The four basic tastes that affect humans are sweet, sour, bitter, and salt. These should be trained along with the tastes for specific foods and liquids. The training of this repertoire should be conducted in the natural environment and under formal training conditions. The instructor should block the other senses (e.g., ask the person to close his eyes and don't let him touch it) and present the stimulus and the question "What does this taste like?" As always, appropriately consequate the response and record the data.

Teaching Self-Awareness (Private Events)

Accurate verbal behavior under the control of internal events represents an advanced form of verbal behavior. Many children suffer from the inability to identify events occurring within their bodies. It is important to be able to tell someone when you are in pain, uncomfortable, sick, or otherwise in need of some help. This problem with nonverbal persons often encourages parents and instructors to immediately begin a language program with procedures to teach this behavior. The importance of expressing one's "wants and needs" is often given as the rationale for teaching one to tact internal events. The first words in a language program are often "toilet," "happy," "sad," "angry," and "tired." However, these verbal responses exemplify a very complicated form of verbal behavior. Teaching this behavior can be very time consuming because the stimulus that should control the verbal behavior is not available to the instructor for differential shaping, hence the acquisition can take some time. If a person has a weak verbal repertoire, other aspects of verbal behavior should be stressed rather than tacting private events.

How do we learn to talk about events that occur within our body? All humans experience stimulation that arises within the body and is accessible to no one but the individual. This stimulation can come from the mechanoreceptors (deep touch, kinesthetic, and vestibular sensors), deep thermoreceptors (internal temperature sensors), and free nerve endings (pain sensors). These sensory systems are affected by any number of environmental events. For example, a virus acquired by contact with a sick person may increase body temperature and result in aversive stimulation from the thermoreceptors, mechanoreceptors, and other receptors of the body. However, it is very difficult to learn to tact these nonverbal stimuli accurately. A verbal child may simply say "I don't feel well" without knowing (tacting) the causes of the pain, while a nonverbal child might say nothing, but they may act differently.

Tacting private events is complicated because members of the verbal community (e.g., parents, instructors, and friends) do not have access to the same stimulation as the child. As a result, they cannot accurately identify, or teach, the relevant features of the event. Verbal responses to external stimuli are easier to teach than responses to internal stimuli. For example, when teaching a child to tact "shoe," an instructor can present or remove the shoe, present other objects, prompt an appropriate response, and differentially reinforce successive approximations to the word. When the stimulus is private, these shaping procedures are difficult to conduct. An instructor cannot present and remove a private stimulus that is inside a person's body and cannot differentially reinforce responses. Yet children with language delays do learn to talk about private events, and it is often important to be able to do so (e.g., sickness). Moreover, since we will never be able to completely solve the problem of privacy, how can this occur? How do we teach verbal behavior that is controlled by stimulation arising within the skin?

Skinner (1945, 1953, 1957, & 1974) has described four methods that members of the verbal community use to teach individuals to tact private events. They are (1) public accompaniment, (2) collateral events, (3) common properties, and (4) response reduction. These methods can be helpful for teaching a child self-awareness.

Public Accompaniment

Frequently a private event is accompanied by an observable public stimulus. For example, a painful internal stimulus may be accompanied by blood and bruises or by observations of the person falling down or bumping into something. An observer who sees these stimuli can safely assume that internal painful stimuli are affecting the free nerve endings. Members of the verbal community use these circumstances to teach children to correctly identify painful sensations. This internal tacting can only be taught in the

natural environment, because the private stimulus cannot be easily presented by the instructor, rather it occurs due to several environmental (including the environment within the skin) variables. For example, if an instructor observes stimuli associated with pain (e.g., blood), the instructor should take the opportunity to teach the child to say "ouch" or "hurt."

Collateral Events

A person may also engage in collateral behavior (e.g., holding his stomach) when a private stimulus is present (e.g., a stomach ache). These collateral behaviors can also be used to teach verbal behavior about private events. Again, training in the natural environment is the only way to establish this verbal repertoire. The instructor should observe (or ask others if necessary) the individual and prompt and consequate the appropriate verbal responses.

Common Properties

Common properties involve circumstances where private stimuli share some of the features of public stimuli. A sensation in the leg may be described as a leg that "fell asleep." Metaphors such as this are frequently used by individuals to describe private events. A patient at a physician's office often uses metaphors to describe private events such as pain (e.g., dull, sharp, or stabbing). These metaphors are used because, as Skinner has pointed out, we don't have a sensory system that allows us to view the inside of our body in the same manner we view the outside of our body. (Technology is changing that situation, but it currently plays only a minor role in the individual's moment-to-moment private events. How often do you have X-rays or CAT scans?) The ability to tact private events by using metaphors represents a rather sophisticated speaker. The instructor should observe the individual in the natural environment and teach these types of tacts when the opportunity arises.

Response Reduction

Response reduction consists of conditions in which a response is learned under public conditions and is later transferred to private conditions. For example, the verbal commu-

nity teaches a person to tact the fact that he is sitting down. Along with the visual (public) stimuli there are kinesthetic (private) stimuli (i.e., the sensations that sitting produces on the muscles, tendons, and joints). A student may be able to say "sitting" when both visual and kinesthetic stimuli are present, but eventually the response can come under the control of the kinesthetic stimuli alone, which are always present. A person may look and see that he is beginning to sit and feel his muscles, etc. moving in a consistent pattern each time. Soon, he learns that he doesn't need to look at his body to tell if he is sitting, because whenever his body moves in that sequence he is moving to a sitting position. Eventually, there is no need to check the public stimuli because the private stimuli are always reliable. This transfer of stimulus control allows one to describe his bodily conditions in the absence of visual or tactual stimuli.

The ability to tact kinesthetic stimuli can be trained by blindfolding the person and asking them to identify their body position and movement (e.g., standing, turning, jumping, twisting). The instructor can move the person's arms, fingers, legs, etc. and ask the student "What do you feel moving?" Responses should be appropriately consequated and recorded.

Summary

Tacts and receptive responses constitute a significant amount of a child's language related behaviors. In order to teach these skills, nonverbal and verbal stimuli should be arranged from simple to complex and appropriate responses differentially reinforced. Training should be conducted on both skills simultaneously and incorporated into the other types of verbal behavior (mixed VB). In addition, training should be conducted in the child's natural environment as well as in formal training sessions. An orderly progression of complexity can be obtained by an analysis of the nature of the stimulus or stimulus configuration controlling the responses. For example, it appears that is it easier to bring a response under the control of a constant stimulus than a moving or relational stimulus. More complex stimuli such as stimuli that are the properties of objects and actions, or stimuli arising within the body, tend to be more difficult to learn to identify.

Chapter 11

Advanced Intraverbal Training

Recall that intraverbal language involves the child's ability to understand and verbally respond to the words of others. A strong intraverbal repertoire is essential for conversations, social interaction, academic activities, and much of what is identified as intelligence. A child who has limited intraverbal skills will suffer in all of these areas. Therefore, it is extremely important that this type of training be a significant part of a child's daily language intervention program. However, this level of language training is not appropriate for all children who have language delays. A child is only ready for the more advanced types of intraverbal training presented in this chapter if he has successfully acquired at least 50-100 tacts and receptive responses, and he is able to emit a number of RFFC responses and the simple intraverbals presented in Chapter 9. In addition, the child's basic mand repertoire should be strong, as well as his imitation and/or echoic skills. In other words, the child should be able to easily demonstrate a number of different types of verbal behavior before complex intraverbal training is added to his daily language program. This level of language ability is reflected in profiles 4 and 5 presented in Chapter 3.

Procedures for Teaching Intraverbal Behavior

Intraverbal training procedures should be conducted simultaneously with training on the other language skills. That is, don't stop teaching new mands or tacts in order to teach intraverbals, simply add the intraverbal procedures to the others discussed thus far. The following procedures for teaching intraverbals involve the transfer of antecedent control from establishing operations (mand), nonverbal (tact), or imitative/echoic stimuli to verbal stimuli that lack point-to-point correspondence to the response (i.e., they don't match). If the child has a strong mand, tact, receptive, or imitative/echoic repertoire, the transfer should occur quickly (via the quick transfer procedure).

Expanding Fill-ins and RFFC Transfer Training

Prior to intensive training on the intraverbals presented in this chapter, instructors should spend some time expanding and generalizing the intraverbals acquired with the procedures suggested in Chapter 9. If a child has acquired a number of fill-in-the-blank intraverbals, then reverse the order of the words so the child must say a new word (Table 11-1). For example, if a child acquired the response "cracker" under the control of "You eat a…," reverse the order to "A cracker is something you…" and prompt the child to say "eat." Activities such as these will help ensure that the acquired intraverbals are not rote responses. In addition, several other people should ask for similar fill-in responses with as much variation in voice, content, context, and motivation level as possible. This broad contact with verbal stimuli will help move the child toward a generalized intraverbal ability. If the child has difficulty with these activities, then he probably is not ready for the more advanced types of intraverbals presented later in this chapter.

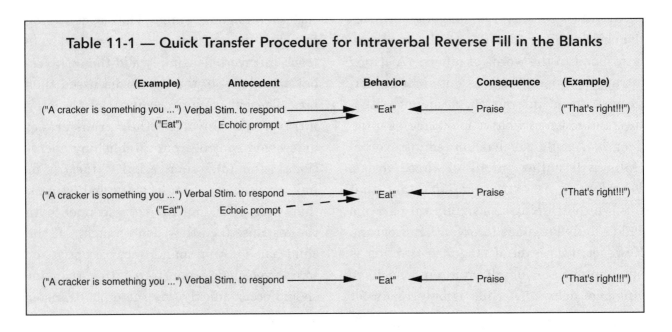

Table 11-1 — Quick Transfer Procedure for Intraverbal Reverse Fill in the Blanks

In addition to expanding and generalizing the fill-ins, the instructor should do the same with the intraverbals acquired through transfer from RFFC (Chapter 9). For example, if the child learned to say "juice" via RFFC trials involving the use of pictures of juice and the verbal stimulus "touch the one you drink," and via fading those pictures and changing the verbal stimulus, then similar procedures of reversal and the generalization described above should be implemented. The child should be able to say "drink" when the instructor says "Juice is something you..." In addition, other items to drink should be included in the transfer process, and other instructors should present these intraverbal trials at different times and in different environmental contexts. Once several of these fill-ins are strong and can be easily reversed, then more advanced types of intraverbal trials should be introduced.

Fill-ins to "Wh" Questions and "Wh" Questions Alone

Responding to questions that begin with "Wh" (e.g., what, who, where, when, why) are often difficult for many language-delayed children. One way to develop this skill is to start with a fill-in-the-blank question, then gradually change the stimulus to a "Wh" question (Table 11-2). For example, following successful responding to the verbal stimulus "You eat a..." the instructor should immediately change the verbal stimulus to "What do you eat?" A correct response is likely (and of course should be reinforced) because the child may have just said "cookie" and will probably repeat this word. The objective of this type of training is to reduce the intraverbal prompt and introduce the child to a carrier phrase (later these phrases can and should be varied). A distracter trial (e.g., "Touch your nose") should be presented, and then the instructor should return to the "What" question. Correct responses should be reinforced and incorrect responses should be followed by a return to the fill-in prompt. Distracter trials and targeted trials should be interspersed with each other until the target response occurs reliably. Variation should be introduced as soon as possible in order to avoid the development of rote responding. Pictures of other foods and slight variations of the questions (e.g., "Tell me what you eat?" "Can you tell me a food?" "Can you name a food?") can be used, as well as other instructors and environmental contexts to promote generalization.

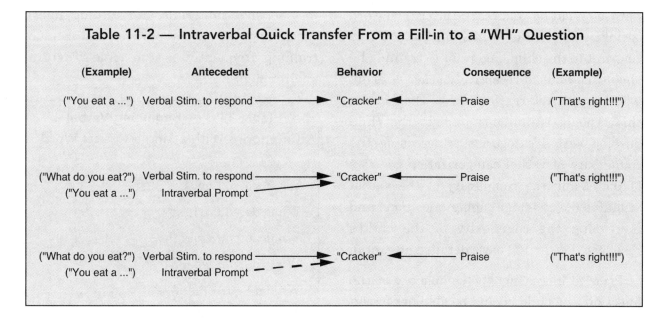

Table 11-2 — Intraverbal Quick Transfer From a Fill-in to a "WH" Question

(Example)	Antecedent	Behavior	Consequence	(Example)
("You eat a ...")	Verbal Stim. to respond	"Cracker"	Praise	("That's right!!!!")
("What do you eat?") ("You eat a ...")	Verbal Stim. to respond Intraverbal Prompt	"Cracker"	Praise	("That's right!!!")
("What do you eat?") ("You eat a ...")	Verbal Stim. to respond Intraverbal Prompt	"Cracker"	Praise	("That's right!!!")

Following the success on one topic, a second topic should be introduced. For example, the instructor might next attempt to shape some animal related intraverbals. If the fill-in "A kitty goes..." correctly evokes "meow," then the procedure described above should be used to transfer control of the word "meow" to the verbal stimulus "What does a kitty say?" These two new intraverbals can be interspersed with each other, as well as with some context related trials such as tact and receptive responses involving a variety of food and animals. These tacts and receptive trials may not only provide a context to talk about foods and animals, but also might help to evoke some novel responses in the intraverbal trials. Additional topics and intraverbal relations should be added slowly (see below), with the rate of adding new material generally based on the child's degree of success.

Answering Simple Questions

The intraverbal repertoire can be analyzed in terms of the complexity of the verbal stimulus presented to the child, and the complexity of the verbal response given by the child (as was done with the tact repertoire in Chapter 10). The most basic form of a verbal stimulus is one that contains a single critical component, like the fill-ins and the "Wh" questions presented earlier. At the beginning level, the verbal stimulus should only contain a few parts, and the content of the verbal stimulus should be common and relevant to the child. For example, the question "What do you drink?" involves the carrier phrase "What do you..." and the critical word "drink." The word "drink" is common and relevant to the child, and prior to training he should be able to receptively select a drink when shown an array of items. The focus of this type of training is to help the child develop verbal categories. Increasing the complexity of verbal categorization consists of increasing the complexity of the verbal stimulus (i.e., asking tougher questions) and increasing the complexity of the child's response (i.e., giving more detailed answers).

Prior to increasing the complexity of the question, the child should be able to correctly respond to a number of simple questions (Table 11-3) with a variety of responses. In order to increase the number of responses to a specific question, the instructor can use an array of pictures as prompts. For example, if the instructor asks the question "Can you tell me an animal," she should follow a single correct response by asking the child to "Tell me more animals." In order to help the child learn a larger class of animals, occasionally present the child with pictures of a few more animals and have the child tact the animals (Table 11-4). Then remove the pictures and ask the child to again name some

animals. If the child gives the same response (e.g., "dog") on each trial, use a novel picture (e.g., cat) as a tact prompt, and then carefully fade out the prompt (Braam & Poling, 1982; Luciano, 1986; Partington & Bailey, 1993). It is very important at this point in training verbal categorization to be alert to rote responding (i.e., giving the same response to each question). The picture prompting procedure can help, but other aspects of generalization should be implemented as well (i.e., use different instructors, settings, materials, and training times). Also, vary the carrier phrases and conduct training frequently in the child's natural environment.

Table 11-3 — Beginning Verbal Categories With a Single Critical Word

What do you eat?

What do you drink?

What do you ride?

What do you wear?

What's your name?

Tell me an animal.

Tell me a fruit.

Tell me a meat.

Tell me a dessert.

Tell me a color.

Tell me a body part.

Sing a song.

What do you sit on?

What do you sleep in?

What do you play?

What can you draw?

More Tact to Intraverbal Training: Intraverbal Functions

Following the successful acquisition of a number of single verbal stimuli relevant to the child's daily life, and prior to increasing the complexity of the verbal stimulus, a variety of other procedures can be conducted to expand and strengthen a child's intraverbal repertoire. One of these procedures involves presenting the child with specific known items (real or pictures) and having him tact them, and then asking questions about the item such as "What do you do with it?" "Where would you find this?" "Who uses this?" For example, when shown a glass of juice, ask the child "What is this?" Following a correct tact response, ask the child "What do you do with this?" "Where do you get more?" Reinforce correct responses, but if the child answers incorrectly, echoically prompt a correct response and then re-present the trial. This type of training begins to teach the child the intraverbal "function" of items and begins to develop the child's ability to talk about things he sees. This training should occur with a variety of pictures and items, and of course, generalized and trained in the natural environment. With some children this kind of activity may precede the simple categorization described above. In any case, the two procedures should be conducted at some time, because they both should help strengthen a child's intraverbal repertoire.

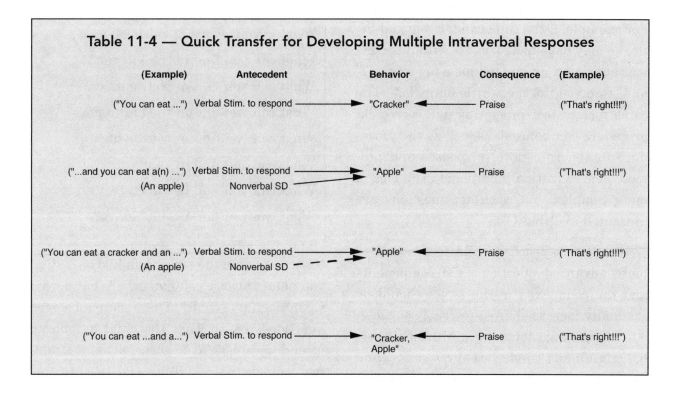

Table 11-4 — Quick Transfer for Developing Multiple Intraverbal Responses

(Example)	Antecedent	Behavior	Consequence	(Example)
("You can eat ...")	Verbal Stim. to respond	"Cracker"	Praise	("That's right!!!")
("...and you can eat a(n) ...") (An apple)	Verbal Stim. to respond Nonverbal SD	"Apple"	Praise	("That's right!!!")
("You can eat a cracker and an ...") (An apple)	Verbal Stim. to respond Nonverbal SD	"Apple"	Praise	("That's right!!!")
("You can eat ...and a...")	Verbal Stim. to respond	"Cracker, Apple"	Praise	("That's right!!!")

Increasing the Complexity of the Question

The questions that children are often asked by adults usually involve more that one critical element, thus requiring that a child be able to attend to more than just one word and a general carrier phrase. For example, the common question "What did you do today?" requires that the child have intraverbal responses related to the words "you," "do," and "today." These are all complicated verbal stimuli and may be hard for a child with limited intraverbal skills to answer. The recommendation is to begin increasing the complexity of questions by using concrete verbal stimuli that a child can already react to in some consist way (i.e., with a tact, receptive response, or mand). For example, if the child can tact big and little, he may have more success with intraverbals such as "Can you tell me a big animal?" and "Can you tell me a little animals?" The same type of tact prompting and correction procedure can be used, as well as the procedure to generate novel responses and promote generalization. Additional examples of more complex, but concrete, questions are presented in Table 11-5.

In order to teach a child to respond to more advanced questions, the components and the complexity of the topics should be gradually increased. As previously suggested, the training should begin with single verbal stimuli and single verbal responses, and then advance to multiple responses and then to multiple stimuli and multiple responses. Following success at this level, the topics should be increased in complexity. For example, "Can you name some fast cars?

Table 11-5 — Multiple Component Intraverbal Questions
Can you name some hot foods?
Can you name some cold foods?
Can you name some snack foods?
Can you name some hot drinks?
Can you name some cold drinks?
Can you name some breakfast foods?
Can you name some dinner foods?
Can you name some water animals?
Can you name some animal that can fly?
Can you name some things with wheels?
Can you name some things that float?
What is your favorite TV show?
Who is your favorite super hero?
What is your favorite video game?
What can you find in the kitchen?
What can you find in your garage?
What can you find in the bathroom?
What can you find in your bedroom?
What can you find in your yard?
What can you find in the grocery store?
What can you find in the library?

"Can you name the street you live on?" "Can you name the city you live in?" "What do you wear when it is cold?" These more advanced questions require that the child be able to attend and respond to three or more stimulus components. A child who reaches this level of intraverbal responding may begin to show a substantial amount of untrained intraverbal language acquisition. Many of the products published by LinguiSystems, especially the HELP series (e.g., Lazzari & Peters, 1994) contain intraverbal training exercises (although not called intraverbal). In fact, this collection of material from LinguiSystems is perhaps the best source of examples of intraverbals, and it demonstrates the wide range of intraverbal training that can (and should) be conducted with children who have language delays.

Intraverbal Expansion

A substantial amount of intraverbal development can occur by requesting that the child expand on the words he says. For example, much of intraverbal development begins in a nonverbal context and the child learns to talk about events in that context. For example, while at a baseball game a child may tact things and events he sees. The technique of prompting intraverbal responses suggested above (i.e., "What do you do with...") can be used with attempts to expand on the responses that the child gives. If the child were to say "He has a bat" (tact), the instructor may say "That's Right! Do you have a bat?" If the child says "Yes" (intraverbal), the instructor can ask other questions about the bat such as "Where do you keep your bat?" If the child say's "In our garage" (intraverbal), the instructor can say "Do you have any other baseball equipment there?" and so on. This type of training is developing the child's ability to maintain a conversation, and is often most successful if it is in a reinforcing context (i.e., children are more willing to talk about things they are interested in and those that are visibly present).

Learning to talk about things when the context is absent is a little more complicated. For example, when the child gets home after the baseball game he may be unable to answer any questions about the game. If he can, it suggests some good intraverbal skills. If the child cannot answer any questions, then some special training may help. A simple procedure to teach a child to talk about past events (always intraverbal) is to gradually increase the time between a concrete event and the question about the event. For example, take the child outside to pet his dog. Have the child tact the dog and the fact that he is petting the dog. Next, come inside and immediately ask the child what he just did. Reinforce correct responses, but if the child cannot respond, repeat the procedure. This time begin asking the child what he did, while walking away from the dog and using prompts if necessary. Gradually increase the time between the event and the question, while reducing any prompts. As with the other language training procedures suggested in this book, conduct the procedure with a variety of activities and use all the basic elements of generalization training.

Conversations on Specific Topics

Another method to strengthen a child's intraverbal repertoire is to pick certain topics and ask the child a series of questions. The questions can consist of those beginning with who, what, where, which, when, how, why, can, do, will, etc. The topics can be brief or extensive and can range from simple to complex. For example, the instructor should pick a topic (this will work best if it is a topic of interest to the child) such as X-Men. Begin the discussion by saying "Let's talk about your X-Men" and start asking the child questions such as "Who is your favorite X-Man?" "What are his powers?" "Where is he from?" "How did he get is powers?" It is important to remember to use the child's responses as opportunities to ask other questions and add other comments to the topic (e.g., "My favorite X-Man is Wolverine. Do you like him?"). Several different topics can be discussed at various levels with the objective being to teach the child to maintain a topic of conversation and acquire the intraverbal ability to engage in multiple verbal exchanges on a single topic. It is also important to attempt to include peers in this activity and prompt this type of verbal interaction between children.

Verbally Sequencing Events

A child's ability to verbally sequence events in his life also requires intraverbal skills. Training this ability can begin in the context of the event and involve either reinforcing events or regular daily routines. For example, if the child likes to play with Mr. Potato Head, ask him "What's next?" as he places the items on the head. If the child successfully responds, begin to gradually remove the items from sight and ask the child "What's next?" (This response is probably part mand and part intraverbal because the child's EO for the item is probably now strong). The instructor should begin establishing a verbal chain such as "You put on his eyes, his ears, and his mouth. What do you put on Mr. Potato Head?" After the child is finished, ask the child the question again. The objective is to get the child to verbally sequence the play activity. This same proce-

dure could be conducted with bedtime routines, hand washing, dressing, toileting, etc.

Advanced Intraverbal and Academic Skills

More advanced intraverbal training can occur on a variety of topics with a wide range of complexity levels (e.g., see the LinguiSystems materials). Newspapers, magazines, and books are good sources of verbal stimuli to present. The instructor can ask the child what he knows about a certain topic, or the instructor can read about topics and then ask the child questions in the manner suggested above. A dictionary is also a good source of verbal stimuli. The instructor can ask the child to define or explain words, give examples, or tell stories about the words or other events suggested by the words. Many of the topics taught in school involve intraverbal skills, and some intraverbal training can begin on topics such as current events ("Did you hear about the earthquake?"), facts ("What type of fuel do you need to put in a car?"), important events, ("When is the president coming to town?"), politics ("Who is the governor?"), and geography ("Where is Lake Tahoe?"). A child who is able to answer these types of questions should be able to benefit from inclusion programs, and he should in general spend a substantial amount of time with typically developing peers (see Chapter 14).

Summary

The intraverbal repertoire involves a child's ability to understand and verbally respond to the words used by others.

Intraverbal interactions constitute a significant part of a typically developing child's language and social interaction skills. If a child has severe language delays, these skills may not evolve from training on mand, tact, or receptive language. Intraverbal skills often need to be specifically taught, and the techniques of behavior modification and the procedures for transferring stimulus control from nonverbal to verbal stimuli are often quite effective. The approach to intraverbal training suggested here is that the instructor consider the complexity of the verbal stimulus and the complexity of the verbal response, and should appropriately sequence the intraverbal tasks so that the child can maintain a high level of success. There are a number of activities that can strengthen a child's intraverbal abilities, such as providing the function of items, verbally categorizing items and events, talking about reinforcing and nonreinforcing items and events, expanding on comments, sequencing events, talking about items and events in the past, and talking about current events. In addition, because a substantial amount of academic training involves intraverbal behavior, a child who is successful with the intraverbals identified above, may benefit more from a typical educational setting. Many of the materials from the publishing company LinguiSystems contain excellent lists of intraverbal questions, and can be of great help to instructors looking for intraverbal training activities.

Chapter 12
Teaching Advanced Mands

In Chapter 5, procedures for teaching a beginning mand repertoire were presented. The procedures suggested in that chapter made use of strong establishing operations (motivation) such as food deprivation and highly preferred items (e.g., music, books, toys, tickles, hugs, juice, swinging). These establishing operations were chosen because they are usually strong and effective motivators for a child. However, there are a limited number of these establishing operations available for a particular child, and it is essential that a child ultimately be able to ask for things other than food and highly preferred items and activities. In fact, a typical child can, if he wants, ask for almost anything he can name. For example, using the procedures in Chapter 7 the tact for chair may have been acquired, but a child also needs to learn to ask (mand) for a chair when no chair is present and he wants one. The purpose of this chapter is to describe procedures that will help the child learn to ask for the many other things that he may need in his daily life.

Establishing Operations

All mands are controlled by establishing operations (Michael, 1988; Skinner, 1957). Michael (1993) defines the establishing operation (EO) as "an environmental event that momentarily alters (a) the reinforcing effectiveness of other events, and (b) the frequen-

cy of occurrence of the type of behavior that had been consequated by those other events" (p. 191). In lay terms (a) the value of reinforcers often change (e.g., first we want it, then we don't want it), when the value is strong we (b) must have a way to get the reinforcer (manding). For example, if a child (a) wants to go visit his grandmother, he needs to be able to (b) mand "Go see grandma?"

Mand training can only be conducted if there is an EO at strength. If the child does not want the item or event, mand training on this item or event should not be conducted. After all, the objective of this type of language training is to teach the child how to ask for things he wants. Therefore, the "want" must be present during training if it is to control language outside of training (i.e., when the child wants something in his natural environment he will be able to ask for it). Because the value of reinforcers change over time, it is important that the instructor learn how to both capture and contrive EOs in order to conduct mand training (Sundberg, 1993b). This focus on EOs can and should occur in both formal training situations and in the child's natural environment. Most of the procedures described below involve methods to contrive EOs in order to teach the many mands a child will need, but an instructor should always be alert to naturally occurring EOs and use them for mand training.

Manding for Missing Items

Many children cannot ask for certain items unless the items are present, yet much of their daily lives involve wanting things that are not present. The objective of the following procedures is to teach the child to mand for missing items. However, the instructor must take special care to establish those missing items as reinforcers. Contriving an establishing operation involves specific manipulations by an instructor to alter the value of a particular object or event. For example, an instructor may give a cassette tape player to a child without a tape in it. When the child attempts to play it, he discovers that his favorite tape is not in the unit. The playing of the music cannot occur until a response is emitted that will obtain the music tape. The response at this point could be nonverbal if the child simply gets the appropriate tape from a drawer, or it could be verbal by the child manding for it with a response such as "I want music." For a child with a defective mand repertoire, these circumstances may lead to negative behavior such as a tantrum or aggression. If this behavior results in obtaining music, then it most likely strengthens an inappropriate form of manding.

Teaching mands controlled by these types of EOs is often difficult, because they can only be taught when the establishing operation is present. This may be difficult because the establishing operation can be a transient variable present only briefly (once it is reinforced the EO may dissipate quickly). Therefore, in order to develop the EO as a controlling variable for mands, the EO must be captured or contrived. Capturing an EO involves the use of EOs as they occur naturally in the child's daily environment and by conducting mand training in these natural settings. For example, if a child is observed to go to the refrigerator, this would be a good time to work on the mands "eat," "food," "drink," or "open." However, the problem with naturally occurring EOs is that they are too infrequent. A long time delay between opportunities to respond can easily further weaken an already tenuous response. This circumstance is often responsible for mands that become "prompt bound" in that imitative, tact, or intraverbal prompts may need to be present, along with the EO, in order for the response to occur.

Contriving EOs may allow for more frequent training trials, as well as provide opportunities for a greater variety of mands. Hall and Sundberg (1987) developed a procedure for contriving EOs with two teenagers who were deaf and had autism. The two children, both of whom had very weak mand repertoires, were taught to complete nonverbal chains of behavior that led to reinforcement. For example, one subject (who liked coffee) was taught to make instant coffee by completing a sequence of steps involving (1) opening the jar of coffee, (2) taking out a teaspoon of coffee, (3) putting it in the cup, (4) pouring hot water in the cup, and (5) stirring the coffee with a spoon. The teenager could tact each item in the chain, but when an item was removed (e.g., the cup) the teenager was unable to produce the correct mand response and often engaged in some form of negative or disruptive behavior. The removal of the cup blocked the response of drinking the coffee, thereby increasing the value of the cup as a reinforcer and thus creating an EO. However, the mand "cup" was not in the teenager's repertoire.

The procedure to teach the mand "cup" consisted of using the variables that controlled the tact (i.e., the actual cup) as a prompt for the response "cup" when the EO was strong. Over successive trials, the object was faded out and control was transferred to the establishing operation. This procedure allowed for the teenager to successfully mand for the missing item. Other items were then removed and the teenager learned to mand for them as well. It is important to note that the negative behavior previously seen under these circumstances no longer occurred. This contrived mand training procedure has been successfully replicated by several researchers with a variety of children and communication systems (e.g., Carroll & Hesse, 1987; Sigafoos, Doss, & Reichle 1989; Sigafoos, Reichle, Doss, Hall, & Pettitt, 1990).

There are many situations which, if arranged properly, can be used to teach mands. Expanding on the music example provided earlier, a mand for music could be taught by using the contrived EO procedure. In order to contrive the EO for music, the cassette tape could be removed from the tape player and the child given the player. Once the child discovers that the player does not work (onset of the EO), prompts could be given to say or sign "music" (implement the quick transfer procedure). The first prompt should be the least intrusive, such as "What do you want?" followed by either an intraverbal or tact prompt, depending on the child's verbal history. An intraverbal prompt might

consist of asking the child "What do you need to put in your cassette player?" For a signing child with less verbal behavior an effective intraverbal prompt might be the English words "sign music." The tact prompt would be the presentation of the cassette tape. These prompts should be faded out as quickly as possible (over the next several trials), and the response ultimately brought under the sole control of the EO.

Fading out the prompts requires careful execution, but this is a critical part of language instruction. Removing prompts too quickly, or too slowly, can result in the failure to transfer. The intraverbal prompt, for example, can be faded out by first dropping off the last word or two in the instructor's question (e.g., "What do you need to put in your..."). Then, during each trial the instructor should continue to reduce her prompt to a "What..." prompt with a questioning look on her face. Finally, just a questioning look, then no special facial prompts. If these additional prompts are not faded out, the response may always be multiply controlled and occur only when more than one of these variables are present.

Learning how to alter the value of objects and events is another important skill for a language instructor. Contriving establishing operations becomes easier once the essential features of the EO and the transfer procedure are understood and practiced. An instructor can often become quite skilled at seizing an opportunity to train a mand. The use of the verbal prompt "What do you want" can be very effective in teaching the child that a mand is needed to obtain what the child wants. Table 12-1 contains some sug-

Table 12-1 — Contriving Establishing Operations
Give the child a bowl of ice cream without a spoon.
Give the child locked box but not a key.
Ask the child to comb his hair but don't give him a comb.
Give the child a sandwich without his favorite meat in it.
Give the child a glass without any liquid in it.
Give the child a cassette tape but not a tape player.
While a child is on a swing don't push him until he asks.
Give the child a chalkboard but no chalk.
Give the child a coloring book but no crayon.
Give the child bread but no peanut butter.
Give the child a chip but no dip.
Give the child scissors but no paper to cut.
Give the child a crayon but no paper.
Bring the child to the computer but don't turn it on.
Give the child a Tupperware container with a reinforcer in it.
Stand in the doorway when a child wants out.
Play a game then stop abruptly.
Give the child a Nintendo game but no controller.
Give the child a drum but no drumsticks.
Give the child some dry Tang but no water.
Give the child some dry hot chocolate but no hot water.
Give the child a soda bottle but no bottle opener.

gestions for ways to contrive EOs. These types of circumstances probably happen throughout a child's day, but often get solved without verbal behavior or go unnoticed due to either no response on the part of the child, or because they evoke negative behavior that gets reinforced and thus becomes the mand. Special training under circumstances where the instructor knows what response topography to prompt may help to increase the chances of developing a generalized mand repertoire (Hall & Sundberg, 1987).

Manding for Action

In Chapter 10 procedures were presented for teaching a child to tact actions (verbs). It is also important that a child learns to mand for actions, as well as emit intraverbal responses involving the same action. When the value of some movement is strong, a child should be able to obtain this reinforcement by emitting some form of verbal behavior. For example, if a child wants an item that is inside a container but cannot open the container, the response "open" should come to strength. The child may be able to emit this response under imitative or tact contingencies, but that is no guarantee that the response will occur when the establishing operation is present. In order to teach this verbal relation, the tact and imitative repertoires can be used to transfer control to the establishing operation. The procedure of contriving the EO might involve putting some form of reinforcement (e.g., a raisin) in a Tupperware container and giving it to the child along with the prompt "What do you need?" or "What do you want?" A partial prompt such as "Want op..." should be given if no response occurs within 5-10 seconds. If the child can emit the response "open" as an echoic, then it should only take a few transfer trials to teach this response as a mand. The procedure should be repeated with a variety of reinforcers and containers. In addition, training should be provided under other circumstances (especially the child's natural environment) where the response "open" would be appropriate, such as opening doors or opening cans of fruit or soda.

For every tact of an action in a verbal repertoire there should be a corresponding mand. Some of these mands will be easier than others, and some certainly are more functional for the child. The focus of early training should be on the more reinforcing and functional relations in an effort to develop a generalized mand repertoire for actions. Verbs such as stand, sit, jump, run, and walk can be taught with the following procedure. Often children are reinforced by telling others to engage in some action (controlling an instructor's motor behavior may be surprisingly reinforcing for some children). In those situations a simple game where the instructor and child tell each other to stand, for example, may be quite effective. First the instructor can say to the child "Tell me to stand." If the child emits the imitative response, the instructor should stand and praise the child. Next, the instructor should mand "You (or use the child's name) stand." The child will most likely stand since this receptive skill is probably strong in his repertoire. Once the turn taking of standing is established with imitative prompts, the prompts should be faded. The verbal prompts "Your turn" or "Now you tell me to do it" can be substituted for the imitative prompt. Other actions should then be tried such as jump. The procedure would be the same except a different action. If this is successful, then the "game" should involve several different mands for actions between both individuals and then in a larger group (the game "Simon says" may further develop this repertoire).

If these procedures for manding actions are tried and the child does not mand the action without prompting and several sessions of training, then the instructor should carefully pick other actions to train. Actions that directly affect the child in some other way may be more effective—for example, mands for throwing or rolling or mands for moving out of the way to a desired object. Training in a group situation may also produce different effects. Have one member of the group play instructor and tell the other members in the group, including the real instructor, to engage in various actions. This can be made into a game and scores kept for each child, with the winner being the one with the greatest number of mands. Whatever method is used, it is important to remember that the specific reinforcement for manding actions is the behavior of the person who is given the instruction.

Mands for Attention and the Removal of Aversives

Some children may need to be specifically taught to mand for attention from others, and to mand to remove aversive stimuli. These mands frequently take the form of negative behavior. In order to reduce this type of behavior, a replacement mand for attention or removal of aversives needs to be established. For example, mands to obtain attention such as "Look," "Watch me," "Mom," "Tap arm," "Raise hand," or stating a persons name, should be trained. The basic procedure of capturing or contriving EOs, and appropriate prompting and fading, can be used to teach these mands. Likewise, mands for the removal of aversives, such as "Go away," "Don't," "Stop," "Give that back," "Leave me alone," may need to be specifically taught. These mands are more complicated because they require that the instructor first present an aversive stimulus to remove. This training might be easiest if this negative EO is captured in the natural environment, and the instructor uses this situation to prompt a more acceptable mand.

Manding for Prepositions, Adjectives, Adverbs, and Pronouns

The ability to tact or emit receptive discriminations involving prepositions, adjectives, adverbs, and pronouns does not, of course, guarantee that a mand for those

same relations will occur when an establishing operation is at strength. Training on these verbal skills when the EO is strong will most likely be necessary for establishing the appropriate mands. For example, a child may be able to distinguish between in and on when presented the corresponding nonverbal stimuli, but when he wants an item put in something, such as a key in a lock, the response may not occur. Instead, as suggested earlier, negative behavior such as whining may occur. In order to teach this type of mand it will be necessary to capture an existing EO, or contrive an EO, and provide specific training.

If the value of the key in the lock is strong for the child, then the quick transfer procedure could be used to transfer control from an imitative prompt to the EO. The instructor says "What do you want?" followed by a brief delay and then the prompt "Say in.". An imitative response should then be reinforced, and the prompt faded on the next trial. If a naturally occurring EO does not exist, then one can be contrived by placing a reinforcing object in a locked box. The procedure could be contrasted with "on" by placing the key on the lock instead of in the box and say "Is this what you want?" Individual procedures for training "on" as a mand should also occur. This type of specific training may be necessary for each preposition and should be conducted under a variety of situations in order to establish a generalized mand repertoire involving prepositions.

The ability to mand for the properties of objects will also probably need direct instruction. If a child has a preference for a certain color, then it may quite easy to establish manding for that color. However, if no preference exists, then specific procedure like the ones previously described will be necessary. Such a procedure may involve placing a reinforcer under one of several different colored plastic cups. The child would then be asked to mand for one of the cups to look for the reinforcer (e.g., "red cup"). A correct response would be followed by receipt of the reinforcer. This procedure could be used for several different adjectives, such "long" versus "short," or "big" versus "little." Training in the natural environment under the control of naturally occurring EOs, like with the other aspects of verbal behavior, will be essential for the further development this repertoire.

Manding for the property of actions would also need special training, as would manding for pronouns. Verbal games can be a useful vehicle for establishing these types of verbal behavior. A game for teaching adverbs might consist of moving a toy horse and cowboy slow and fast. The quick transfer procedure would involve the use of delays and imitative prompts to get the child to mand for fast movements versus slow movements. Taking turns between the instructor and the child, or perhaps even more effectively, between children can be an effective way to develop a variety of responses. Mands for pronouns could be taught also in the group situation where turn taking is the game and responses such as "mine" and "yours" are prompted and trained.

These various "parts of speech" may all need to be trained individually, but soon they will need to be placed together in a "sentence." The next section will describe procedures for developing larger and more grammatical units of verbal behavior as mands. The first procedures presented will involve the development of "mand frames," then procedures for teaching multiple component responses will be presented.

Teaching the "I Want..." Mand Frame and Mand Sentences

A mand is often embedded within a response frame that has a history of reinforcement. The "I want..." frame can be useful in establishing a generalized mand repertoire. The child's response "I want" can become equivalent to the response "I have an active EO." Training now must be given on emitting the particular response form linked to that EO. If a child can mand using single response forms, then the captured EO procedure can help expand the response form to include the "I want..." frame. For example, a child says/signs/points to "juice" as a mand. At that point the instructor prompts "Say I want juice" and requires the child to emit a imitative response; then she conducts a transfer trial consisting of the prompt "What do you want?" The instructor may need to prompt the first part of the response with "I..." A child who can emit "I want" before a specific topography can help an instructor discriminate between a response that is a tact and one that is a mand. There are several other mand frames that can help develop the mand repertoire, such as "Can I..." "Will you..." "Give me..." etc.

This procedure may be a useful starting point for the development of more grammatically accepted mand sentences. Mands that contain only a single response form are often considered rude or inappropriate for a skilled speaker. Often, however, it is difficult to get a child to emit the "I want" response. Under these circumstances it may be more useful to pursue teaching multiple responses that involve specific features of the desired item. For example, it may be easier to teach the child to mand "apple juice," or "grape juice." If so, then the emphasis should be placed on expanding the mand topography this way rather then always allowing a single response form. The quick transfer procedure can be used to link together nouns and verbs, as well as nouns, verbs, adjectives, etc. Prompts such as "Say the whole thing," and incidental teaching procedures, can be helpful in establishing these larger response units.

A skilled mander often softens his mand in many ways. The response "Please" is an acceptable way to increase the probability that a listener will provide the specific reinforcement. However, the controlling variables for this response are quite complicated, and it is usually best taught within a mand frame such as "I want... please." Eventually, the two procedures of teaching mand frames along with teaching multiple responses can be combined as in the response "I want apple juice please."

Mands for Information

Questions are mands because they occur under the control of establishing operations and are consequated by specific reinforcement. This, of course, is why young children reach a point in verbal development where questions begin to occur at a high rate. Questions are very important for verbal development because they allow a speaker to acquire additional verbal behavior. Once an early language learner can ask questions, then the acquisition of verbal behavior begins to accelerate rapidly. For example, a child might ask "What's that?" and the parent says "hammer," then the child might say "I want hammer" or "That's a hammer." If an individual can easily emit a number of mands, and does so with multiple component response forms, then he should be taught how to mand for information with the question words where, what, who, which, when, how, and why.

Where. The mand "Where?" involves asking for the location of a desired item. In order to teach this type of question, an establishing operation must be present or created. One way to do it is to play a game where a reinforcer is hidden under one of two colored cups. The instructor then moves the cups around and echoically prompts the child to ask "Where is the cracker?" (or simply, "Where cracker?"). At first the imitative response should be reinforced, then prompts faded and reinforcement withheld until less prompted responses occur. Other objects for concealment of the item should then be used such as bowls, hats, paper, etc., as well as different reinforcers. Also, instructors should make use of the natural contingencies involving "where" throughout the child's day. Prompts such as "Where is your coat?" or "Can you say 'Where is my coat?'" can make the verbal relation more functional while increasing the strength of this type of mand.

What. The response "What?" is a mand when the response occurs under the control of the establishing operation involving the increased value of some verbal information. This response can often be taught by again playing a game where the instructor and the child take turns asking for the names of known items presented. The instructor should ask "What is this?" then after the child responds prompt him with "Your turn, you ask me." Additional prompts may be necessary to get the child to respond initially. After turn taking is established, unfamiliar items should be placed in front of the child. This type of training, along with training under the natural contingencies of the daily environment, can help establish the "What?" mand.

Who. A similar procedure can be used for teaching "Who?" but persons should be used instead of objects. Real persons, or pictures of people in different professions (e.g., policeman, fireman), should be presented in a game and turn-taking format. The responses may require extensive prompting at first, but the child should be reinforced for approximations and prompts should be faded. Training in the natural environment should also occur.

Which. This type of question involves a mand for a specific item or information about a specific item from an array of items. A game to teach this mand could consist of presenting the child with a number of similar items that differ in color (e.g., jelly beans). First ask the child "Which one do you want?" Then, following the child's turn, prompt him with "Your turn, you ask me."

When. "When?" is a mand for information involving time. This type of question might be taught by first telling the child that a reinforcing event is going to occur. This may help to create an EO for information involving the passage of time. The instructor can prompt the child to ask, for example, "When are we going?" and reinforce this with information about when the departure is planned. This type of training is perhaps best done under the natural contingencies of day-to-day events.

How. This is a more difficult question then the others. Asking "How?" might be taught by first demonstrating some activity, such as constructing a toy or a reinforcing object that would require some specific skill or behavior to operate—for example, a mechanical robot with a remote control. The instructor can then prompt the child to ask "How?" and then reinforce the child by showing them how to operate the toy. Prompts should be faded and trials conducted under natural contingencies as often as possible.

Why. This mand involves asking for the causes of behavior or events. These are perhaps the most difficult questions to teach. A possible way to teach this mand is to perform some action in the presence of the child, such as opening the toy robot's battery compartment. The child should be prompted to ask "Why did you open it?" and the instructor should respond "To check the batteries." Then, have the child open it and the instructor should ask the "Why?" question. Trials on other types of actions and in the natural environment will probably be necessary for the further development of this mand.

These procedures for question asking are general and meant to be only examples of how these repertoires might be developed. It often takes several trials across a wide variety of situations to establish these reper-toires firmly. Specific techniques will depend on the individual child, and on the degree to which, for example, the behavior of another person functions as reinforcement for that child. The game aspects of the pro-cedures have been quite helpful in the past. These procedures often work well in a group situation with several questions developed simultaneously. For example, one child in the group is instructed to close his eyes or turn away from the group. A second child is then given some object that would function as reinforcement for the first child. The child who was given the object then hides it somewhere. The first child is then told he can have the object if he can find out who hid it and where. This type of activity is often enjoyable to children and teaches coopera-tion along with question asking.

Arranging the Daily Verbal Environment

A primary objective at this point in teach-ing language is to increase the frequency of functional words occurring throughout a child's day. Many (if not most) of the early forms of verbal behavior for an early lan-guage learner consist of mands (one need only spend time with young children to be convinced of this). Parents and instructors need to establish an environment that requires and reinforces mands. Simple prompts such as "What do you want?" can have big effects. Rather than giving rein-forcers away use them as an opportunity to evoke a mand. A typical child may emit thousands of mands a day. A language-training program that is in effect only a short time each day, or even worse a few times a week, will have a low probability of producing a fluent mander.

Capturing and contriving EOs and requir-ing responses are good ways to increase the frequency of mands. There are several other activities that can help promote mands as well. The focus of the daily intervention should be on all types of language (i.e. imita-tive, receptive, RFFC, mand, tact, and intraverbal). Require the child to talk as much as possible. Responses that are part mand and part tact (e.g., when playing catch with a ball, request the child ask for the ball) may easily be worked into the daily routine. Also, interspersing trials on the other verbal operants with the mand can be helpful. Tact, receptive, and intraverbal trials at varying levels should occur as many times as possible each hour. For example, ask the child to identify common objects in the daily environment, to answer fill-in questions, and receptively identify objects and activities. The more frequently these trials are con-ducted, the easier it becomes to verbally respond.

Summary

In order for a response to be a mand it must occur under the control of an establish-ing operation. Therefore, training this type of language must involve capturing or con-triving EOs. All words acquired as tacts and intraverbals may at some point need to occur as mands (some of these words may be more useful than others). Special training is usu-ally required to teach children to mand for missing items, to mand using the different parts of speech, and to mand for verbal information. The captured and contrived EO procedures are two ways to be assured that an EO is at strength. These procedures should be conducted as often as possible, and the child should be required to mand throughout the day. It is important to remember that if the object needs to be present for a mand to occur, then the response is also part tact. In order to train a pure mand, the response must be solely under the control of the establishing operation.

Chapter 13

The Need for Both Discrete Trial and Natural Environment Training

Children with autism have historically provided unique challenges to the professionals who work with them. Perhaps the most complex task faced by these professionals is the development and implementation of effective language intervention programs. Language is complex, and for many nonverbal children with autism it often requires a substantial amount of skill and effort on the part of parents and teachers to develop a successful communication repertoire. Many specific language skills must be directly taught to these children, and careful programming provided in order for generalization and spontaneity to occur. In addition, these children need to eventually be able to acquire new types of language skills without highly trained staff or a carefully programmed individualized educational environment. A substantial amount of literature on autism suggests that a behavioral approach can best provide these necessary elements for successful language instruction (Maurice, Green, & Luce, 1996).

However, in the behavioral literature there are several quite different approaches to language instruction for children with autism. Two common approaches have been identified as discrete trial training (e.g., Lovaas, 1981; Lovaas, Koegel, Simmons, & Long, 1973; Smith, 1993), and the natural language paradigm (e.g., Koegel, O'Dell, &

Koegel, 1987; Laski, Charlop, & Schreibman, 1988). There are several variations of these two different approaches to language training (e.g., Guess, Sailor, & Baer, 1976; Halle, 1987; Hart & Risley, 1975; Hart & Rogers-Warren, 1978; Kent, 1974). Koegel, Koegel, and Surratt (1992) provided a summary of the basic elements of these two approaches (Table 13-1) and they will be briefly reviewed here.

The main aspect of discrete trial training (DTT, also called analog training by Koegel, et al., 1992) is that language intervention is conducted in a highly specified and structured manner. The instructor chooses and presents a specific stimulus related to a target skill, and when the student responds correctly (perhaps with prompting) the response is reinforced with strong reinforcers such as food. Incorrect responses typically result in the use of a correction procedure, and training on a specific skill is often repeated until a mastery criterion is met. Language skills are divided into a number of independent tasks (or drills), and mass trial training typically occurs in a designated situation (e.g., at a table). In addition, the instructor often presents a command to respond to a specific task in a slightly louder voice, with the clear indication to the child that he is expected to respond. Some approaches to discrete trial training

(DTT) recommend punishing nonresponding and incorrect responses with verbal reprimands usually in the form of a loud "No!" Discrete trial training can be very effective (e.g., Smith, 1993), especially when compared to the indirect type of language intervention (e.g., large group and activity-based instruction) common to many special education classrooms.

Table 13-1 — Comparison of Discrete Trial Training and Natural Environment Training

	Discrete Trial (Analog)	Natural Environment (NLP)
Stimulus items	a. Chosen by clinician b. Repeated until criterion is met c. Phonologically easy to produce irrespective of whether they were functional in the natural environment	a. Chosen by child b. Varied every few trials
Interaction	a. Clinician holds up stimulus item; stimulus item not functional within interaction	a. Clinician and child play with stimulus item (i.e., stimulus item is functional within interaction)
Response	a. Correct response or successive approximations reinforced verbally (except self-stimulation)	a. Looser shaping contingency so that attempts to respond are also reinforced
Consequences	a. Edible reinforcers paired with social reinforcers	a. Natural reinforcers (e.g., opportunity to play with the item) paired with socialreinforcers

---

The essential features of natural environment training (NET, also called the Natural Language Paradigm (NLP) by Koegel, et al., 1987) involve focusing on the child's immediate interests and activities as a guide for language instruction. NET is looser and conducted in the child's typical daily environment (e.g., his home, a playground, the community), rather than in a formal teaching arrangement. Stimulus and response variation is stressed, and the consequences for correct verbal responses are specific to the child's interest or activities, rather than consequences that are irrelevant to the response (e.g., giving a child the ball for identifying a ball rather than giving him an M&M). There are a number of language training approaches and techniques that have been based on this general orientation (e.g., incidental teaching, milieu teaching), and these, along with NLP, have been successful in teaching a variety of language delayed children more advanced language skills (e.g., Halle, 1987; Hart & Risley, 1975; Hart & Rogers-Warren, 1978; Koegel, O'Dell, & Koegel, 1987; Warren & Kaiser, 1986).

Both DTT and NET have been shown to be effective. However, these quite different approaches to language instruction have generated a substantial amount of discussion and disagreement among professionals as to which method is the most effective. In a recent series of research, DTT (identified by the authors as analog training) was contrasted with NET (identified by the authors as the natural language paradigm) in an attempt to determine which behavioral approach to language instruction produced better results (Elliot, Hall, & Soper, 1991; Koegel, Koegel, & Surratt, 1992). The findings of these studies were somewhat mixed with Elliot, et al. (1991), who made their assessments under conditions favoring analog training to assure against bias, reporting no statistical difference between the two methods. However, these authors concluded that "Because natural language teaching has many strengths, few drawbacks, and produces equal generalization and retention under disadvantageous conditions, it is strongly supported as preferable for people with autism and mental retardation" (p. 444). Koegel, et al. (1992), using a different methodology, found that "teaching language to autistic children in a natural teaching context typically produced more correct target behavior than an analog approach. The results also added to the literature by showing that the children exhibited considerably less disruptive behavior during the natural language conditions" (Koegel, et al., 1992, p. 151).

Given these results, it would seem that a practitioner should conduct natural language training rather than discrete trial training with children with autism.

However, the issue as to which approach is the most effective may not be that simple. First, since there is such a wide variation among children with autism, no single approach would probably work for all children. Second, a fundamental problem with the different behavioral approaches to language training presented in the literature (such as the two described above) is that they are not based on a behavioral analysis of language. Rather, while they employ behavioral techniques (e.g., prompting, reinforcement) to teach language skills, they (often unknowingly) are guided by a traditional cognitive or biological analysis of language (e.g., Brown, 1973; Chomsky, 1957; Piaget, 1926; Pinker, 1994). Unfortunately, these traditional analyses of language tend to neglect important environmental variables and often blend useful distinctions that might be essential to guiding language intervention programs for children with autism. The use of the traditional distinctions between expressive and receptive language common to most of the above-cited research is a hallmark of these traditional analyses of language.

The purpose of this chapter is to further examine DTT and NET, but with the help of Skinner's (1957) functional analysis of verbal behavior. Skinner's analysis of verbal behavior has been used as a conceptual tool to help analyze a variety of topics in the analysis of language, such as the acquisition of language by children (e.g., Bijou & Bear, 1965), the acquisition of language by apes (e.g., Savage-Rumbaugh, 1984; Sundberg, 1996), language assessment (Partington & Sundberg, 1998; Spradlin, 1963; Sundberg, 1983), the use of Facilitated Communication (e.g., Hall, 1993; Sundberg, 1993), stimulus equivalence (e.g., Hall & Chase, 1991), and schizophrenic hallucinations (e.g., Burns, Heiby, & Tharp, 1983; Layng & Andronis, 1984). There are many theoretical analyses of language available to the professional, but Skinner's (1957) analysis of language and its focus on environmental variables, can be a valuable guide for the assessment and development of a language intervention program.

The essential feature of Skinner's analysis of verbal behavior is that language is learned behavior under the control of a variety of different environmental variables. Skinner (1957) identifies and functionally classifies these different types of environmental variables and has suggested a number of different verbal operants. In general, Skinner goes beyond the traditional classification of receptive and expressive language by distinguishing between receptive language and 5 functionally independent types of expressive language (echoic/motor imitation/copying-a-text, mand, tact, intraverbal, textual/transcriptive). There are also many subtypes, extensions, and combinations of these basic "elementary verbal operants," as Skinner calls them. The distinction between the mand, tact, and intraverbal is quite complex, and thus frequently not recognized by professionals. However, this distinction often reveals important information regarding the pragmatic aspects of expressive communication, especially for the analysis of defective or delayed language skills. By using Skinner's elementary verbal operants as a tool to classify the types of language behavior focused on in training, the distinction between DTT and NET can be more closely examined. Table 13-2 contains a comparison of the two approaches across the different elementary verbal operants. This comparison will be described in more detail below.

Mand

Perhaps the most significant difference between DTT and NET is that NET primarily involves the basic elements of mand training (i.e., the use of establishing operations and specific reinforcement), while DTT primarily involves the basic elements of receptive, tact, echoic, and imitation training (i.e., verbal and nonverbal stimulus control and nonspecific reinforcement). There is an extensive body of research on the many differences between mand training and training on the other types of verbal behavior (for reviews see Brady, Saunders, & Spradlin, 1994; Oah & Dickenson, 1989; Shafer, 1994). Perhaps the most important distinction between these types of verbal behavior is the role of the establishing operation as an independent variable in the mand (Michael, 1988, 1993). Previous research has shown that use of the EOs and specific reinforcement can facilitate language acquisition (e.g., Braam & Sundberg, 1991; Carroll & Hesse, 1987; Hall & Sundberg, 1987; Stafford, Sundberg, & Braam, 1988). From a practical point of view, language training can be a lot more successful and fun for a child if his on-going establishing operations guide language intervention, especially for manding. However, as will be discussed shortly, the child must also learn verbal behaviors not solely related to his current establishing operations.

Table 13-2 — A Comparison of Discrete Trial Training and Natural Environment Training Using Skinner's Elementary Verbal Operants		
	Discrete Trial Training	Natural Environment Training
Mand operations	Not specifically trained, EO not used, specific reinforcement not and nonverbal stimulus control	Focus on establishing and use of specific reinforce but multiply controlled if verbal or nonverbal stimuli present
Receptive	Specifically trained, focus on verbal and nonverbal stimulus control	Specifically trained, but multi ply controlled if EO and contex tual stimuli present
Tact	Specifically trained, focus on nonverbal stimulus control	Specifically trained, but multi ply controlled if EO and specific reinforcement present
Echoic	Specifically trained, focus on vocal verbal stimulus control	Specifically trained, but multi ply controlled if EO, object, and specific reinforcement present
Imitation	Specifically trained, focus on visual motor stimulus control	Specifically trained, but multi ply controlled if EO, object, and specific reinforcement present
Intraverbal	Not specifically trained, multiply controlled if EO, object, and	Specifically trained, but multi ply controlled if EO, object, and specific reinforcement present specific reinforcement present

Receptive, Tact, Echoic, and Imitation

Much of a typically developing child's language is controlled by what he sees and hears in his daily environment. Receptive, tact, echoic, and imitation are types of verbal behavior that are evoked by these verbal and nonverbal stimuli in that environment. DTT may be more suited for teaching these types of verbal behavior because of the high rate of trials often required and the absence of the EO as a source of control in training. In fact, it may be possible that training in the absence of the EO helps the child learn how to work and attend for extended periods of time, which is required for success in a typical school. However, it is often the case that strong forms of reinforcement, or even mild aversive control, are needed to be successful because many of the tasks are irrelevant to the child's current EOs, and are out of context.

Receptive, tact, echoic, and imitation training can also be conducted with NET, but with EOs and specific reinforcement as variables that may facilitate the acquisition of these skills (e.g., Carroll & Hesse, 1987). However, it may be difficult to conduct a high rate of training trials, and a special effort must be made to ensure that the responses ultimately are not multiply controlled by EOs and specific reinforcement. For example, a child might be successful at receptively identifying a Winnie the Pooh video tape in a natural context, but his success may be multiply controlled by not only the video and the verbal instruction but also by the establishing operations related to the video the presence of other stimuli associated with the video (e.g., a VCR, TV), and getting to watch the video. It should be pointed out that multiple control is not necessarily a bad thing; in fact, these additional variables may facilitate the initial acquisition of some types of language. However, the problem with multiple control is that EOs, specific reinforcement, and other forms of verbal and nonverbal stimulus control, may not be present outside of the original NET conditions, thus possibly reducing the probability of generalizing these types of verbal responses to less interesting but still important environmental conditions.

Intraverbal

Intraverbal behavior is not a major focus in the early phases of either approach.

However, training on this verbal skill is essential for the development of conversations, social interaction, and certain types of academic behavior. NET seems more conducive to intraverbal training, and procedures are often included to increase intraverbal responding (e.g., "expansion" in incidental teaching). However, when intraverbal behavior is taught, both approaches may unintentionally develop multiply controlled responding if training does not include conditions where the EO, specific reinforcement, and nonverbal stimuli are eliminated as independent variables (i.e., the child ultimately needs to acquire pure intraverbal behavior).

In summary, a comparison between DTT and NET shows that these two approaches focus on different types of verbal behavior. Both teach receptive and expressive language, but Skinner's (1957) analysis of verbal behavior shows that NET primarily involves mand training by incorporating the child's current establishing operations and the delivery of specific reinforcement. In comparison, DTT primarily involves tact, receptive, echoic, and imitation training by using nonverbal and verbal stimuli and nonspecific reinforcement. However, intraverbal behavior typically is not a major focus of either approach. Since elements of each type of training can benefit children with autism, a more effective approach might consist of a combination of DTT and NET, with intervention programs guided by Skinner's analysis of verbal behavior as a conceptual framework. The practical advantages and disadvantages of DTT and NET will now be examined in order to further identify the strengths and weaknesses of each approach.

Some of these advantages and disadvantages are presented in Tables 13-3 to 13-6. Other comparisons of DTT and NET are available in the literature, and the reader is referred to these for additional information (e.g., Elliot, Hall, & Soper, 1991; Spradlin & Siegel, 1982).

Advantages of DTT. Perhaps the main advantage of DTT is that a high rate of training trials on specific verbal operants can be conducted. With this clear focus and emphasis on specific language skills, the training program is easier to script, and the procedures can be conducted by staff who have only minimal training. The training stimuli (e.g., specific target items to label) can be clearly identified and collected prior to training sessions, the targeted responses are measurable and easy to take data on, and the consequences are easy to deliver (e.g., food). In addition, this type of training is more conducive to a classroom structure, where it is often impossible to follow each child's EO as it occurs. Thus, it is possible that this arrangement is an effective way to teach the types of verbal behaviors that are not related to the EO and specific reinforcement, or skills that may need an extensive number of training trials to acquire.

Table 13-3 — The Advantages of Discrete Trial Training

❑ Allows for a high number of training trials

❑ Easy for many different staff members to implement (a scripted curriculum is used)

❑ May be a good way to develop tact, receptive, echoic, and imitative behaviors

❑ Easier to run in a classroom setting

❑ Instructional stimuli and detailed curriculum provided for staff

❑ Target responses are known and easily identified

❑ Contrived consequence is easy to deliver

❑ Data collection is relatively straightforward

❑ Progressive steps in the curriculum clearly identified (e.g., nouns, verbs, pronouns)

❑ Progress (or the lack of progress) is very observable

❑ May help to establish stimulus control of "learner repertoires" (e.g., child learns to attend, learns that if he does respond he gets reinforced, learns how to make discriminations, learns to sit and work, acquires an increased tolerance of demands)

Disadvantages of DTT. There are a number of disadvantages of DTT that should be considered (Table 13-4). While DTT may facilitate a child's acquisition of specific verbal responses, the formal structure of the language interaction is different from that found in the natural environment. The natural environment does not contain strong prompts to respond, including an implicit threat that one must respond, nor does it

Table 13-4 — The Disadvantages of Discrete Trial Training

❏ Requires special procedures to ensure generalization

❏ Prompts to respond (including aversive prompts) often not present outside of the training session

❏ Child's current EOs not used in training and may even compete with training

❏ Mainly teacher-initiated activities

❏ Mand training is difficult because it requires using EOs and specific reinforcement

❏ Intraverbal behavior typically not taught as a separate verbal operant

❏ Immediate and powerful reinforcers often not available outside of the training session

❏ The drill nature of the training may generate rote responding

❏ Non-functional nature of the training may generate escape and avoidance behaviors (possibly increasing the need for the use of aversive control or powerful contrived reinforcers)

❏ The interaction between the speaker and listener is very different from that observed by typical speakers and listeners

❏ Language and language trainers may become paired with aversive situations

❏ Trials that are presented in a scripted manner reduce the trainer's ability to expand on responses or mix up the verbal operants, as in typical verbal interactions

always contain the immediate delivery of powerful reinforcers. Therefore, extensive efforts to establish generalization and thin out reinforcement must be included in the program. In addition, DTT is primarily teacher initiated and does not make use of the child's on-going EOs, which not only neglects opportunities to teach mands but also possibly contributes to potential behavior problems. Another disadvantage of DTT is that the drill nature of the training may generate rote responding and inhibit spontaneous verbal behavior because of the tight stimulus control that is often established. Also, specific skills are typically isolated and taught independently (e.g., tacting, imitation, receptive); however, in typical verbal interactions the different types of verbal behavior (e.g., receptive, mand, tact, intraverbal) are mixed together in a conversation. Also, the interaction between a speaker and listener in the natural environment is very different from the interaction observed in standard DTT (e.g., where the instructor commands each specific response from the child).

Advantages of NET. There are several advantages of conducting language instruction in a child's natural environment. Perhaps the most significant variable is the use of the child's current motivation (establishing operations) and the immediate environmental context as guides for the language training process. This type of training not only teaches manding but reduces the need for elaborate generalization procedures, because the training is conducted in the context of natural events in the child's daily environment that are typically the focus of generalization procedures used in DTT (e.g., Koegel & Johnson, 1989; Koegel, et al., 1992). In addition, the child may exhibit fewer negative behaviors because of the focus on his motivation and the use of consequences directly related to that motivation (Hall & Sundberg, 1987; Koegel, Koegel, & Surratt, 1992; Stafford, Sundberg, & Braam, 1988). NET may also promote more spontaneous verbal behavior because of the focus on EO control rather than trainer stimulus control.

A skillful trainer can use EOs and specific reinforcement to teach tacts, intraverbals, and other important verbal and nonverbal skills. For example, if a child shows interest in playing with a train set, it may be quite easy to teach the mand "train," as well as tacts for items related to the train, such as track, light, caboose, engine, wheels, etc., and intraverbals such as "It's a choo choo..." This teaching strategy not only allows the instructor to teach each type of verbal behavior, but the instructor can more easily bring together these different types of verbal behavior as they relate to the current environmental context (e.g., the presence of a train set). This type of interaction typically does not occur in DTT.

Table 13-5 — The Advantages of Natural Environment Training

❏ Use of the child's interests (EOs) to guide language instruction

❏ Best conditions to teach manding

❏ Use of the stimuli in the child's natural environment as target stimuli

❏ Reduced need for elaborate generalization procedures

❏ Reduced amount of negative behavior

❏ Reduced need for aversive control

❏ Easier to teach intraverbal behavior as a separate verbal operant

❏ The verbal interaction is much more characteristic of typical verbal interactions

❏ More opportunities for trainers to be paired with successful verbal interactions

❏ Verbal responses can be mixed together more easily under the environmental conditions that may evoke them later

❏ The training conditions are closer to those of kindergarten and how child may be taught in the future

Disadvantages of NET. There are a number of disadvantages of NET as well. Perhaps the main problem is that extra effort must be made to eliminate the EO, specific reinforcement, and other contextual prompts from the language training activities. Attempts to conduct only tact or intraverbal training may be less successful because of the absence of EOs and specific consequences in a language training session. Therefore, conducting language training in the natural environment requires a sophisticated set of skills on the part of the language trainer/parent to move beyond this type of multiply controlled manding. Teaching staff exactly how to conduct this training is much more complicated, because it is hard to predict the child's EOs and behaviors, and there is no scripted curriculum for the teacher to follow. In addition, the amount or training trials and the types of training activities may be limited in the natural environment because the child's interests may be limited and because of the often cumbersome and time consuming nature of delivering specific reinforcement (e.g., "Take me swimming").

Using primarily the child's EOs to initiate and guide language interactions may be a sharp contrast with the daily contingencies in the child's real world. The child may be required to follow the adult's EOs, and comply with adult's verbal stimuli, while his EOs are ignored or are not understood (as is probably the case with a substantial amount of early parent-child relationships). While strong EOs may provide good opportunities to teach more advanced language skills and should be capitalized on, the child must also be able to comply to specific educational routines and instructions delivered by a teacher

if the child is to succeed in a typical classroom (Lovaas, 1977). That is, teaching language also involves the establishment of nonverbal (tact) and verbal (receptive, intraverbal, textual) stimulus control. In fact, for some children an extensive focus on their EOs (mands) may interfere with the establishment of these other types of antecedent control, especially verbal stimulus control (e.g., compliance, receptive discriminations).

Combining DTT and NET for Daily Language Instruction

Language intervention for children with autism should involve teaching all the different elementary verbal operants, under a variety of environmental contexts, while being assured that each type of verbal behavior can stand on its own and can be mixed together (Skinner, 1957). For example, the success of a child's tact repertoire should not be dependent on the presence of mand variables (i.e., EOs and specific reinforcement), just like the tact should be able to lead to a relevant intraverbal if the conditions warrant it. DTT and NET are both effective procedures and each offers specific advantages for teaching certain types of verbal behavior. The exclusive use of only one of these approaches may be less effective then the combination of the two, guided by Skinner's analysis of verbal behavior.

Unfortunately, the terms that have evolved as descriptors for these two approaches are somewhat misleading. Technically, a "discrete trial" is a three-term contingency consisting of a stimulus-response-consequence relationship (e.g.,

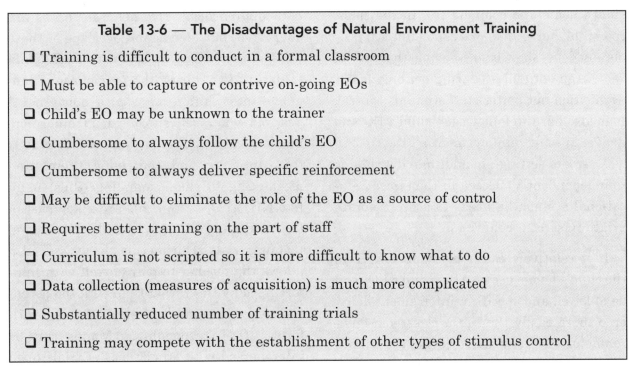

Table 13-6 — The Disadvantages of Natural Environment Training

❑ Training is difficult to conduct in a formal classroom

❑ Must be able to capture or contrive on-going EOs

❑ Child's EO may be unknown to the trainer

❑ Cumbersome to always follow the child's EO

❑ Cumbersome to always deliver specific reinforcement

❑ May be difficult to eliminate the role of the EO as a source of control

❑ Requires better training on the part of staff

❑ Curriculum is not scripted so it is more difficult to know what to do

❑ Data collection (measures of acquisition) is much more complicated

❑ Substantially reduced number of training trials

❑ Training may compete with the establishment of other types of stimulus control

staff hold up a car, child says "car," staff say "Right!"). Recently, however, "discrete trial" has come to be used by parents and educators as a descriptor for an entire approach to language instruction, usually that of Lovaas. However, discrete trials are not restricted to the implementation of an entire program (which is often requested by parents), but can be conducted in a variety of environmental situations with substantial variation (e.g., Leaf, 1997).

"Natural language" is also a term that suggests other possible meanings. For example, it may suggest linguistically interacting with the child in a manner similar to how one would interact with a typically developing child in a noneducational environment. However, if the child is nonverbal or is limited in his verbal abilities, the informal and casual language instruction provided by parents of typical children may be markedly inadequate for a child with autism (much of the work on incidental and milieu

training, which preceded NLP, was conducted with higher functioning children). However, for many children, an effective way of teaching them the different types of verbal behavior is to use the elements of the child's natural environment (i.e., current EOs, events, activities, materials) to intensively conduct discrete trials. The term "natural environment" is not much better, but seems to at least put the focus on the child's immediate environment rather than on developmental processes.

There are two general instructional settings for most children with autism: a special education classroom provided by the local school district and the child's home environment. Language training on all the elementary verbal operants should be conducted in both of these environments, using both DTT and NET techniques. However, depending on the child and the available staff, it may be easier to conduct more DTT in the child's classroom and more NET in the child's home and community. In the classroom, higher rates of responding can be obtained by sharply increasing the rate of reinforcement and producing not only faster acquisition but better staff stimulus control. It is also hard to follow each child's EO and deliver specific reinforcement all the time in a classroom setting. In addition, if a child is to independently succeed in the typical educational system, he needs to acquire appropriate classroom behaviors.

It is relatively easier to conduct NET in the child's home, because the child's EOs can be followed and specific reinforcement delivered more easily than in a classroom environment. Also, a wider variety of the stimuli associated with verbal behavior can be accessed for training (e.g., lights, toys, people, sounds, smells). However, at home there is much less of a demand on the child then at school (as is of course the case for typical children), thus high demand tasks (such as language training for some low verbal children) might be difficult to complete. In addition, DTT may be more difficult at home because reinforcers may be less effective, as they are often available noncontingently at home. However, the careful use of EOs to conduct discrete trial training on mands and other types of verbal behavior (with discrete trials) can generate a substantial amount of verbal behavior.

Finally, it is most important to consider the existing skills of the individual child when determining how to best approach his language needs. The balance between DTT and NET may change frequently during the language acquisition process, but training should always include both approaches. Five general phases are suggested, but blends and overlaps of these phases may vary widely with each child (Table 13-7). During the first phase of language intervention for, say, a nonverbal 3 year old who rarely sits down, a trainer may be more successful following the child's EOs (by capturing and contriving them) and attempting to shape manding (thus, more like NET). Discrete trials are a key part of this training, but they are discrete mand training trials. During this phase, NET also allows the teacher to pair herself with reinforcing activities rather than with the potential aversive stimuli often associated with formal DTT responding. Mands can be interspersed with other types of trials (e.g., receptive, echoic, imitation) in an effort to begin establishing stimulus control in addition to EO control (Michael, 1982). While a majority of the training may be conducted in the child's natural environment, some DTT training can begin to occur at a table or on the floor.

In Phase 2, the other verbal operants should become more of a focus of training, but mand training should still be conducted at every opportunity. Training should be conducted with both types of general approaches, but during this phase the child should be learning how to work for extended periods of time in a formal language session conducted at a table or desk. In Phase 3, more of a focus should be placed on the acquisition of academic like behaviors, such as letters and numbers, and more complex language relations, such as prepositions and adjectives. Training on these more complex skills (which are often quite unrelated to a child's current EOs) should be conducted at

Table 13-8 — The Changing Emphasis of DTT and NET as the Child Learns Language

Phase 1. NET > DTT	Focus on early manding, pairing, compliance, stimulus control
Phase 2. NET = DTT	Focus on mand, tact, receptive, imitation, echoic, and intraverbal
Phase 3. DTT > NET	Focus on academic activities and specific skill development
Phase 4. NET > DTT	Focus on learning from group instruction, from peers, and without a highly structured learning environment, training is more like that of typical kindergarten and first grade classrooms
Phase 5. DTT > NET	Focus on academic skills and structured learning characteristic of later elementary classrooms

a table or desk and for extended period of time (e.g., 15-20 minutes between breaks). NET can still be used to teach and help generalize these academic skills and should still be conducted whenever possible.

The objectives of Phase 4 and Phase 5 are to move the child closer to a less restrictive and more typical educational setting. Once the child has acquired a substantial amount of verbal behavior, it is important to teach him how to learn new verbal responses from the natural environment (actually this training should be occurring to some degree all along). That is, the child should be able to learn language in the absence of a specific language-training structure (e.g., group instruction, activity-based instruction) and from peers. Much of the activities in a typi-

cal kindergarten and first grade classrooms are of this type, and have the major advantages of typically speaking peers. Phase 5 suggests a shift back to more structured educational activities characteristic of typical later elementary classrooms.

In conclusion, both DTT and NET can be effective for teaching receptive and expressive language to children with autism. However, a functional analysis of the skills focused on in training shows that these two procedures target different types of expressive language. NET is primarily based on mand training by incorporating the child's current establishing operations and the delivery of specific reinforcement, while DTT is primarily based on tact, receptive, echoic, and imitative training by using nonverbal and verbal stimuli and nonspecific reinforcement. Intraverbal training is not a major focus of either approach, but is an essential type of verbal behavior. A more complete approach to teaching language to children with autism may consist of a combination of DTT and NET procedures, with Skinner's (1957) analysis of verbal behavior as a conceptual framework for the intervention program.

Chapter 14
Critical Elements of an Effective Educational Program

It is often a difficult task to find an appropriate educational program for a child with autism or a severe language delay. Typically there are a variety of special and regular education classrooms available in any given community; however, the parents' and educators' task is to consider all the options and determine which would be most beneficial for the child. In some situations, there may not be a single classroom environment that can provide all of the appropriate educational opportunities. Therefore, it may be necessary to provide educational services in more than one environment or create a truly individualized educational environment.

When considering the options, it is important to remember that there are several outcomes desired for any educational program. The most important outcome is that the child acquires skills that are both immediately useful to him and allow him to learn additional skills without highly trained staff and individualized instruction. Ideally, the child should acquire skills that enable him to learn from what he sees and hears every day, while interacting with a variety of individuals (e.g., aunts, uncles, neighbors, peers). In order to meet these goals, it is essential to identify an educational environment that can effectively teach the child.

Determining an appropriate educational environment involves a four-step process.

These steps include: (1) defining the child's needs, (2) reviewing the features of existing educational options (regular education and special education options), (3) reviewing the teaching skills of the instructional staff, and (4) selecting the best option or options for the child, including the possibility of adding consultation services (e.g., behavioral consultation, speech therapy, occupational therapy, inclusion specialist). These four steps will be discussed in more detail below.

Defining The Child's Needs

The child's educational needs should be defined through the development of an Individualized Education Program (IEP). Specific educational objectives that identify the skills the student should learn during the upcoming 6 to 12 months are the heart of the IEP. These IEP objectives should clearly identify specific skills that will be immediately useful to the child and result in the child being able to acquire additional skills without highly structured teaching.

The results of the assessment presented in Chapters 2 and 3 should provide the basis for many of the child's educational objectives (i.e., skills to be acquired). It may be appropriate to include one or several educational objectives for every area of the assessment in which the child did not receive the highest score for that area (See Chapter 3 for sample objectives). Additional objectives may also be included to further advance skills in those areas in which the maximum score was obtained and to address other areas that are not specifically targeted in this assessment (e.g., motor skills, self-help skills, disruptive behavior).

These written educational objectives should also clearly identify the behaviors that will be exhibited by the child in order to demonstrate that the skills have been acquired. It is also important to include the conditions under which the child will be expected to demonstrate the skills, and the measurable criteria to determine attainment of the objectives. Clearly specified objectives also make it possible to develop an on-going data collection system to track the child's progress. Additionally, the child's program should be periodically reviewed to determine if it is effective in teaching the child new skills.

Comparing Educational Programs

In most geographical areas, there are only a limited number of educational programs that may be available for a child with language delays. The options range from intensive home-based programs developed for a specific child to inclusion in a regular education classroom. Between these two extremes there is often a wide range of special education programs. These programs include both special schools and traditional self-contained, special education classrooms. Additionally, it is often possible to provide services utilizing a combination of these options.

All types of educational programs have certain features that may be either beneficial or detrimental for any individual child. A review of the advantages and disadvantages of four types of programs will be provided in an attempt to clarify some of the major distinctions between educational options. The types of teaching environments to be considered include: (1) intensive home-based instruction, (2) intensive individual instruction in a public or private school, (3) a typical special education classroom, and (4) inclusion within a regular classroom.

It should be noted that there are wide variations in the services that are delivered within each type of teaching environment. As such, it is impossible to identify exactly which type of classroom is appropriate for a particular child. However, it is hoped that by providing a description of these programs a more informed decision can be made.

Intensive Home-based Programs

One educational option that has recently emerged for young children with autism or severe language delays is an intensive home-based educational program. Many of these individualized programs have been established because of the lack of appropriate services available through the local school districts, and because of the published empirical research that has demonstrated the effectiveness of intensive home-based early intervention programs (Lovaas, 1987; McEachin, Smith, & Lovaas, 1993).

There are several major components of an intensive home-based educational program. In these programs, services are often provided on a one-student-to-one-instructor basis.

The services are typically provided for approximately 25 to 40 hours per week, with the majority of the instruction being provided in a databased, discrete trial learning format. The instructional personnel are often the child's parents and several college students who are interested in working with special education students, and who have received pre-service training on the instructional methodology and program for a particular child. The instructional program is designed and monitored by a consultant who has had advanced training in the instructional methods being utilized. Team meetings are scheduled on a regular basis (e.g., weekly) for all of the instructional team members to review the child's performance and to coordinate changes in the instructional program.

There are several advantages of this type of instructional program. One of the most important benefits is that the program is individualized to meet the needs of a particular child. Because the instructional staff do not need to respond to the needs of other students, specific procedures are developed and modified based solely upon the individual child's behavior and rate of skill acquisition. Some additional advantages of this type of instruction are that it allows for a high rate of responding by the child, and the parents are actively involved in the program so training can occur throughout the child's day.

Although the intensive home-based programs have been effective for many children, there are also disadvantages associated with this type of program. The most significant problems involve the locating, training, monitoring, and maintaining of the instructional staff and the child's lack of appropriate peer models for language and social interaction.

The assembly and maintenance of instructional staff is often a formidable task that requires a major parental commitment. Parents are often the ultimate team leaders for this type of program and frequently spend considerable amounts of time recruiting and scheduling staff to provide the services. The scheduling includes both the day-to-day delivery of services (e.g., when staff are sick, changes in the staffs' schedules), and the training of new staff when previously trained staff are no longer able to work with the child. The coordination of the instructors, both logistically and with regards to the continuing supervision and training, is reported by many parents to be a "full-time job."

Another concern is that frequent staff turnover often results in the use of individuals who have limited training and experience. Because many of the individuals employed to provide training have not had extensive instruction in the teaching methodology, many of the procedures that are implemented become limited in scope to ensure consistency across the various trainers. Additionally, changes in procedures are typically not made until the team meets to decide on the programmatic changes. As a result, the interventions may often miss naturally occurring motivational situations and miss opportunities for the generalization of the child's acquired skills.

The other major disadvantage of an intensive home-based program is the child's lack of peers. This issue may not initially be a critical factor for some children, but as a child acquires new skills, it is important to consider the availability of models of language, classroom routines, and social interaction with other children. Once a child is learning to attend to the actions of others, it is important to arrange for him to benefit from the models provided by other children. It is often difficult to arrange for peer interaction for a child who requires individual instruction and supervision. However, some contact can be made by involvement in community based programs (e.g., gymnastics, ice skating) or part-time enrollment in preschool programs.

Intensive Individualized School-based Programs

There are some classrooms in both private and public schools that are designed to provide a more intensive, individualized program than is found in a typical special education classroom. These types of programs usually provide data-based instruction delivered by staff with a high level of training. Services are usually provided with a low ratio of students to instructors (e.g., 1 or 2 students to each instructor). In general, this type of specialized instruction can provide considerable individualization in the teaching methods, but it like home-based programs, may lack models of appropriate behavior necessary to help develop subtle social interaction skills. The advantages and disadvantages of this type of classroom will be examined in more detail below.

There are several benefits of a highly individualized educational program. One benefit is that the staff have often received considerable amounts of specialized training. There is also immediate access to colleagues and specialists who can make timely recommendations regarding educational interventions for a specific child.

Another benefit of this type of special education program is the use of a low student-to-teacher ratio (e.g., 2 to 1). Because the staff have to attend to the needs of fewer children, they can work intensively on the development of specific skills for each child. They can also provide a much higher number of individualized training trials on critical skills than is possible in other types of classrooms. The limited number of children per instructor also makes it possible to easily adjust the program based upon the moment-to-moment changes in motivational conditions of the child, and to quickly deliver a wider variety of individualized reinforcers.

In the highly individualized educational program, it is often possible to provide a greater degree of consistency in responding to the child's behavior. Because there are fewer staff, it is usually easier to arrange for greater precision in the use of prompts, error correction procedures, and reinforcers used in teaching. Thus, it is possible to rapidly teach new skills because the educational staff can consistently require and reinforce the highest level of responding. Additionally, because there are fewer children affected by instances of disruptive behavior, it is often easier to ensure that these undesired behaviors do not get reinforced.

While there are advantages of a highly individualized educational program, there are also some disadvantages. Although the program may be effective in rapidly teaching new skills, this type of environment often does not have models of language and social interactions exhibited by typically developing peers. This lack of peers may result in fewer opportunities for the development of generalized language and social interaction skills.

In addition, in a highly individualized educational program, the number and types of words and objects used in teaching sessions are often limited. This limitation of words and objects may be beneficial for some children because it allows a child to acquire new skills that may never be acquired unless presented in such a specific manner. However, this same feature may be detrimental to a child who quickly acquires new responses and benefits from the immediate generalization of the response across a wide variety of items and activities. For example, when children in less specialized classes discuss the topic "dogs," their discussion may include a variety of words such as "K-9's," "Dalmatians," "Poodles," "mutts," "the pound," "strays," "mangy," etc. A child who is able to quickly learn new words may miss out on that learning opportunity if he is only exposed to simpler words such as "Says woof, woof," "Eats a bone," "Barks," etc.

Another disadvantage with the highly individualized educational program is that it provides limited occasions for social interaction with typically developing peers. However, similar to the children who participate in home-based instruction, it is often the case that many children also lack the skills used during the interaction process (e.g., the child doesn't attend to others, he has no method of letting his needs and wants be known, he can't follow directions, he actively resists being prompted to do an activity). For such children, the lack of appropriate models and peers with which to interact may not be immediately critical. However, other children who do directly benefit from observing peer models and from engaging in social interactions with peers may miss out on the opportunity to develop a wide variety of social skills.

Finally, a highly structured environment often does not teach the child how to adjust to changes in routines. By its design, the highly structured classroom or teaching situation has a consistent schedule of learning activities. This type of schedule may be critical for some children to acquire skills; however, it may not help the child learn to adapt to the changes that are characteristic of less structured learning environments.

Traditional Special Education Classroom

There is usually a wide range of special education classrooms available in most communities. These classrooms usually share several common characteristics, although the composition of the students and the focus of the educational activities may vary considerably between the classrooms. The typical special education classroom is often comprised of approximately 10 to 12 students, and is staffed by one teacher and one or two instructional assistants. In most situations, the main format of teaching involves small group instruction, and these classrooms are typically located on regular education campuses.

The special education classroom provides several important advantages for a child with special needs. The group instruction model used in these classrooms may foster generalization because discussions are loosely structured allowing for the acquisition of a variety of language skills related to the classroom activities and topics of conversation. Also, the daily classroom routines provide the opportunity for the child to learn to follow the actions of the other students without relying on adults to lead him from one activity to the next. In addition, the special education classroom staff will usually tolerate some disruptive behavior that is not readily accepted in regular education classrooms. Finally, the availability of access to interactions with typically developing peers can provide numerous models of language and social interaction skills.

However, there are several aspects of the traditional special education classroom that may result in this educational option not being appropriate for some children. Although special education staff have usually had classes or training in providing instruction to students with various disabilities, they have usually not had intensive training in behavior modification nor the behavioral approach to language instruction. There are often staff consultants with greater amounts of expertise who can provide additional input; however, the availability for providing input for a particular child is often very limited. Additionally, because of the higher ratio of students to instructors (e.g., 4 or 6 to 1), there is an emphasis on

small group instruction, thus not much individual instruction is available for any particular student. As such, the child with severe language delays often does not receive a high enough rate of teaching trials necessary to acquire many language skills. In addition, since it is difficult to take individualized data in this teaching model, it is sometimes difficult to determine what the children are learning.

Inclusion in Regular Education

Historically, children with severe language delays have been educated in special education classrooms that provided minimal, if any, contact with typically developing peers. More recently, a wide range of options have evolved that allow children with language delays to participate in educational opportunities with typically developing peers. This range of options includes having regular education students participate in the learning activities of a child with language delays, having the child participate in some of the regular education students' academic and non-academic activities, and having the child with language delays fully participate in a regular education classroom. Any of these options could include the child participating either independently or with the assistance of a 1:1 instructional aide.

Probably one of the greatest advantages of inclusion in a regular education classroom is the ongoing models of typical language and social interactions. Effective communication involves a number of social skills that a child needs to develop. It is not only important to have the right words to say, but also to have the skills of knowing how and when to say those words. For some children, being included in an environment in which these subtle skills are constantly modeled increases the probability that these skills will be acquired. The interactions with typical peers provide numerous models of appropriate language for the child to imitate. There are a wide variety of words and inflections used during common classroom tasks and numerous models of interacting with others. These models may be beneficial for the acquisition of subtle social interaction skills that may not be observed in highly structured environments.

Although there are advantages to participation in regular educational programs, there are also some disadvantages (Chesley & Calaluce, 1997). Perhaps the most significant disadvantage for the autistic or severely language-delayed child is the decreased ability to provide individualized instruction. For some children, full or partial inclusion may not result in the child to acquiring the basic language skills, because these rudimentary skills are not the major focus of the regular education program.

Even though the regular education classroom is rich with models of language and social interactions, the child who does not have basic communication skills may not attend to the critical aspects of these models, and therefore may not be successful in acquiring these skills. Additionally, if attempts are made to teach the basic communication skills in the regular education classroom, the educational staff are typically inadequately trained in the specialized methodology necessary to teach those skills.

Even if the staff have the skills to teach language, managing the learning process in a regular education classroom is a complex task. It is often difficult to make the necessary accommodations for the child with severe language delays. There is very little time for individual instruction, and it is also difficult to deliver individualized reinforcers and to capture the motivation of an individual child to encourage participation in language instruction activities.

Another potential problem with inclusion programs is that peers typically do not have the skills required to help the child with severe language delays. Special training, such as how to use and fade prompts is usually required in order for the peers to actually help the child. Peers who may be attempting to "help" a child may actually be over-prompting and essentially doing the task for the child with language delays. The peers must be taught the importance of only using prompts when actually necessary and fading those prompts as soon as possible. Without such training, the child with severe language delays may never learn to respond independently.

Finally, in regular education classrooms, there is less tolerance of disruptive behaviors because of the negative impact on the other children in the classroom. In addition, without appropriate training, the natural reactions of peers may unintentionally increase undesirable behaviors. For example, when a child engages in disruptive behavior when he is not allowed access to a certain item, the typically developing peer may directly reinforce the behavior by providing the child with the desired item such as to make the child "feel better." Thus the peer's attempts to "help" may actually increase instances of disruptive behavior, and therefore decrease the likelihood that the child will be successful in a regular education classroom.

Summary of Educational Programs Review

There are a variety of potential educational environments for children with severe language delays. However, each option has both advantages and disadvantages, depending upon the needs of the individual child. Clearly, it is important to identify those aspects of the educational environment that are the most important to the child at his current level of skill development. Once the most advantageous type of instructional environment has been identified, it is still necessary to review the available classrooms that provide that type of environment and to determine which classroom can meet the needs of the child.

Reviewing Potential Programs

There are several factors that should be considered when reviewing a classroom or program in relation to the needs of a particular child (Table 14-1). These issues include the classroom curriculum, the philosophy of the classroom, skills of the instructional staff, compatibility with the existing student population, and administrative aspects of the classroom environment.

The Classroom Curriculum

It is important that the chosen classroom have a specific written curriculum that matches the needs of the child. The curriculum should include a structured sequence of skills that is consistent with the skill level of the child, and it should allow for the tracking of child's progress in acquiring those skills.

The child should have a clearly specified and measurable set of educational objectives that should allow for an on-going review of the child's progress in relation to those objectives and the classroom curriculum. In addition, the curriculum should allow for the individualization and adjustment of the learning activities based upon the child's progress. This flexibility in the learning activities is critical to ensure that the instruction is able to be adjusted according to the changing needs of the individual child.

Table 14-1
Educational Options Survey

Classroom: _____   **Date:** _____

School: _____

Teacher: _____   **Time observation started:** _____

Type of classroom: _____   **Time observation ended:** _____

Classroom environment
Is the physical layout of the classroom conducive to skill acquisition?
Are there any other factors which may interfere with the learning process?
Are the furniture, materials, and restrooms appropriate for the child?

Staff & students
How many students are in the classroom?
How many instructional staff are in the classroom?
What are the characteristics of students in the classroom?
Are the other children in the classroom a reasonable match for the child?
Do the students exhibit excessive disruptive behavior that may interfere with teaching and learning?

Schedule & curriculum
What is the orientation of the curriculum (e.g., academic, self-help, community-based, language-based)?
Is there a clearly defined classroom schedule?
Does the schedule allow adequate amounts of time to teach critical skills?
Do the staff appear to know and follow the classroom schedule?
Does the classroom curriculum match the needs of the child?
Are there skills that the child needs to learn that can't be addressed within the classroom?

Teaching process
Do the children and staff in the classroom appear to be happy?
Do the children appear to be motivated to during teaching sessions?
Do the staff provide frequent praise to the students?
Do the staff appear to be able to competently handle the learning activities for the students?
If there are instances of disruptive behavior, do the staff appear to handle the situation appropriately?
Are data being collected on skill acquisition?
Are the students given clear instructions during teaching sessions?
Are the children required to actively and frequently respond during teaching sessions?

Table 14-1
Educational Options Survey

Teaching process (Continued)

Do the instructors provide a high rate of reinforcement for correct responses?

Do the instructors provide a high rate of praise or other reinforcement for appropriate social behavior (Catch the children being good)?

Do the staff use prompts as needed and appear to be fading the use of those prompts?

Is teaching occurring in both structured and non-structured situations?

Does there appear to be instructional programming for the generalization of acquired skills?

Do the staff intersperse easy and more difficult tasks in teaching sessions?

Do the staff use alternative forms of communication (e.g., ASL, picture communication)?

Was there active teaching of requesting skills?

Was there active teaching of labeling skills?

Was there active teaching of conversational skills?

Was there active teaching of receptive language skills?

Was there a mixture of the various types of verbal responses required in teaching sessions (i.e., not only one type of response required in a session)?

Consultation & support staff

If the classroom staff need advanced input, who would provide it?

What is the availability of those consultants?

What support staff are available to the classroom?

    Behavior Specialist

    Speech Therapist

    Occupational Therapist[

    Integration specialist

How much time do the consultants spend in the classroom?

Questions to ask about the program

What is the length of instructional day?

How many school days are there in the school year?

Is the summer program the same or different from regular school year?

Will students be leaving or entering the classroom soon?

Are there opportunities for integration with regular education students?

Who will be responsible for monitoring the child's skill acquisition?

What opportunities are there for parents to learn new teaching skills?

How do the educational staff and parents share information regarding the child's skill acquisition?

Classroom Orientation

All educational environments have a certain focus that guides the delivery of instruction. For example, the primary focus of most regular education classrooms is on teaching academic skills. Special education classrooms, however, vary considerably in their focus and philosophical orientation. Some special education classes place an emphasis on academic skills while other classrooms emphasize functional skills (e.g., self-help skills) and community-based instruction (e.g., how to utilize existing community services). Other classrooms emphasize vocational skills or focus on participation in a regular education environment as the major instructional activities, while some classrooms emphasize teaching language skills. Thus it is important to identify these differences and match the child's needs with the specific program. It should be pointed that often parents are assured that since the IEP is "individualized" that the child's needs will be met. However, rarely is it the case that the main focus of a classroom will truly change for a single child.

Philosophy of the Staff /Teacher in Control of Acquisition

One of the most critical aspects of any educational program relates to the staff's analysis of their control over the learning process. "Teaching" refers to the ability to expedite the learning process of the child. Many individuals can provide "an enriched environment" and "opportunities" for children to acquire skills, and all children can learn to some extent. However, to actually "teach" language skills, one must be an effective behavior shaper. Some instructors view the child's skill acquisition as being a direct result of their teaching activities. This orientation suggests that most children can acquire skills if it is possible to identify the appropriate teaching strategies. These instructors often believe that the child may or may not be able to "catch-up" to other children of the same age, but believe the learning process is greatly influenced by the instructional staff teaching activities. Other instructors view the child's lack of progress as less indicative of their teaching skills, but rather more of a result of factors beyond their control (e.g., biological limitations, cognitive impairments, poor parental practices, or simply a result of the disabling condition).

Basic Behavior Modification

Effective teaching occurs when staff believe they actively shape the child's skills, and the staff have strong basic behavior modification skills. In order to effectively teach new skills, instructors (e.g., teacher, instructional assistants, speech therapists) must have specific teaching competencies required to teach skills (including language skills), and they must teach in a manner that maintains the child's motivation to participate in the learning process. It is beyond the scope of this chapter to address all of the factors related to the analysis of behavior and behavior modification techniques. There are numerous texts available for individuals to learn more about these specific skills (e.g., Cooper, Heron, & Heward, 1987; Martin & Pear, 1995).

Augmentative Communication

The educational staff should be capable of teaching non-vocal methods of communication (as described in Chapter 4) to those children who cannot speak. Although vocal communication should be the goal of language instruction, the use of sign language or a picture-based system of communication may provide a necessary bridge to speech and language to some children. Thus the educational staff's skills in teaching these non-vocal methods of communication are critical for the non-vocal child.

Language Analysis and Teaching Skills

In order to provide effective instruction to the language-delayed child, the staff must be knowledgeable in the methods of teaching language skills. The teaching staff should be able to arrange for a child to develop all types of the verbal responses such that the child can say a word (or use American Sign Language) to request an item (mand), name the item (tact), talk about the item (intraverbal), etc. As is described throughout this book, once the child has acquired a particular response, it is possible to teach several new verbal skills by carefully changing some of the words used in the instructions or the materials presented to the child. The ability to systematically change the task and capitalize on the opportunity to teach language during ongoing daily situations is essential to the development of effective verbal skills. The staff must also program for generalization to avoid rote responding and to develop a functional set of verbal skills. The educational staff should also foster spontaneous language by the child, because the child who initiates an interaction has a greater opportunity for participation in social situations than the child who only responds when required to respond.

The Classroom Environment

In addition to the staff's teaching skills, there are a number of other factors related to an effective educational environment. These factors include the staff-to-child ratio, the length of the instructional day, the number of school days in the academic year, the classroom's daily schedule, the physical layout of classroom, the availability of parent education and classroom involvement, data collection regarding the acquisition of skills, the availability of appropriate peer models, and the extent to which the staff are required to implement behavior reduction programs for other children in the classroom who exhibit disruptive behavior. Although some issues related to these factors were discussed earlier, a review of these specific factors is presented below.

Staff-to-Student Ratio

The classroom should provide adequate staffing and a sufficient amount of instructional time for the children. If the classroom is staffed at a ratio of 1 teacher and 1 instructional assistant to 12 children, it is virtually impossible to provide appropriate services to a child who does not learn in group-teaching situations. If a child only responds to instructions that are presented directly to him, and only when he is fully attending to the instructor, participation in learning activities will only occur when the ratio of instruction is at or near 1 staff to 1 or 2 children.

Length of the Instructional Day

The length of the child's school day is another important variable in an effective program. In order to acquire effective communication skills, it is often necessary to provide several hundred teaching trials under a wide variety of conditions each day. A child with severe language delays who is only provided with a few hours (i.e., two or three hours) of instruction by competent teaching staff is not likely to make adequate progress.

It is sometimes argued that a young child can't tolerate a long day at school (e.g., 5 hours per day). This argument is often indicative of the failure to adapt the teaching strategies to meet the needs of the child. Although young children often take naps during the day, they are typically active and exploring their environment many hours each day. While it might be unreasonable to require the child to sit at a table or in a small group situation for many hours, the instruction can be arranged in a less structured manner.

Number of School Days in the Academic Year

The number of days is the school year is an important factor for many children. Although regular education programs are typically 180 days per year, this schedule may not be adequate for a child who does not consistently maintain newly acquired skills. Many children with language delays will

lose new skills in a few days if they do not use those skills. In such situations, a break in the school schedule of four or more weeks can result in a major setback for some children. Therefore, for those children, it is critical that the school year be constructed such that there are no major breaks in the school year, and no major changes in the staff or educational strategies used during the summer months.

In many school systems, the instruction provided during the summer months varies considerably from the services provided during the regular school year. For those children who require highly structured teaching in order to acquire new skills, it is important to ensure that there is consistency in the instruction throughout the year.

Classroom's Daily Schedule

Another important environmental variable in the classroom is the child's daily schedule. In order to increase the child's on-task time during the school day, it is necessary to strategically schedule specific activities between table tasks and non-table tasks. It is also critical to vary the tasks according to both the level of difficulty for a child and according to the type of responses required for the task. For example, many children will frequently begin to "go off-task" if a learning session lasts for too long. The amount of time before the child is no longer actively responding varies according to the amount of reinforcement obtained, the child's success, and the difficulty of the task. Tasks that are difficult for the child should be relatively short in duration and interspersed between sessions in which the tasks are generally easier for the child. For many young children, it is often beneficial to change learning activities approximately every 15 to 30 minutes.

Scheduled changes in types of activities are also an important issue. For example, when children are required to come into the classroom for teaching sessions after being outdoors for recess, the transition is often difficult because the children are required to go from a highly reinforcing activity (i.e., self-determined play) that involves a considerable amount of movement (e.g., running, swinging) to a situation in which the staff require the child to sit quietly and attend to the teacher. One method of lessening the contrast is to have the children return to an activity that is either highly reinforcing table task (e.g., snack, child determined activity), or to an activity that allows the child to move while doing a task (e.g., an art project in which he may need to gather materials).

The sequencing of the educational tasks is also an important variable that affects the acquisition of skills. Typically, children will be able to remain "on-task" longer if their tasks vary in terms of level of difficulty (i.e., not all difficult tasks presented in a row). A sequence of too many difficult tasks often results in the child engaging in "off-task behaviors" or disruptive behaviors to escape from the learning tasks.

Physical Layout of the Classroom

The physical layout of the classroom is also a factor related to skill acquisition. Many children with language delays are easily distracted by the actions of others. A classroom in which the child is able to view the activities of others may not be conducive to learning. For such children, it may be helpful to minimize the child's visual field when the child is participating in a learning task. The strategic positioning of room dividers (e.g., bookcases, toy shelves, partitions), and the positioning of the child such that his visual field is away from the activities of others, can result in a more productive learning environment.

Parent Education and Involvement

Parents play a major role in the development of a child's skills. Therefore, in order for the educational program to be successful, it is very important that the parents be involved in the program. No matter how sophisticated the teaching strategies may be, it is important that the parents help their child use or further develop his skills at home and in the community. At a minimum, parents should know what the child knows, and what the child is currently learning at school, so they can maintain and generalize the child's skills. Ideally, provisions should be made (e.g., parent education classes) to allow parents to acquire teaching skills they wish to learn, such as to ensure the highest level of consistency with the child.

Skill Acquisition Data

In order to ensure the effectiveness of the instruction, it is important to document the child's acquisition of skills. Although skill acquisition can occur in the absence of data collection systems, data allow the teacher to determine if their intervention strategies are working. Teachers who maintain data on skill acquisition can make timely adjustments in the teaching methods and avoid extended periods of time using ineffective educational interventions. Additionally, data also helps to ensure that when the child acquires a skill he can rapidly move onto the next area in the curriculum.

Disruptive Student Behavior

One final factor affecting a child's rate of learning is the behavior of the other children in the classroom. When the children follow the teacher's directions and classroom routines, the teacher can teach the children. However, in some situations, the competent teacher is assigned too many children who exhibit disruptive behavior. Although the teacher has the technical skills to be an effective teacher, the frequency of incidents that require immediate and intensive intervention often result in an inability to provide instruction to the children.

Decision Making: Selecting The Best Option

One of the most critical decisions for a child's IEP team is the selection of the appropriate learning environment for meeting the child's educational needs. The decision regarding placement and services will ultimately determine both what and how much the child will learn. Therefore, it is extremely important that the team make a decision based upon the child's needs and upon all of the possible options for meeting those needs.

Once the child's learning needs have been identified, and the existing options have been reviewed and considered, the next step is to select an educational environment. The options include selecting one of the existing environments, creating a unique learning environment, or arranging for participation in a combination of learning environments. The decision is easy if there currently exists an environment in which the educational staff have the necessary skills, the environment is appropriate for the child, and an opening exists within that particular classroom. However, there is often not a direct match between the child's needs and the options currently available within the educational system.

When a direct match between the child's needs and existing options is not available, there are two alternative arrangements that should be considered. These options include a combination of educational environments and services or the creation of a unique educational environment. Although both of these alternatives are usually more difficult to establish and maintain, they may be necessary for a certain period of time.

The main consideration for the selection of any educational environment should be what the child will be able to learn in that environment. Ideally, the child should be learning skills that allow him to learn from his everyday experiences, such that specialized instruction is not required for the acquisition of new skills. No matter how nice the environment seems (e.g., the staff are "caring" individuals, the peers are "accepting and helpful"), the critical issue is whether the child will learn the skills he needs to learn. If the environment can't accomplish this task, it is not an appropriate option.

Because skill acquisition is the main issue for the educational environment, it is absolutely essential that the teacher's skills, and her ability to use those skills, be considered the most important factor in the decision making process. In many situations, a skilled teacher could teach a critical skill in a matter of days or weeks, whereas other less skilled teachers may never be able to teach the skill.

If one or more teachers have the ability to teach the critical skills to the child, the next important decision is whether the instructor's environment will allow for the child to learn those skills. Almost all special education classrooms provide instruction that varies to some degree from the primary focus of the classroom. Specifically, some modifications can be made within any individual classroom to help accommodate the needs of individual learners. However, it is important that the required adjustments are not so great as to disrupt the learning of the other children and does not require radical shifts in the teaching activities. In general, it is desirable to have a fairly close match between the needs of the individual being considered and the needs of the other children in the existing classroom.

If the teacher has the necessary skills and the classroom provides reasonably close match between the child's needs and the needs of the other children in the class, the placement in the classroom may serve as the major foundation of the educational program. Additional consultation services (i.e., behavioral consultation, speech therapy,

occupational therapy) may be required to help address some of the needs of the child.

However, if the teacher can teach the critical skills, but doesn't have the environment to meet many of the needs of the child, other options must be considered. One possible option is for the educational program to be conducted in more than one environment. Some of the educational services can be provided by the skilled instructor in the "less than ideal" environment, so as to ensure that critical skills are acquired, while some of the child's day is spent in a different environment (e.g., with socially appropriate peers but in an environment in which the critical skills would not be acquired due to the lack of effective teaching opportunities).

A second option is to arrange for effective services to be provided in the more appropriate social environment. Although this option may appear to be an easy solution, it can often fail because the specialized teaching methodology may not be acquired by the educational staff, or because the adjustments in the overall focus of the instruction is too great for that classroom. Therefore, before this option is implemented, it is important to have a clear commitment from all individuals involved to provide the necessary behavior and resources to make the option successful.

In some situations, none of the options listed above will seem likely to produce the critical learning outcomes for the child. In this situation, it may be most appropriate to design an effective short-term educational program to teach those skills that will allow the child to successfully learn in one of the other programs. It may be necessary to develop the highly individualized program with the input of individuals who are experts in the specific instruction required by the child. The establishment of this type of program is often very labor intensive in that it involves establishing a totally unique program. Once established, these types of programs can be very difficult to maintain because the program is based upon the participation of individuals with specific teaching skills. The loss of certain key staff can result in a failure of the program. Additionally, because the program is often not a regular part of the educational system, monitoring of the child's progress is often a concern. However, in spite of these disadvantages, this option may be the only one available to effectively produce the desired learning outcomes for the child.

In summary, there are three key issues with respect to selecting an appropriate environment for a child. The first issue is the identification of critical skills that the child must learn in order to acquire additional skills without highly specialized instruction. The second issue is what types of environment(s) and additional services are or can be made available to teach those skills. The third, and probably most important factor, concerns the teaching skills of the instructional staff. It is possible to have well defined educational objectives, an appropriate type of educational environment, and still make little or no progress in the development of the critical skills because of a teacher's inability to effectively teach those skills. The acquisition of those critical skills is the determinant of the success in the child's educational career, and it is one of the most important determinants of his partici-

pation in, and enjoyment of, family and community activities throughout his life.

Reviewing the Outcomes: A Continual Process

The process of determining an appropriate educational environment is not a singular decision to be made for the child. Rather, it is necessary to continually make decisions during the child's school years in order to arrange a progression of environments in which the educational emphasis changes as the child's needs change. Parents are consumers of educational services for their child. The task of selecting appropriate educational services will continue throughout the child's educational career. However, at each point in the child's development, decisions must be made regarding the appropriate educational placement for that moment.

One of the most important aspects involved in the decision making process is that of continually attending to both the learning needs of the child and to the rate of skill acquisition. Although it is often possible to become too concerned with each day's skill development, it is also possible to not adequately monitor the changes that are occurring. There will undoubtedly be many days in which it appears as if there is no skill acquisition; however, there should not be several months in which there is not an increase in the critical skills. The careful review of the acquisition of skills in relation to the overall goal of the program is an ongoing process, which should occur on an informal basis at least every other month. By carefully observing the rate of skill acquisition in relation to the educational objectives, it is possible to make changes or adjustments in the program. Those changes may be necessary to arrange for the interventions to become more effective in teaching the critical skills, or hopefully, may be necessary because the child has learned skills that will now allow him to effectively learn in a higher-level educational setting.In 1957 B. F.

Appendix:
A Behavioral Approach to Language

Skinner wrote the book *Verbal Behavior*. In this book Skinner provided an analysis of language based on the same environmental principles of behavior he previously used to analyze nonverbal behavior (Skinner, 1938, 1953). Readers may recall that it was Skinner's analysis of nonverbal behavior that lead to the field commonly known as behavior modification. In his treatment of language, Skinner proposes that language is *behavior* that is primarily caused by environmental variables such as reinforcement, motivation, extinction, and punishment. This view of language differs substantially from other views that assume language is primarily caused by cognitive or biological variables (e.g., Brown, 1973; Chomsky, 1957; Neisser, 1978; Piaget, 1926; Pinker, 1994). While the arguments over what causes language continue, the theory that has produced the most effective applied results for children with autism or other developmental disabilities is Skinner's behavioral approach (Maurice, Green, & Luce, 1996).

The behavioral approach analyzes language by its formal and functional properties (Catania, 1974; Skinner, 1957). The formal properties of language consist of the physical description of specific response topographies, or classes of responses (e.g., nouns, verbs, adjectives, pronouns). It also includes the syntactical order of phrases, and adherence to grammatical conventions. The formal properties of verbal behavior also include articulation, intonation, pitch, emphasis, and so on. The functional properties of verbal behavior consist of the circumstances under which responses occur, more specifically, an analysis of the discriminative stimuli, establishing operations (motivation), and consequences that control a response, or class of responses (also known as pragmatics).

In Skinner's (1957) analysis of verbal behavior he distinguished between several different types of functional control. This analysis has resulted in a classification system that allows for the identification of these functionally different types of language. Based on this system, Skinner (1957) identified and named these verbal relations (see Table A-1). In addition to receptive language, he presents the following types of expressive behavior: echoic (and imitation), mand, tact, intraverbal, textual, and transcriptive (spelling). A brief description of these separate language repertoires will be presented below.

Table A-1 — The Behavioral Classification of Language

Receptive	Following instructions or complying with the mands of others. A tendency to touch a picture of a dog when asked to touch the dog.
Echoic	Repeating what is heard. A tendency to say "dog" after someone else says "dog."
Imitation	Copying someone's motor movements. A tendency to clap after someone else claps.
Tact	Naming or identifying objects, actions, events, etc. A tendency to say "dog" because you see a dog.
Mand	Asking for reinforcers that you want. A tendency to ask for a dog because you want one.
RFFC	Identifying specific items when given some description (its function, features, or class) of the item. A tendency to touch a dog when someone says "Which one barks?"
Intraverbal	Answering questions or conversations where your words are controlled by other words. A tendency to say "dog" when someone else says "Lassie."
Textual	Reading written words. A tendency to say "dog" because you see the written word "dog."
Writing	Writing and spelling words when spoken to you. A tendency to write "dog" because you hear it spoken.

Receptive Language and Receptive by Function, Feature, and Class (RFFC)

Receptive language consists of nonverbally responding to the language of others. This skill is often identified as the behavior of a listener. Hearing someone say "Touch the chair" while touching the chair is an example of receptive language. Many children with language delays have a substantial amount of receptive language, but lack many of the expressive types of language presented below. Another aspect of receptive language is the ability to identify objects, actions, etc., when they are not specifically named, but rather described or identified in some other way such as by the features of an item. For example, the ability to touch a turtle when someone says "What animal has a shell?" is a receptive response, but it is controlled by a feature of the object rather than the specific name of the object. Many children with language delays are unable to emit this more complicated type of receptive language.

The Echoic Repertoire

In the echoic relation the stimulus is auditory and the response is speaking (echoing what one hears). The consequences for echoic behavior consist of nonspecific conditioned reinforcement (Table A-2). Saying "apple" after someone else says "apple" is an example of echoic behavior. In the process of acquiring a verbal repertoire, a child learns to echo the sounds and words of others. The ability to duplicate these sounds is essential in learning to identify objects, actions, and so on. "An echoic repertoire is established in the child through 'educational' reinforcement because it is useful to the parents, educators, and others" (Skinner, 1957, p. 56). For example, if a child can say "bear" (or a reasonable approximation) after a parent says "bear," then it becomes possible to teach the child to say "bear" in the presence of the bear by using a transfer of stimulus control procedure. A parent might say, "That's a bear, can you say bear?" If the child can respond "bear," then the parent says "Right, now what is that?" Eventually, the child will learn to say "bear" without an echoic prompt. This often occurs in only a few trials. The echoic repertoire is very important for teaching language to children with language delays. Many children can echo sounds and words, but frequently the words do not occur "spontaneously" or under the desired type of control. In addition, the echoic repertoire can be very useful in teaching more advanced forms of language as well as improving articulation.

Table A-2 — Technical Definitions of Skinner's (1957) Elementary Verbal Operants

CONTROLLING VARIABLES	RESPONSE	CONSEQUENCE
Verbal stimulus with point-to-point correspondence and formal similarity	Echoic Imitation Copying-a-text	Nonspecific reinforcement
Nonverbal stimulus	Tact	Nonspecific reinforcement
Establishing operations	Mand	Specific reinforcement
Verbal stimulus without point-to point correspondence or formal similarity	Intraverbal	Nonspecific reinforcement
Verbal stimulus with point-to-point correspondence, but without formal similarity	Textual Transcriptive	Nonspecific reinforcement
Verbal stimulus	Nonverbal behavior (Receptive language)	Nonspecific reinforcement

The Imitation Repertoire

The echoic repertoire involves the vocal musculature while the imitative repertoire involves the fine and gross motor movements of the skeletal muscles. The tendency to stand up when some one else stands up exemplifies gross motor imitation. The tendency to touch your ear when someone else touches his ear exemplifies fine motor imitation. In imitation the stimulus is visual (verses the auditory stimulus of the echoic) and the response is visual (verses the auditory response of the echoic).

Perhaps the most obvious linguistic use of the imitation repertoire is in facilitating the acquisition of sign language. Imitation is extremely important for the deaf population and plays a major role in sign language acquisition for a deaf child with deaf signing parents. The imitation repertoire has the same functional properties as the echoic repertoire, and can help a deaf child acquire the names of objects, actions, relations, and so on. Imitation is also critical for the teaching of sign language to hearing children who are nonvocal. Many children do not have a strong enough echoic repertoire for vocal language instruction, and a lot of time is spent on teaching echoic behavior rather than more useful types of verbal behavior. A strong imitative repertoire can allow an instructor to immediately begin working on teaching more advanced forms of language by using sign language. This can allow a child to almost immediately communicate with others without using inappropriate behavior as a response form.

The Tact Repertoire

Skinner (1957, pp. 81-146) suggested the term "tact" as a descriptor for the type of verbal relation in which the form of the response is controlled by a prior nonverbal stimulus (Table A-2). Saying "chair" in the presence of a chair is a tact. The consequences for the tact, like those for echoic and imitative behavior, usually involve some type of conditioned reinforcement (or nonspecific reinforcement). In common sense terms, the tact can be thought of as naming the physical features of the environment. The nonverbal environment consists of objects (nouns), actions (verbs), relations (prepositions), properties of objects and actions (adjectives and adverbs), and so on. There are a great number of nonverbal stimuli in the environment, and these nonverbal stimuli can affect any one of the different sensory systems (e.g., we can name things we see, hear, smell, taste, touch, etc.).

The Mand Repertoire

The mand (Skinner, 1957, pp. 35-51) is a type of verbal relation where the form of the response is controlled by a motivational variable such as deprivation or aversive stimulation (Table A-2). Michael (1982a, 1988, 1993) has termed these motivational variables "establishing operations" (EOs). The consequences for the mand are quite different from those for the other types of verbal relations in that the mand specifies what would function as reinforcement for the speaker (the consequence is specific to the establishing operation). In common sense terms, the mand is a type of verbal behavior where the speaker asks for what he wants.

A child's tendency to say "When are we going to eat?" is a mand where the form of the response is controlled by the motivational variable of food deprivation, and the reinforcing consequences of food are specific to food deprivation.

The mand becomes a strong form of verbal behavior because of the specific reinforcement characteristic of this verbal relation, and the fact that this reinforcement often satisfies a strong deprivation condition or removes some aversive stimulus. A child very quickly learns how to ask for what he needs or wants. Asking for help, directions, instructions, and for information are mands, as are most other questions asked by children and adults. Manding often gets something, hence it is said that the mand directly benefits the speaker by allowing him to directly control the behavior of a listener, while satisfying personal establishing operations by obtaining specific reinforcement. In addition, much of the negative behavior observed in children who have limited verbal abilities may be mands.

The Intraverbal Repertoire

Intraverbal behavior allows a speaker to talk about objects and events even though those objects and events are not physically present. In order to be an effective speaker, a person must acquire this repertoire. For example, a speaker would be very limited if he could only identify animals when they were present and not when someone said "What animal lives in the water?" or "What animal has a long neck?" Technically, the intraverbal (Skinner, 1957, pp. 71-78) is a type of verbal relation where the form of the

response is controlled by antecedent verbal stimuli that lacks point-to-point correspondence to the response. That is, the stimulus and the response do not match. The consequences for the intraverbal usually involves some form of conditioned reinforcement (Table A-2). Some examples of intraverbal behavior would be the tendency to respond "dog" when asked to name an animal, "apple" when asked to name a fruit, or "California" when asked to name a state.

A large number of children with language delays have strong receptive skills, and strong tact repertoires, but weak mand and intraverbal skills. The importance of the mand and intraverbal repertoires in everyday verbal interactions is frequently underestimated in the language training programs currently available for children with autism or other developmental disabilities. The emphasis in many programs is on extensive receptive training and expressive training, which mainly focuses on the development of the tact repertoire. When a child has virtually no vocal behavior, it is very common to provide receptive language training rather than pursue a new response topography such as sign language. However, when sign language training is provided, it often only involves programs that focus primarily on receptive skills and tacting. And when a typical verbal repertoire fails to develop, the blame is placed on the child's handicapping condition, the inadequacies of sign language, or the failure of behavior modification techniques. Rarely is the problem identified as the failure to teach mands and intraverbals along with tacts. This is an example of the importance of behavioral theory as a guide to language assessment and training.

A common situation in work with language-delayed children is that a child can emit hundreds of words/signs for objects and actions (tacts) but "rarely uses his words/signs" or fails to talk/sign "spontaneously." A more careful analysis of each child's verbal repertoire may show that his verbal behavior is under the strong stimulus control of the nonverbal stimulus and a verbal prompt by the instructor (e.g., What is that?"). The response has not been effectively transferred to other types of control, specifically, to establishing operations and to verbal stimuli that lack point-to-point correspondence to the response. For example, a person who has been trained the receptive skill of touching a bike when asked "Can you find the bike?" and to sign "bike" when shown a bike, or picture of a bike (tact), and asked "What is this?" will not necessarily be able to sign bike when one is a strong form of reinforcement but absent (mand), or when someone says "What has two wheels?" (intraverbal). These two verbal relations (mand and intraverbal) are under a type of control that is often not visible or identifiable to a listener, hence are termed "spontaneous" as if there were no control, or as if some internal cognitive device was active. These views typically hinder progress in acquiring verbal behavior because they mask the appropriate environmental controlling variables.

The Textual Repertoire

In the textual relation a vocal response is controlled by a visual written stimulus (either cursive, printed, typed, or fingerspelled), and there is a match (point-to-point correspondence) between the stimulus and the response product (Table A-2). The consequence for this type of language is also conditioned reinforcement. In common sense terms, this is reading out loud (without any implications that the reader "understands" what is being read). In some respects, textual behavior is like echoic behavior except the stimulus and the response product are in different sense modes, and do not physically resemble each other. Seeing the word "apple" written on the board and saying "apple" is a lot harder than simply copying the word "apple." Transforming a written word to a spoken word is obviously a difficult repertoire exemplified by the fact that so many people have strong mand, tact, and intraverbal repertoires, but are illiterate. A behavioral analysis of this repertoire and the use of behavioral procedures could greatly change this situation.

Textual behavior is often viewed as complex behavior that is beyond the reach of many children with language delays. However, textual behavior can be acquired by bringing a vocal response under the control of a written stimulus. Transfer of stimulus control procedures are very effective in teaching this repertoire. If a person can say "apple" when he sees an apple, it is often not to difficult to transfer stimulus control from the object to the written stimulus; keep in mind that the response "apple" is always the same behavior. Reading comprehension, quite different from textual behavior, involves a child's receptive, mand, tact, and intraverbal repertoires.

The (Transcriptive) Spelling Repertoire

When asked to spell the word "pencil" a child's response "p-e-n-c-i-l" is a form of verbal behavior where there is point-to-point correspondence between the stimulus and the response product and no formal similarity (Table A-2). The stimulus and the response product are in the same sense mode, but they do not physically resemble each other, thus this type of verbal behavior is not formally similar. Spelling is a difficult repertoire to acquire due to the non-phonetic nature of the English language. Many of the words in our language are not spelled like they sound, hence it is very difficult to shape an appropriate discriminative repertoire. A child with language delays can learn to spell if he has a good echoic repertoire, can tact the nonverbal stimulus, and has some reinforcers available to him. The procedures consist of transferring stimulus control from echoic to textual by using prompts and fading the prompts.

Summary

Skinner's elementary verbal operants are the result of his analysis of the environmental contingencies responsible for the behavior of the speaker and listener. This analysis provides a new framework for language assessment and training. That is, in addition to measuring the physical properties of the response form such as mean length of utterances, syntax, pitch, intonation, etc., a complete account of verbal behavior must also include an analysis of the behavior under receptive, echoic, imitative, mand, tact, intraverbal, and written conditions.

Biklen, D. (1990). Communication unbound: Autism and praxis. Harvard Educational Review, 60, 291-314.

Bijou, S. W., & Baer, D. M. (1965). Child development II: Universal stage of infancy. Englewood Cliffs, NJ: Prentice-Hall.

Bloom, L. (1974). Developmental relationship between receptive and expressive language. In R. L. Schiefelbusch and L. L. Lloyd (Eds.). Language perspectives, acquisition, retardation, and intervention. (pp. 285-311). Baltimore: University Park Press.

Bondy, A. S., & Frost, L. A. (1993). Mands across the water: A report on the application of the picture-exchange communication system in Peru. The Behavior Analyst, 16, 123-128.

Bonvillian, J. D., Nelson, K .E., & Rhyne, J. (1981). Sign language and autism. Journal of Autism and Developmental Disorders, 11, 125-137.

Braam, S. J., & Poling, A. (1982). Development of intraverbal behavior in mentally retarded individuals through transfer of stimulus control procedures: Classification of verbal responses. Applied Research in Mental Retardation, 4, 279-302.

Braam, S. J., & Sundberg, M. L., (1991). The effects of specific versus nonspecific reinforcement on verbal behavior. The Analysis of Verbal Behavior, 9, 19-28.

Brady, N. C., Saunders, K. J., & Spradlin, J. E. (1994). A conceptual analysis of request teaching procedures for individuals with severely limited verbal repertoires. The Analysis of Verbal Behavior, 12, 43-54.

Breuning, S. E., & Davis, V. L. (1981). Reinforcement effects on the intelligence test performance of institutionalized retarded adults: Behavior analysis, directional control, and implications for habilitation. Applied Research in Mental Retardation, 2, 307-321.

Brown, R. (1973). A first language: The early stages. Cambridge, MA: Harvard University Press.

Burns, C. E. S., Heiby, E. M., & Tharp, R. G. (1983). A verbal behavior analysis of auditory hallucinations. The Behavior Analyst, 6, 133-143.

Carroll, R. J., & Hesse, B. E. (1987). The effects of alternating mand and tact training on the acquisition of tacts. The Analysis of Verbal Behavior, 5, 55-65.

Carr, E. G. (1979). Teaching autistic children to use sign language: Some research issues. Journal of Autism and Developmental Disorders, 9, 345-359.

Carr, E. G., Binkoff, J. A., Kologinsky, E., & Eddy, M. (1978). Acquisition of sign language by autistic children I: Expressive labelling. Journal of Applied Behavior Analysis, 11, 489-501.

Catania, A. C. (1992). Learning. Englewood Cliffs, NJ: Prentice-Hall.

Charlop-Christy, M. H., & Kelso, S. E. (1996). How to treat the child with autism. Claremont CA: Claremont McKenna College Press.

Chesley, G. M., & Calaluce, P. D., Jr. (1997). The deception of inclusion. Mental Retardation, 35, 488-490.

Chomsky, N. (1957). Syntactic structures. The Hague: Mouton and Company.

Clarke, S., Remington, B., & Light, P. (1988). The role of referential speech in sign language learning by mentally retarded children: A comparison of total communication and sign-alone training. Journal of Applied Behavior Analysis, 21, 419-426.

Cooper, J., Heron, W., & Heward, W. (1987). Applied behavior analysis. Englewood Cliffs, NJ: Prentice-Hall.

Dougher, M. J. (1994). Stimulus equivalence, functional equivalence, and the transfer of function. In S. C. Hayes, L. J. Hayes, M. Sato, & K. Ono (Eds.), Behavior analysis of language and cognition (pp. 71-90). Reno NV: Context Press.

Drash, P.W., & Tudor, R.M. (1993). A functional analysis of verbal delay in preschool children: Implications for prevention and total recovery. The Analysis of Verbal Behavior, 11, 19-29.

Elliott, R. O. Jr., Hall, K., & Soper, H. V. (1991). Analog language teaching versus natural language teaching: Generalization and retention of language learning for adults with autism and mental retardation. Journal of Autism and Developmental Disorders, 21, 433-447.

Fristoe, M., & Lloyd, L. L. (1977). Manual communication for the retarded and others with severe communication impairments: A resource list. Mental Retardation, 15, 18-21.

Frost, L. A., & Bondy, A. S. (1994). The picture exchange communication system training manual. Cherry Hill, NJ: Pyramid Educational Consultants, Inc.

Green, G., & Shane, H. C. (1993). Facilitated communication: The claims vs. the evidence. Harvard Mental Health Letter, 10, 4-5.

Guess, D., Sailor, W. S., & Baer, D. M. (1976). A functional speech and language program for the severely retarded. Lawrence KS: H & H Enterprises.

Hall, G. A. (1993). Facilitator control as automatic behavior: A verbal behavior analysis. The Analysis of Verbal Behavior, 11, 89-97.

Hall, G. A., & Chase, P. N. (1991). The relationship between stimulus equivalence and verbal behavior. The Analysis of Verbal Behavior, 9, 107-119.

Hall, G. A., & Sundberg, M. L. (1987). Teaching mands by manipulating conditioned establishing operations. The Analysis of Verbal Behavior, 5, 41-53.

Halle, J. (1987). Teaching language in the natural environment: An analysis of spontaneity. Journal of the Association for Persons with Severe Handicaps, 12, 28-37.

Halle, J. W., Baer, D. M., & Spradlin, J. E. (1981). Teachers' generalized use of delay as a stimulus control procedure to increase language use in handicapped children. Journal of Applied Behavior Analysis, 14, 389-409.

Hart B., & Risley T. R. (1975). Incidental teaching of language in the preschool. <u>Journal of Applied Behavior Analysis, 8</u>, 411-420.

Hart, B., & Rogers-Warren, A. (1978). A mileau approach to language teaching. In R. Schiefelbusch (Ed.), <u>Language intervention strategies</u> (pp. 193-235). Baltimore, MD: University Park Press.

Haskew, P., & Donnellan, A.M. (1992). <u>Emotional maturity andwell-being: Psychological lessons of facilitated communication.</u> New York: DRI Press.

Hurlbut, B. I., Iwata, B. A., & Green, J. D. (1982). Nonvocal language acquisition in adolescents with severe physical disabilities: Blissymbol versus iconic symbol formats. <u>Journal of Applied Behavior Analysis, 15,</u> 241-258.

Judd, N., Endicott, K., & Sundberg, M. L. (1997, February). <u>The use of written prompts in the early language acquisition in a child with autism.</u> Poster presented at the 15th Annual Conference of the Northern California Association for Behavior Analysis, Oakland, CA.

Kent, L. (1974). <u>Language acquisition program for the retarded or multiply impaired.</u> Champaign, IL: Research Press.

Keogh, W., & Reichle, J. (1985). Communication intervention for the "difficult to teach" severely handicapped. In S. Warren & A. Rodgers-Warren (Eds.), <u>Teaching functional language</u> (pp. 157-196). Baltimore: University Park Press.

Koegel, R. L., & Johnson, J. (1989). Motivating language use in autistic children. In G. Dawson (Ed.), <u>Autism: Nature, diagnosis, and treatment</u> (pp. 310-325). New York: Guilford.

Koegel, R. L., Koegel, L. K., & Surratt, A. (1992). Language intervention and disruptive behavior in preschool children with autism. <u>Journal of Autism and Developmental Disorders, 22</u>, 141-153.

Koegel, R. L., O'Dell, M. C., & Koegel, L. K. (1987). A natural language teaching paradigm for nonverbal autistic children. <u>Journal of Autism and Developmental Disorders, 17</u>, 187-200.

Laski, K. E., Charlop, M. H., & Schreibman, L. (1988). Training parents to use the natural language paradigm to increase their autistic children's speech. <u>Journal of Applied Behavior Analysis, 21</u>, 391-400.

LaVingna, G. (1977). Communication training in mute, autistic adolescents using the written word. <u>Journal of Autism and Childhood Schizophrenia, 7,</u> 135-149.

Layng, T. V. J., & Andronis, P. T. (1984). Toward a functional analysis of delusional speech and hallucinatory behavior. <u>The Behavior Analyst, 7</u>, 139-156.

Lazzari, A. M., & Peters, P. M. (1994). Handbook of exercises for language processing. East Moline, IL: LinguiSystems, Inc.

Leaf, R. (1997, February). <u>Illusions, delusions, and conclusions of discrete trial training.</u> Symposium conducted at the 15th Annual Conference of the Northern California Association for Behavior Analysis, Oakland, CA.

Lovaas, O. I. (1977). <u>The autistic child: Language development through behavior modification</u>. New York: Irvington.

Lovaas, O. I. (1981). <u>Teaching developmentally disabled children: The ME book</u>. Baltimore: University Park Press.

Lovaas, O. I., Koegel, R., Simmons, J.Q., & Long, J. (1973). Some generalization and follow-up measures on autistic children in behavior therapy. <u>Journal of Applied Behavior Analysis, 6</u>, 131-166.

Luciano, C. (1986). Acquisition, maintenance, and generalization of productive intraverbal behavior through transfer of stimulus control procedures. <u>Applied Research in Mental Retardation, 7</u>, 1-20.

Malott, R.W., Whaley, D., & Malott, M. (1994). <u>Elementary principles of behavior</u> (2nd Ed.). Englewood Cliffs, NJ: Prentice-Hall.

Martin, G. L., & Paer, J. J. (1995). <u>Behavior modification: What is it and how to do it.</u> Englewood Cliffs, NJ: Prentice-Hall.

Maurice, C., Green, G., & Luce, S.C. (1996). <u>Behavior interventions for young children with autism</u>. Austin, Texas: Pro Ed.

McNaughton, S. (1976). Bliss symbol—an alternative symbol system for the non-vocal pre-reading child. In G .Vanderheiden & K. Gillery (Eds.), <u>Non-vocal communication techniques and aids for the severely physically handicapped</u>. Baltimore: University Park Press.

Michael, J. (1982). Distinguishing between discriminative and motivational functions of stimuli. <u>Journal of the Experimental Analysis of Behavior, 37</u>, 149-155.

Michael, J. (1983). Evocative and repertoire-altering effects of an environmental event. <u>The Analysis of Verbal Behavior, 2,</u> 19-21.

Michael, J. (1985). Two kinds of verbal behavior plus a possible third. <u>The Analysis of Verbal Behavior, 3,</u> 1-4.

Michael, J. (1988). Establishing operations and the mand. <u>The Analysis of Verbal Behavior, 6</u>, 3-9.

Michael, J. (1993). Establishing operations. <u>The Behavior Analyst, 16</u>, 191-206.

Mirenda, P. (1985). Designing pictorial communication systems for physically able-bodied students with severe handicaps. <u>Augmentative and Alternative Communication, 1</u>, 58-64.

Moores, D. F. (1978). <u>Educating the deaf: Psychology, principles, and practices</u>. Boston: Houghton Mifflin Company.

Mowrer, O. H. (1950). <u>Learning theory and personality dynamics.</u> New York: The Ronald Press Company.

Novak, G. (1996). <u>Developmental psychology: Dynamical systems and behavior analysis</u>. Reno, NV: Context Press.

Oah, S., & Dickinson, A. M. (1989). A review of empirical studies of verbal behavior. <u>The Analysis of Verbal Behavior, 7,</u> 53-68.

O'Neill, R. E., Horner, R. H. Albin, R. W., Sprague, J. R., Storey, K. Newton, J. S. (1997). <u>Functional assessment and program development for problem behaviors.</u> Pacific Grove: Brooks/Cole.

Osgood, C. E. (1953). <u>Method and theory in experimental psychology.</u> New York: Oxford University Press.

Partington, J. W., & Bailey, J. S. (1993). Teaching intraverbal behavior to preschool children. <u>The Analysis of Verbal Behavior, 11,</u> 9-18.

Partington, J. W., & Sundberg, M. L. (1998). <u>The assessment of basic language and learning skills.</u> Danville, CA: Behavior Analysts, Inc.

Partington, J. W., Sundberg, M. L., Newhouse, L., & Spengler, S. M. (1994). Overcoming an autistic child's failure to acquire a tact repertoire. <u>Journal of Applied Behavior Analysis, 27,</u> 733-734.

Piaget, J. (1926). <u>The language and thought of the child.</u> (M. Cook translation). London: Routledge and Kegan Paul, Ltd.

Pinker, S. (1994). <u>The language instinct.</u> New York: William Morrow & Company.

Potter, B., & Brown, D. (1997). A review of studies examining the nature of selection-based and topography-based verbal behavior. <u>The Analysis of Verbal Behavior, 14,</u> 85-103.

Poulton, K. T., & Algozzine, B. (1980). Manual communication and mental retardation: A review of research and implications. <u>American Journal of Mental Deficiency, 85,</u> 145-152.

Reichle, J., Sigafoos, J., & Remington, B. (1991). Beginning an augmentative communication system with individuals who have severe disabilities. In Remington, B. (Ed.), <u>The challenge of severe mental handicap.</u> Chichester: Wiley & Sons.

Reichle, J., York, J., & Sigafoos, J. (1991). <u>Communication programming for persons with severe handicaps: Vocal and augmentative strategies.</u> Baltimore: Paul H. Brookes

Romski, M. A., & Sevcik, R. A. (1988). Augmentative and alternative communication systems: Considerations for individuals with severe intellectual disabilities. <u>Augmentative and Alternative Communication, 4,</u> 83-98.

Savage-Rumbaugh, E. S. (1984). Verbal behavior at the procedural level in the chimpanzee. <u>Journal of the Experimental Analysis of Behavior, 41,</u> 223-250.

Shafer, E. (1993). Teaching topography-based and stimulus selection-based verbal behavior to developmentally disabled individuals: Some considerations. <u>The Analysis of Verbal Behavior, 11,</u> 117-133.

Shafer, E. (1994). A review of interventions to teach a mand repertoire. <u>The Analysis of Verbal Behavior, 12,</u> 53-66.

Sigafoos, J., Doss, S., & Reichle, J. (1989). Developing mand and tact repertoires with persons with severe developmental disabilities with graphic symbols. Research in Developmental Disabilities, 11, 165-176.

Sigafoos, J., Reichle, J., Doss, S., Hall, K., & Pettitt, L. (1990). "Spontaneous" transfer of stimulus control from mand to tact contingencies. Research in Developmental Disabilities, 11, 165-176.

Sisson, L. A., & Barrett, R. P. (1983). A review of nonspeech communication systems with autistic and mentally retarded individuals. In S. E. Breuning, J. L. Matson, & R. P. Barrett (Eds.), Advances in mental retardation and developmental disabilities, Vol 1 (pp. 97-123). Greenwich, CT: JAI Press.

Skinner, B. F. (1945). The operational analysis of psychological terms. Psychological Review, 52, 270-277.

Skinner, B. F. (1953). Science and human behavior. New York: Free Press.

Skinner, B. F. (1957). Verbal behavior. New York: Appleton-Century-Crofts.

Skinner, B. F. (1974). About behaviorism. New York: Knopf.

Sloane, H. N., & MacAuley, B. D. (Eds.) (1968). Operant procedures in remedial speech and language training. Boston: Houghton Mifflin.

Smith, T (1993). Autism. In T. R. Giles (Ed.). Effective Psychotherapies (pp. 107-133). New York: Plenum.

Snell, M. E. (1987). Systematic instruction of persons with severe handicaps. Columbus: Charles E. Merrill Co.

Spradlin, J. E. (1963). Assessment of speech and language of retarded children: The Parsons language sample. Journal of Speech and Hearing Disorders Monograph, 10, 8-31.

Spradlin, J. E. (1974). Development of receptive language. In R. L. Schiefelbusch & L. L. Lloyd (Eds.). Language perspectives, acquisition, retardation, and intervention. (pp. 285-311) Baltimore: University Park Press.

Spradlin, J. E., & Siegel, G. (1982). Language training in natural and clinical environments. Journal of Speech and Hearing Disorders, 47, 2-6.

Stafford, M. W., Sundberg, M. L., & Braam, S. (1988). A preliminary investigation of the consequences that define the mand and the tact. The Analysis of Verbal Behavior, 6, 61-71.

Sundberg, C. T., & Sundberg, M. L. (1990). Comparing topography-based verbal behavior with stimulus selection-based verbal behavior. The Analysis of Verbal Behavior, 8, 31-41.

Sundberg, M. L. (1980). Developing a verbal repertoire using sign language and Skinner's analysis of verbal behavior. Unpublished doctoral dissertation, Western Michigan University.

Sundberg, M. L. (1983). Language. In J. L. Matson, & S. E. Breuning (Eds.), Assessing the mentally retarded (pp. 285-310). New York: Grune & Stratton.

Sundberg, M. L. (1987). <u>Teaching language to the developmentally disabled.</u> Prince George, B.C.: College of New Caledonia Press.

Sundberg, M. L. (1990). <u>Teaching verbal behavior to the developmentally disabled.</u> Pleasant Hill, CA: Behavior Analysts, Inc.

Sundberg, M. L. (1993a). Selecting a response form for nonverbal persons: Facilitated communication, pointing systems, or sign language? <u>The Analysis of Verbal Behavior, 11,</u> 99-116.

Sundberg, M. L. (1993b). The application of establishing operations. <u>The Behavior Analyst, 16,</u> 211-214.

Sundberg, M. L. (1996). Toward granting linguistic competence to apes: A review of Savage-Rumbaugh, et al.'s Language comprehension in ape and child. <u>Journal of the Experimental Analysis of Behavior, 65,</u> 477-492.

Sundberg, M. L., Michael, J., Partington, J. W., & Sundberg, C. A. (1996). The role of automatic reinforcement in early language acquisition. <u>The Analysis of Verbal Behavior, 13,</u> 21-37.

Sundberg, M. L., Milani, I., & Partington, J. W. (1977, August). <u>The use of sign language with hearing mentally impaired persons.</u> Paper presented at the 85th Annual Meeting of the American Psychological Association, San Francisco, CA.

Sundberg, M. L., Ray, D. A., Braam, S. J., Stafford, M. W., Rueber, T., & Braam, C. (1979). The use of B.F. Skinner's analysis of verbal behavior for language assessment and training. <u>Western Michigan University Behavioral Monograph #8.</u> Kalamazoo, MI: Western Michigan University

Terrace, H. (1963). Discrimination learning with and without "errors." <u>Journal of the Experimental Analysis of Behavior,6,</u> 1-27.

Touchette, P. E. (1971). Transfer of stimulus control: Measuring the moment of transfer. <u>Journal of the Experimental Analysis of Behavior, 15,</u> 347-354.

Vanderheiden, G. C., & Lloyd. L. L. (1986). Communication systems and their components. In S. W. Blackstone (Ed.), <u>Augmentative communication: An introduction</u> (pp. 49-161). Rockville, MD: American Speech-Language-Hearing Association.

Van Riper, C. (1978). <u>Speech correction principles and methods</u> (6th ed.). New York: Prentice-Hall.

Vaughan, M. E., & Michael, J. L. (1982). Automatic reinforcement: An important but ignored concept. <u>Behaviorism, 10,</u> 217-227.

Vernon, M., & Koh, S. D. (1970). Early manual communication and deaf children's achievement. <u>American Annual of the Deaf, 115,</u> 527-536.

Warren, S. F., & Kaiser, A. P. (1986). Incidental language teaching: A critical review. <u>Journal of Speech and Hearing Disorders, 51,</u> 291-299.

Watkins, C. L., Pack-Teixteira, L., & Howard, J. S. (1989). Teaching intraverbal behavior to severely retarded children. <u>The Analysis of Verbal Behavior, 7,</u> 69-81.

Wheeler, D. L., Jacobson, J. W., Paglieri, R. A., & Schwartz, A. A. (1993). An experimental assessment of facilitated communication. Mental Retardation, 31, 49-60.

Winokur, S (1976). A primer on verbal behavior. Englewood Cliffs, NJ: Prentice-Hall.

Wolff, P. H. (1969). The natural history of crying and other vocalization in early infancy. In B. M. Foss (Ed.), Determinants of infant behavior (Vol. 4). London: Methuen.

Wraikat, R., Sundberg, C. T., & Michael, J. (1991). Topography-based and selection-based verbal behavior: A further comparison. The Analysis of Verbal Behavior, 9, 1-17.

Young, R. M., Bradley-Johnson, S., & Johnson, C. M. (1982). Immediate and delayed reinforcement on WISC-R performance of mentally retarded students. Applied Research in Mental Retardation, 3, 13-20.

Zangari, C., Lloyd, L. L., & Vicker, B. (in press). Augmentative and alternative communication: An historic perspective. Augmentative and Alternative Communication.

Zwiebel, A. (1987). More on the effects of early manual communication on the cognitive development of deaf children. American Annual of the Deaf, 132, 16-20.

Also available from www.AVBPress.com

Verbal Behavior Milestones Assessment and Placement Program: The VB-MAPP

The VB-MAPP provides educators and parents with a new generation of assessment for children with autism or other developmental disabilities that is based on B.F. Skinner's analysis of language, the principles of Behavior Analysis, and developmental milestones. The VB-MAPP offers a comprehensive and well-grounded assessment approach that can also help to identify barriers that impede learning and language and assist in providing direction in developing an individualized intervention program. Each VB-MAPP set contains an Individual Protocol and an Instruction Guide.

Features:

❑ **Milestones Assessment.** Focuses on 170 milestones that serve as the foundation of language, learning, and social development.

  ■ Sequenced across three developmental levels (0-18 months, 18-30 months, and 30-48 months)

  ■ Includes objective measurement criteria for treatment or research outcomes

  ■ Echoic assessment by Barbara Esch, Ph.D., BCBA, CCC-SLP

  ■ Color-coded for ease of use

❑ **Barriers Assessment.** Focuses on 24 barriers that may impede a child's acquisition of new skills.

❑ **Transition Assessment.** A summary assessment of 18 areas that serves as a guide for planning the child's educational needs.

❑ **Task Analysis and Skills Tracking.** A checklist of approximately 900 skills that support the milestones and can be used for daily curriculum activities and skill tracking.

❑ **VB-MAPP Instruction Guide.** Provides the scoring criteria, examples, and a further explanation for each milestone, barrier, and transition measure, as well as the general scoring instructions and tips for the tester. The guide also contains a basic overview of Skinner's analysis of verbal behavior and how to use it for language assessment.

❑ **Placement and IEP Goals.** Helps to interpret the assessment results for each of the 170 milestones, establish intervention and curriculum priorities, and develop IEP goals that are measurable, meaningful, and manageable.